PRENTICE HALL LITERATURE

PENGUIN EDITION

Teaching Resources

Unit 5
Disillusion, Defiance, and Discontent

The American Experience

PEARSON
Prentice
Hall

Upper Saddle River, New Jersey
Boston, Massachusetts

ISBN 0-13-165223-0

1 2 3 4 5 6 7 8 9 10   09 08 07 06 05

Contents

UNIT 5

"The Turtle" from *The Grapes of Wrath* by John Steinbeck

"old age sticks" and "anyone lived in a pretty how town" by E. E. Cummings

"The Unknown Citizen" by W. H. Auden

Benchmark Test 7

Diagnostic Test 8

"The Far and the Near" by Thomas Wolfe

"Of Modern Poetry" and "Anecdote of the Jar" by Wallace Stevens

"Ars Poetica" by Archibald MacLeish

"Poetry" by Marianne Moore

"In Another Country" by Ernest Hemingway

"The Corn Planting" by Sherwood Anderson

"A Worn Path" by Eudora Welty

"Chicago" and "Grass" by Carl Sandburg

"The Night the Ghost Got In" by James Thurber

from *Here Is New York* by E. B. White

Benchmark Test 8

Diagnostic Test 9

from *Dust Tracks on a Road* by Zora Neale Hurston

"The Negro Speaks of Rivers," "Ardella," "Dream Variations," and "Refugee in America" by Langston Hughes

"The Tropics in New York" by Claude McKay

"From the Dark Tower" by Countee Cullen

"A Black Man Talks of Reaping" by Arna Bontemps

"Storm Ending" by Jean Toomer

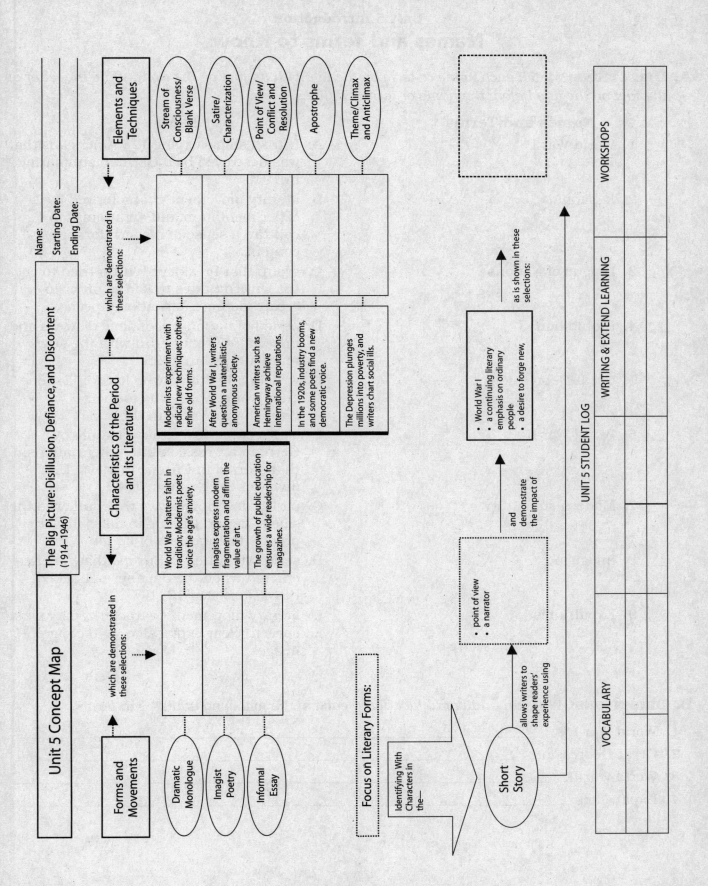

Unit 5 Concept Map

The Big Picture: Disillusion, Defiance, and Discontent
(1914–1946)

Name:

Starting Date:

Ending Date:

Forms and Movements

which are demonstrated in these selections:

- Dramatic Monologue
- Imagist Poetry
- Informal Essay

Characteristics of the Period and its Literature

- World War I shatters faith in tradition; Modernist poets voice the age's anxiety.
- Imagists express modern fragmentation and affirm the value of art.
- The growth of public education ensures a wide readership for magazines.

- Modernists experiment with radical new techniques; others refine old forms.
- After World War I, writers question a materialistic, anonymous society.
- American writers such as Hemingway achieve international reputations.
- In the 1920s, industry booms, and some poets find a new democratic voice.
- The Depression plunges millions into poverty, and writers chart social ills.

which are demonstrated in these selections:

Elements and Techniques

- Stream of Consciousness/ Blank Verse
- Satire/ Characterization
- Point of View/ Conflict and Resolution
- Apostrophe
- Theme/Climax and Anticlimax

Focus on Literary Forms:

Identifying With Characters in the—

Short Story

allows writers to shape readers' experience using

- point of view
- a narrator

and demonstrate the impact of

- World War I
- a continuing literary emphasis on ordinary people
- a desire to forge new,

as is shown in these selections:

UNIT 5 STUDENT LOG

VOCABULARY			WRITING & EXTEND LEARNING			WORKSHOPS	

1

Name _____   Date _____

Unit 5 Introduction
Names and Terms to Know

A. DIRECTIONS: *Match each name or term on the left with its fact on the right. Write the letter of the fact on the line before the name or term it defines.*

Names and Terms	**Facts**
___ 1. World War I	A. British ship carrying 128 Americans that was destroyed by a German submarine in 1915
___ 2. *Lusitania*	B. literary movement characterized by experimentation and an attempt to capture a sense of modern form and content
___ 3. League of Nations	C. group that President Wilson tried to get the United States to join in order to create lasting international peace
___ 4. Prohibition	D. period of national economic distress and uncertainty that began with the stock market crash in 1929
___ 5. Great Depression	E. writers and others who lived in Europe after World War I, due to their disenchantment with the U.S.
___ 6. World War II	F. series of battles, caused mainly by German aggression into other nations, that started in Europe in 1914; U.S. involvement began in 1917
___ 7. Modernism	G. period describing laws that outlawed the sale of liquor, leading to mass illegal production and sale of liquor
___ 8. Imagism	H. series of battles in Europe that America entered when the Japanese attacked Pearl Harbor in 1941
___ 9. Expatriates	I. literary movement characterized by plain speech, clear expression, and concrete images

B. DIRECTIONS: *Write an additional fact about each of the following names and terms.*

1. World War I: _____

2. Great Depression: _____

3. World War II: _____

4. Expatriates: _____

Name _____ Date _____

DIRECTIONS: *Use the hints below to help you answer the Focus Questions. You will find all of the information in the Unit Introduction in your textbook.*

1. For what reasons did the United States enter World War I?
    Hint: What was the general American attitude toward entering a European conflict? ____

    _____

    _____

    Hint: What key events led to American involvement in the war? _____

    _____

    _____

2. What was the impact of the Great Depression on the government and the people of the United States?
    Hint: How many people were affected by the Great Depression? _____

    _____

    _____

    Hint: How did the Great Depression affect presidential politics? _____

    _____

    _____

3. In what ways did American literature reflect the uncertainty and disillusionment of this period?
    Hint: Why did people move to Europe? _____

    _____

    _____

    Hint: Think about the mood and attitude expressed in literature of this period. _____

    _____

    _____

Vocabulary Warm-up Word Lists

Study these words from the selection. Then, complete the activities.

Word List A

attendant [uh TEN duhnt] *adj.* secondary; helping; auxiliary
  During the operation, Dr. Marlin served as an <u>attendant</u> surgeon, helping Dr. Silver.

deferential [def uh REN shuhl] *adj.* very respectful
  In the ruler's presence, the chief minister was extremely <u>deferential</u>.

digress [dy GRES] *v.* to wander away from a topic or route
  Professor Potter's tendency to <u>digress</u> during lectures confused his students.

dusk [DUSK] *n.* twilight
  Bats generally leave their roost at <u>dusk</u> to forage during the night and then return at dawn.

obtuse [uhb TOOS] *adj.* ignorant; insensitive
  Marla seemed <u>obtuse</u> in her failure to understand Jim's main point during the meeting.

presume [pree ZOOM] *v.* to make an unjustified assumption
  Don't <u>presume</u> to judge the evidence without carrying out a thorough investigation.

ragged [RAG uhd] *adj.* worn away; irregular
  The beggar's clothing was worn, almost <u>ragged</u>.

snicker [SNIK er] *v.* to joke or laugh scornfully or mockingly
  The would-be stand-up comic was embarrassed to hear the audience <u>snicker</u> at him.

Word List B

fasted [FAST uhd] *v.* abstained from food and water
  During the holy month of Ramadan, Rehman <u>fasted</u> from sunrise to sundown every day.

malingers [muh LING erz] *v.* stays or remains past the proper time for departure
  Every evening, the stray dog <u>malingers</u> on that corner, hoping for a handout.

meticulous [muh TIK yoo luhs] *adj.* painstaking; extremely conscientious
  Jenna, who is a certified public accountant, is always <u>meticulous</u> in her calculations.

overwhelming [oh ver WELM ing] *adj.* irresistible; extremely persuasive
  Having found the evidence against him <u>overwhelming</u>, the jury convicted the defendant.

scuttling [SKUT uhl ing] *v.* moving quickly in an irregular fashion, as from fear
  <u>Scuttling</u> away to safety, the mice had been frightened by the cat's sudden appearance.

sprawling [SPRAW ling] *v.* spreading the limbs in a relaxed or awkward position
  At the end of each workday, Mike would be <u>sprawling</u> in an easy chair, extremely tired.

tedious [TEE dee uhs] *adj.* wearisome; tiresome; boring
  Some factory workers find that their tasks are repetitive and <u>tedious</u>.

wreathed [REETHD] *adj.* crowned
  The statue of the Olympic victor had a crown of olive leaves <u>wreathed</u> around its head.

Name _____ Date _____

"The Love Song of J. Alfred Prufrock" by T. S. Eliot
Vocabulary Warm-up Exercises

Exercise A *Fill in each blank in the paragraph below with the appropriate word from Word List A. Use each word only once.*

The emergency operation, a kidney transplant, began in mid-afternoon and was not over until [1] _____. Dr. Linda Graziano was in charge, and Dr. Bill Robertson was the [2] _____ surgeon who assisted her. Bill had graduated from medical school only recently, and he was very [3] _____ toward his chief, treating her with the greatest respect. He would never boldly [4] _____ to [5] _____ from the task at hand. Although he did not want his silence to be interpreted as if he were ignorant or [6] _____, he felt it was more diplomatic to wait until Linda addressed him first. At last they were ready to remove the diseased kidney. Bill was about to [7] _____ when he saw how [8] _____ and worn out the old organ was. Linda was more respectful of her patient, saying, "Thank goodness we were able to give this man a new kidney."

Exercise B *Revise each sentence so that the underlined vocabulary word is logical.*

Example: Because the ocean was so <u>turbulent</u>, we felt swimming was safe.
  Because the ocean was so <u>turbulent</u>, we felt swimming would be dangerous.

1. Omar <u>fasted</u> all month, eating his fill.
   _____

2. Since the memory of them <u>malingers</u>, we have forgotten them entirely.
   _____

3. A <u>meticulous</u> teacher doesn't bother to prepare lesson plans in advance.
   _____

4. A wrestler with <u>overwhelming</u> strength can be easily defeated.
   _____

5. Animals that are <u>scuttling</u> across the floor generally move slowly and carefully.
   _____

6. Someone <u>sprawling</u> in an armchair usually looks formal and extremely polite.
   _____

7. If you find a book <u>tedious</u>, you can hardly put it down.
   _____

8. The statue showed the hero's feet <u>wreathed</u> with a crown.
   _____

"The Love Song of J. Alfred Prufrock" by T. S. Eliot
Reading Warm-up A

Read the following passage. Pay special attention to the underlined words. Then, read it again, and complete the activities. Use a separate sheet of paper for your written answers.

Throughout his childhood, James had heard rumors about the old man who lived across the street, Mr. Gray. The neighborhood kids claimed that he had been kidnapped by spies after inventing a secret radar device. As a joke, they would ring his doorbell, then hide behind the bushes and gleefully <u>snicker</u> at him when he answered and found no one there.

One evening last summer, James saw Mr. Gray looking through someone else's mail, then slamming the box shut in frustration. His wrinkled clothes and battered hat gave him a <u>ragged</u> appearance. The sun had just begun to set, and in the dimming light of <u>dusk</u>, he looked stranger than ever. For a moment, the old man met James's stare, and time seemed to stand still.

"Who are you looking at?" Mr. Gray said. "Are you the one who's been stealing my mail? You look too smart to do something so <u>obtuse</u>."

James almost ran away, but Mr. Gray seemed lonely and almost frightened, and he hesitated. The old man started up a complaint about the neighborhood kids, but he had difficulty concentrating, and soon began to <u>digress</u> to a story about the supermarket. Then a woman in a white nurse's uniform came out of the old man's house, carrying a cane in her hand. She asked Mr. Gray to please come back inside, and he began to argue, shaking his head. He said that just because he was old, people should not <u>presume</u> he was helpless. The nurse soothed him with her quiet, <u>deferential</u> voice, full of respect, and James felt ashamed.

For the first time, James thought about what it would be like to grow old, and the challenges that accompany an aging body and mind. He watched Mr. Gray move unsteadily toward his house, his <u>attendant</u> nurse holding him by the arm.

1. Underline the words in this sentence that give a clue to the meaning of <u>snicker</u>. Define **snicker** in your own words.

2. Circle the words in this sentence that give a clue to the meaning of <u>ragged</u>. What is an antonym for **ragged**?

3. Underline the words in this sentence that give a clue to the meaning of <u>dusk</u>. Use the word **dusk** in an original sentence.

4. Underline the words in this sentence that give a clue to the meaning of <u>obtuse</u>. What is the opposite of **obtuse**?

5. Circle the words in this sentence that hint at the meaning of <u>digress</u>. What is a synonym for **digress**?

6. Circle the words in this sentence that offer a clue to the meaning of <u>presume</u>. Use **presume** in an original sentence.

7. Circle the words that help explain the meaning of <u>deferential</u>. What is an antonym for **deferential**?

8. Underline the words that give a clue to the meaning of <u>attendant</u>. Use **attendant** in an original sentence.

"The Love Song of J. Alfred Prufrock" by T. S. Eliot
Reading Warm-up B

Read the following passage. Pay special attention to the underlined words. Then, read it again, and complete the activities. Use a separate sheet of paper for your written answers.

Our concepts of heroes in literary works have been shaped to a great degree by the heroes of epic poetry. Epics are long poems composed in a serious style and focused on the deeds and adventures of a heroic protagonist. The hero is usually nobly born and often possesses great, <u>overwhelming</u> strength. Heroes typically reflect the values and ideals of an entire nation or culture. They are figures easy to visualize as honored in <u>wreathed</u> statues, with crowns symbolizing the tribute and admiration of all the people.

The opposite of the hero in literature is the antihero. Eliot's J. Alfred Prufrock embodies this type. Prufrock's "love song" is far from romantic, to put it mildly. The speaker, full of self-doubt and self-pity, is all too aware that he is <u>tedious</u> in his fumbling efforts at romance. <u>Meticulous</u> to a fault, Prufrock offers a detailed scrutiny of his emotions, showing that he is a young man grown prematurely old. An epic hero is a larger-than-life character who, typically, is <u>sprawling</u> across the pages of the poem that celebrates him. An antihero like Prufrock, by contrast, is smaller-than-life, resembling a frightened animal or insect <u>scuttling</u> for safety. By the end of an epic, the hero has usually feasted at one or more great banquets to celebrate his glorious deeds. It is truer of an antihero to say that he has often <u>fasted</u>, choosing not to take part in the typical routines of everyday life.

If an antihero like Prufrock falls so far short of our expectations, why do we remember him? Perhaps his memory <u>malingers</u> because his self-consciousness and apprehension are deeply human personality traits. Perhaps, even though we might not care to admit it, there is a little of Prufrock in all of us.

1. Underline the words in this sentence that hint at the meaning of the word <u>overwhelming</u>. What are two antonyms for *overwhelming*?

2. Circle the words in this sentence that hint at the meaning of <u>wreathed</u>. Use *wreathed* in an original sentence.

3. Underline the words in this sentence that hint at the meaning of <u>tedious</u>. What is the opposite of *tedious*?

4. Underline the words in this sentence that hint at the meaning of <u>meticulous</u>. What are two synonyms for *meticulous*?

5. Circle the words in this sentence that hint at the meaning of <u>sprawling</u>. Write a definition of *sprawling* in your own words.

6. Circle the words in this sentence that give a good clue to the meaning of <u>scuttling</u>. What is an antonym for *scuttling*?

7. Underline the words in this sentence that hint at the meaning of <u>fasted</u>. Write an original sentence about a person who has *fasted*.

8. Underline the word in the previous sentence that hints at the meaning of <u>malingers</u>. What is the opposite of *malingers*?

"The Love Song of J. Alfred Prufrock" by T. S. Eliot
Literary Analysis: Dramatic Monologue

A **dramatic monologue** is a poem or speech in a play or novel in which a character speaks his or her thoughts aloud about a crucial event or feeling in the character's life. In "The Love Song of J. Alfred Prufrock," Prufrock is speaking to a silent companion—perhaps a part of himself. What Prufrock says reveals a deep split between what he desires and his ability to achieve his desires. Several times in the poem, Prufrock repeats these questions: "Do I dare?" and "How should I presume?" These repeated lines may suggest that Prufrock wishes to act but is deeply afraid of failure and rejection.

DIRECTIONS: *Read the lines from the poem and answer the questions on another sheet of paper. Give examples from the poem as evidence to support your interpretation.*

1. In the following lines, what might Prufrock wish he could dare to do?

   Time to turn back and descend the stair, / With a bald spot in the middle of my hair— / (They will say: "How his hair is growing thin!") / My morning coat, my collar mounting firmly to the chin, / My necktie rich and modest, but asserted by a simple pin— / (They will say: "But how his arms and legs are thin!") / Do I dare / Disturb the universe?

2. What could these lines show Prufrock is afraid of? To what does he compare himself? Why is this an apt comparison?

   And I have known the eyes already, known them all— / The eyes that fix you in a formulated phrase, / And when I am formulated, sprawling on a pin, / When I am pinned and wriggling on the wall, / Then how should I begin / To spit out all the butt-ends of my days and ways? / And how should I presume?

3. What might Prufrock want to do at this point? Why is he unable to do it?

   Shall I part my hair behind? Do I dare to eat a peach? / I shall wear white flannel trousers, and walk upon the beach. / I have heard the mermaids singing, each to each.

   I do not think that they will sing to me.

Name _____   Date _____

"The Love Song of J. Alfred Prufrock" by T. S. Eliot
Reading Strategy: Listen

Listening to the way a poem sounds often can be as important as the words themselves. Writers use sound effects and musical devices to enhance the poem's mood and meaning. One device they sometimes use is **alliteration,** which is the repetition of consonant sounds at the beginning of words or accented syllables. Other effects often used are repetition, rhyme, and rhythm. All of these devices are present in the following excerpt from "The Love Song of J. Alfred Prufrock."

> Time for you and time for me,/ And time yet for a hundred indecisions,/ And for a hundred visions and revisions./ Before the taking of a toast and tea.

Notice the repetition of the word *time*. It suggests that Prufrock is trying to convince himself that there is an abundance of time in which to be indecisive. The rhyming of *indecisions, visions,* and *revisions* gives the lines a fluid internal structure and a pleasing sound. The rhythm flows in beats, evoking the feeling of time passing. The excerpt ends with the alliteration of *t*'s giving the line a sharp, prim and proper feel.

These musical qualities occur throughout "The Love Song of J. Alfred Prufrock," and to appreciate them, you must listen as you read.

DIRECTIONS: *Read each of the following excerpts aloud. On the lines following each one, note which musical devices are being used. Explain how they contribute to the musicality of the poem.*

1. "The yellow fog that rubs its back upon the window-panes, / The yellow smoke that rubs its muzzle on the window-panes.

   _____

   _____

   _____

2. "And indeed there will be time/ To wonder, 'Do I dare?' And 'Do I dare?'/ Time to turn back and descend the stair,/ With a bald spot in the middle of my hair—"

   _____

   _____

   _____

3. "I have seen the moment of my greatness flicker,/ And I have seen the eternal Footman hold my coat and snicker."

   _____

   _____

   _____

"The Love Song of J. Alfred Prufrock" by T. S. Eliot
Vocabulary Builder

Using the Prefix di-

A. DIRECTIONS: *Each of the following sentences includes an italicized word that contains the prefix* di- *(or dis-), meaning "away" or "apart." Fill in the blank with a word or phrase that completes the sentence and reveals the meaning of the italicized word.*

1. When the botanist *dissected* the flower, she _____.

2. When an elected official is *divested* of his or her office, it is _____.

3. If a company produces a *diverse* line of products, each product is _____.

4. If I *divert* a child's attention from something, she will _____.

5. The protesters tried to *disrupt* the meeting, causing it to _____.

Using the Word List

insidious	digress	malingers	meticulous	obtuse

B. DIRECTIONS: *Replace each bracketed word or phrase with one of the words in the Word List.*

1. We suspect that the boy often [fakes illness] _____ when he claims he is too sick to go to school in the morning but feels well enough to go to a ball game in the afternoon.

2. Robert was such a [neat and careful] _____ cook that his kitchen was usually spotless.

3. Although Denise hinted that she would like to date him, Ramon seemed too [dense] _____ to understand.

4. The constant criticism and teasing that Laverne received from her older brother had a(n) [damaging] _____ effect on her self-confidence.

5. Pardon me if I [stray] _____ from the subject, but I have some interesting news.

"The Love Song of J. Alfred Prufrock" by T. S. Eliot
Grammar and Style: Adjectival Modifiers

Adjectival modifiers are phrases or clauses that modify or describe a noun or pronoun. They may begin with a preposition, a present or past participle, a relative pronoun, or the infinitive form of a verb.

These lines from "The Love Song of J. Alfred Prufrock" show four types of adjectival modifiers.

Prepositional phrase:	Is it perfume *from a dress*
Participial phrase:	I know the voices *dying with a dying fall*
Adjective clause:	The yellow fog *that rubs its back upon the window-panes*
Infinitive phrase:	There will be time *to murder and create*

A. PRACTICE: *Underline the adjectival modifier in each of the following lines from "The Love Song of J. Alfred Prufrock." In the blank, identify the type of adjectival modifier each one is.*

1. "Arms that are braceleted and white and bare" _____

2. "My necktie . . . asserted by a simple pin" _____

3. "a bald spot in the middle of my hair" _____

4. "Time to turn back and descend the stair" _____

5. "the smoke that rises from the pipes/Of lonely men" _____

B. Writing Application: *Describe each of the nouns below, using the type of phrase or clause identified in parentheses.*

1. children's faces (adjective clause)

   _____

2. a room (infinitive phrase)

   _____

3. bright light (prepositional phrase)

   _____

4. loud noises (participial phrase)

   _____

5. bitter taste (prepositional phrase)

   _____

Name _____ Date _____

"The Love Song of J. Alfred Prufrock" by T. S. Eliot
Support for Writing

To prepare to write a **character analysis** of J. Alfred Prufrock, enter information from the poem in the graphic organizer below. To respond to each heading, write examples from the poem.

The Character of J. Alfred Prufrock

What J. Alfred Prufrock does with his time	What J. Alfred Prufrock thinks/feels about love
_____ _____ _____	_____ _____ _____
What J. Alfred Prufrock thinks/ feels about himself	What J. Alfred Prufrock thinks/ feels about other people
_____ _____ _____	_____ _____ _____
What other people would say about J. Alfred Prufrock	
_____ _____ _____	

On a separate page, write a draft of your character analysis, using evidence from the poem to support the statements you make about J. Alfred Prufrock. When you revise your work, be sure to replace vague language with more specific and descriptive words.

"The Love Song of J. Alfred Prufrock" by T. S. Eliot
Support for Extend Your Learning

Listening and Speaking

Choose a classmate as a partner to **role-play** an interview between J. Alfred Prufrock and a talk-show host. Try to find out why Prufrock has such low opinion of himself. How can you improve his self-image? Take turns playing each character. Follow these tips:

- Create a list of interview questions that require explanations rather than "yes" or "no" answers.
- Make sure that Prufrock's responses fit his character, as it is described in the poem.

Research and Technology

As you gather material for a **report** on Modernism in art, literature, and popular culture, enter your findings in the graphic organizer below.

Modernism and its Effects

Modernism's influence on art:
Modernism's influence on literature:
Modernism's influence on popular culture:

As you prepare your report, download graphics from the Internet to accompany your conclusions about the Modernism movement.

"The Love Song of J. Alfred Prufrock" by T. S. Eliot
Enrichment: Art

Readers of "The Love Song of J. Alfred Prufrock" must form a mental image of Prufrock. The passage that follows gives the reader some clues about Prufrock's appearance.

> Time to turn back and descend the stair,
> With a bald spot in the middle of my hair—
> (They will say: "How his hair is growing thin!")
> My morning coat, my collar mounting firmly to the chin,
> My necktie rich and modest, but asserted by a simple pin—
> (They will say: "But how his arms and legs are thin!")

DIRECTIONS: *Make a sketch of a realistic, an abstract, or an impressionistic representation of J. Alfred Prufrock.*

1. Before you begin, reread the poem and list any characteristics that you could incorporate into your sketch. What do you know about his personality? Does he hide his insecurity and inner doubts? How do his posture, body language, and facial expression either reveal or successfully hide how he feels inside?

   _____

   _____

   _____

   _____

   _____

2. If possible, conduct some research to ascertain how gentlemen dressed around 1910. What would a morning coat look like? A collar and necktie with a simple pin? Make notes or sketches here of details you will include in your portrait.

3. Draw your sketch of J. Alfred Prufrock on a separate sheet of paper. Share your work with a classmate and compare your sketches. What do the sketches have in common? How are they different?

"The Love Song of J. Alfred Prufrock" by T. S. Eliot
Selection Test A

Critical Reading *Identify the letter of the choice that best answers the question.*

____ 1. Who participates in the dramatic monologue of "The Love Song of J. Alfred Prufrock"?
  A. the speaker of the monologue
  B. the speaker and a silent listener
  C. two people speaking to each other
  D. two people speaking the same words

____ 2. In The Love Song of J. Alfred Prufrock," what two things are compared here: "When the evening is spread out against the sky / Like a patient etherized [asleep] upon a table"?
  A. the speaker and the listener
  B. the evening and the sky
  C. the evening and a patient
  D. a patient and a table

____ 3. Where is repetition used in these lines from "The Love Song of J. Alfred Prufrock": ". . . there will be time/ For the yellow smoke that slides along the street / Rubbing its back upon the window–panes;/ There will be time, there will be time"?
  A. in the first and second lines
  B. in the first and last lines
  C. in the first and third lines
  D. in the second and third lines

____ 4. Whose thoughts and feelings are expressed in "The Love Song of J. Alfred Prufrock"?
  A. those of the listener
  B. those of the women
  C. those of the speaker
  D. those of men

____ 5. What is the poet's view of love in "The Love Song of J. Alfred Prufrock"?
  A. Love has disappointed him.
  B. Love has made his life worthwhile.
  C. He has always avoided love.
  D. He will avoid love from now on.

___ 6. What are the women doing who are "talking of Michelangelo" in "The Love Song of J. Alfred Prufrock"?

A. The women are ignoring the speaker.

B. The women are discussing art.

C. The women are gossiping about someone.

D. The women are listening to a poem.

___ 7. How do you know that end rhyme is used in these lines from "The Love Song of J. Alfred Prufrock": "My morning coat, my collar mounting firmly to the chin, / My necktie rich and modest, but asserted by a simple pin—"?

A. Words in both lines start with the same sound.

B. Words in each line are repeated.

C. The end word in each line rhymes exactly.

D. The end word in each line almost rhymes.

___ 8. When the speaker says he is "pinned and wriggling on the wall" in "The Love Song of J. Alfred Prufrock," what image does he create?

A. the image of a wall

B. the image of a pin

C. the image of an insect

D. the image of a dancer

___ 9. Why is the speaker afraid of "the eternal Footman," who is holding his coat in "The Love Song of J. Alfred Prufrock"?

A. The eternal Footman is a symbol of death.

B. The eternal Footman is a former friend.

C. The eternal Footman is a servant.

D. The eternal Footman is a criminal.

___ 10. How is repetition used in these lines from "The Love Song of J. Alfred Prufrock"?

After the sunsets and the dooryards and the sprinkled street,
After the novels, after the teacups, after the skirts that trail / along the floor—

A. The end words in the lines rhyme.

B. Many words start with the same sound.

C. The first word of each line is repeated.

D. The sunsets are like skirts.

Vocabulary and Grammar

____ **11.** Which word best replaces *digress* in this sentence: "I try to focus on one task, but I often *digress*"?
    A. add
    B. wander
    C. believe
    D. discover

____ **12.** Which sentence contains an adjectival modifier that modifies a noun?
    A. You and I will leave.
    B. I see water that sits in puddles.
    C. Women come and go.
    D. I have known them well.

Essay

13. In "The Love Song of J. Alfred Prufrock," the reader never knows exactly where the speaker is going or what he is doing. What might this absence of a setting mean to the poem? Write a brief essay to give your ideas about why this poem has no specific setting.

14. In "The Love Song of J. Alfred Prufrock," the speaker says, "I have seen the moment of my greatness flicker." What might be a "moment of greatness" in someone's life—an opportunity that he or she might miss as it "flickers" and then is gone? Write a brief essay to give your ideas about events in life that are opportunities for greatness.

Name _____ Date _____

"The Love Song of J. Alfred Prufrock" by T. S. Eliot
Selection Test B

Critical Reading *Identify the letter of the choice that best completes the statement or answers the question.*

____ 1. "The Love Song of J. Alfred Prufrock" is written in the form of
    A. an epic poem.
    B. a prose poem.
    C. a dramatic monologue.
    D. a dramatic dialogue.

____ 2. What best describes the mood of the evening "spread out against the sky / Like a patient etherized upon a table"?
    A. hopeful
    B. suspenseful
    C. romantic
    D. melancholy

____ 3. When Eliot describes "The muttering retreats / Of restless nights in one-night cheap hotels / And sawdust restaurants with oyster-shells," he is referring to love's
    A. hidden dangers.
    B. sometimes sordid surroundings.
    C. mysterious power.
    D. sometimes shameful deceits.

____ 4. What natural association links Prufrock's observations of the yellow fog with his thoughts about there being "time yet for a hundred indecisions / . . . Before the taking of a toast and tea"?
    A. the connection between fog and tea
    B. the similarity between the murky fog and his indecisive thoughts
    C. the relationship between the yellow color of the fog and the color of sunlight
    D. the parallel between the mysterious nature of fog and the nature of love

____ 5. In a dramatic monologue, an imaginary character addresses
    A. the cast of the play.
    B. only one other character.
    C. fewer than three characters.
    D. a silent listener.

____ 6. What musical device does Eliot use in the following excerpt from "The Love Song of J. Alfred Prufrock"?
    Before the taking of a toast and tea.

    A. alliteration
    B. internal rhyme
    C. simile
    D. narrative

_____ 7. In the following lines, what sound device lends musicality to the poem?

Have known the evenings, mornings, afternoons, / I have measured out my life with coffee spoons.

    A. end rhyme
    B. repetition
    C. alliteration
    D. iambic pentameter

_____ 8. Which of the following quotations from the poem uses the musical device of repetition?
    A. "Is it the perfume from a dress/ That makes me so digress?"
    B. "I grow old . . . I grow old . . ./ I shall wear the bottoms of my trousers rolled."
    C. "Then how should I begin/ To spit out the butt-ends of my days and ways?"
    D. "I should have been a pair of ragged claws/ Scuttling across the floors of silent seas."

_____ 9. In a dramatic monologue, the thoughts and feelings that are expressed are those of the
    A. poet or playwright.
    B. protagonist.
    C. character who is speaking.
    D. antagonist.

_____ 10. How does Prufrock think others view him?
    A. as a fully accepted member of his social set
    B. as a menacing figure
    C. as a heroic figure
    D. as an aging, conventional person of little consequence

_____ 11. Which statement best describes the attitude about human relationships expressed in the poem?
    A. People are their own best companions.
    B. People can learn from the experiences of others.
    C. True understanding between two people is impossible.
    D. Without love or friendship, life is meaningless.

_____ 12. What image is suggested by the use of repeated vowel and consonant sounds in the following line from "The Love Song of J. Alfred Prufrock"?

By sea-girls wreathed with seaweed red and brown.

    A. blowing wind
    B. drowning
    C. aging
    D. rolling waves

Vocabulary and Grammar

_____ 13. Which phrase is most nearly the same in meaning to *insidious*?
    A. subtly treacherous
    B. boldly evil
    C. obviously hostile
    D. deeply secret

_____ 14. The word *digress* means to
A. remove from political office.
B. elaborate on an aside.
C. exit from a room.
D. stray from the subject.

_____ 15. Which of the following words means the opposite of *obtuse?*
A. overweight
B. insightful
C. unintelligent
D. thin

_____ 16. Which of the following italicized phrases is an example of a participial phrase?
A. "Is it perfume *from a dress*"
B. "I know the voices *dying with a dying fall*"
C. "The yellow fog *that rubs its back upon the window-panes*"
D. "There will be time *to murder and create*"

_____ 17. Which of the following italicized phrases is an example of an infinitive phrase?
A. "Is it perfume *from a dress*"
B. "I know the voices *dying with a dying fall*"
C. "The yellow fog *that rubs its back upon the window-panes*"
D. "There will be time *to murder and create*"

Essay

18. J. Alfred Prufrock's disillusionment with his life and his uncertainty about himself reflect life in the early decades of the twentieth century. In an essay, discuss Prufrock's personality, beliefs, and experiences. Is Prufrock a typical man of his times, or is he unusual? Why do you think Eliot chose to write about a man like Prufrock? Use specific details from the poem as evidence of your interpretation of Prufrock.

19. "The Love Song of J. Alfred Prufrock" is written in the form of a dramatic monologue. Write an essay explaining how the use of this form combined with poetic images enables the poet to present a memorable and moving portrait of Prufrock. Why is the dramatic monologue a particularly revealing form? Would a short story about Prufrock have been as effective as Eliot's dramatic monologue in verse? Support your points with details from the poem.

20. The title of a poem may provide clues to its interpretation. Sometimes the clues are obvious, sometimes not. Write an essay in which you interpret the meaning and significance of the title "The Love Song of J. Alfred Prufrock." Do you think this "love song" is about love in any sense? Is it a typical song? Present evidence from the poem to back up your interpretation.

Vocabulary Warm-up Word Lists

Study these words from the selections. Then, complete the activities.

Word List A

bashful [BASH fuhl] *adj.* shy; easily embarrassed
  Because of his <u>bashful</u> nature, Andy tended to avoid parties.

blunts [BLUNTS] *v.* makes less sharp; tones down; makes weaker or ineffective
  Her newspaper column successfully <u>blunts</u> the force of the criticism by the mayor's
  opponents.

clangs [CLANGS] *n.* loud ringing noises
  We heard the <u>clangs</u> of the fire truck as it rushed toward the scene of the blaze.

mediocre [mee dee OH kuhr] *adj.* average; barely adequate
  Most voters found the candidate's credentials <u>mediocre</u>, and he was defeated at the polls.

petals [PET uhlz] *n.* any of the inner leaves of a flower
  The <u>petals</u> of a day lily form a beautiful bell shape.

rend [REND] *v.* to rip or tear
  As you handle that old manuscript, please try not to <u>rend</u> or damage any of the pages.

scowling [SKOWL ing] *v.* frowning in anger or disapproval
  When Noah reached the finish line in third place, he was <u>scowling</u> in disappointment.

suspicion [sus PISH uhn] *n.* feeling of mistrust; underlying feeling
  According to police, several people were under <u>suspicion</u> for the robbery.

Word List B

apparition [ap uh RISH uhn] *n.* ghost; mysterious or supernatural figure
  Tales about haunted houses often include mentions of an <u>apparition</u>.

bizarre [bi ZAHR] *adj.* weird; extremely strange
  We were amazed when <u>bizarre</u> green lights appeared around the setting sun.

dogma [DOG muh] *n.* strongly held belief
  Political opponents seldom agree on issues of <u>dogma.</u>

eddies [ED eez] *n.* swirling bodies of water or liquid
  The water often forms <u>eddies</u> as it goes down the sink drain.

instantaneously [in stuhn TAYN ee uhs lee] *adv.* at once; instantly
  When a crack of thunder follows a lightning flash almost <u>instantaneously</u>, the storm is nearby.

rumbling [RUM bling] *v.* making a deep-pitched noise
  <u>Rumbling</u> with iritation, the lion opened its mouth and bared its huge teeth.

tatters [TAT uhrz] *n.* worn, ragged, or torn strips
  Seth's coat was in tatters, so he finally bought a new one.

unheeded [un HEED uhd] *adj.* ignored; not noticed
  Our warnings went <u>unheeded</u>, and Mike went hiking despite the threat of storms.

Poems by Ezra Pound, William Carlos Williams, and H. D.
Vocabulary Warm-up Exercises

Exercise A *Fill in the blanks, using each word from Word List A only once.*

Cliff was determined to ask Mary to marry him, but because he was so
[1] _____ and shy, he had trouble planning how to propose to her. Walking home late one evening, he was frowning and [2] _____ in frustration. Every plan he could think of seemed [3] _____ and unsatisfactory. He had the [4] _____ that an elaborate dinner, a bouquet of flowers with stunning [5] _____, or a dance hall date were all clichés. A stale scenario would [6] _____ the impact of such an important moment for Mary. Also, it would painfully [7] _____ his own heart not to be able to come up with an original plan. He really needed a striking, original idea. A fire engine suddenly roared past, and its [8] _____ nearly deafened Cliff. He had to think of a strategy this very night, he told himself.

Exercise B *Decide whether each statement below is true or false. Circle* T *or* F, *and explain your answer.*

1. An <u>apparition</u> is often presumed to be a ghost.
   T / F _____

2. If you consider someone's behavior <u>bizarre</u>, you find it normal and understandable.
   T / F _____

3. People do not generally believe very firmly in a <u>dogma</u>.
   T / F _____

4. <u>Eddies</u> in the water swirl in a circular motion.
   T / F _____

5. A reaction that occurs <u>instantaneously</u> happens very rapidly and suddenly.
   T / F _____

6. A <u>rumbling</u> noise has a deep pitch.
   T / F _____

7. If your clothing is in <u>tatters</u>, it is usually neat and clean.
   T / F _____

8. <u>Unheeded</u> advice makes a deep impression on the listener.
   T / F _____

Name _____   Date _____

Poems by Ezra Pound, William Carlos Williams, and H. D.
Reading Warm-up A

Read the following passage. Pay special attention to the underlined words. Then, read it again, and complete the activities. Use a separate sheet of paper for your written answers.

Some of William Carlos Williams's imagist poems, such as "The Red Wheelbarrow," are extremely brief, consisting of only a few words. Williams was hardly shy or bashful, however, about writing long poems. In fact, his greatest work, in the opinion of many critics, is *Paterson*. This is a philosophical epic in verse consisting of five books, published between 1946 and 1958. This poem's central character is a mythic being named Paterson, who also stands for the city of the same name in northern New Jersey. From many hints and clues in the poem, the reader has the suspicion that Paterson also represents the poet himself. Williams, in fact, lived in the nearby town of Rutherford.

As Paterson roams the city, he is alternately scowling at the area's industrial chaos and rejoicing in the complex energy of modern, urban life. Social injustice may tear at his emotions and rend his heart with sadness Then the echoing clangs of a fire engine on the move lift his spirits. The city's history as one of the pioneering centers of the Industrial Revolution in America offers the speaker an inspiring story. Compared with that history, much of modern-day Paterson seems to him mediocre, or even sub-standard. Williams blunts his criticism of modern life, however, by toning down the negative and paying tribute to the power of the artistic imagination.

The portrait of city life that Williams presents in *Paterson* is, like real life itself, many-sided and complex. Reading the poem is like watching the petals of a large exotic flower slowly opening and unfolding. In the end, although Williams expresses many reservations about life as he sees it, he nevertheless celebrates the human spirit.

1. Underline the word in this sentence that gives a clue to the meaning of bashful. Use the word *bashful* in an original sentence.

2. Circle the words in this sentence that give a clue to the meaning of suspicion. Write a definition for *suspicion* in your own words.

3. Underline the words that give a clue to the meaning of scowling. What is an antonym for *scowling*?

4. Circle the words that offer a clue to the meaning of rend. What are two synonyms for *rend*?

5. Circle the words in this sentence that offer clues to the meaning of clangs. Would *clangs* produce a loud or a soft noise?

6. Underline the word in this sentence that gives a clue to the meaning of mediocre. What are two antonyms for *mediocre*?

7. Circle the words in this sentence and the next sentence that give a clue to the meaning of blunts. Use the word *blunts* in an original sentence.

8. Underline the words in this sentence that hint at the meaning of petals. Use the word *petals* in an original sentence.

Poems by Ezra Pound, William Carlos Williams, and H. D.
Reading Warm-up B

Read the following passage. Pay special attention to the underlined words. Then, read it again, and complete the activities. Use a separate sheet of paper for your written answers.

Ezra Pound greatly admired the Chinese poet, Li Po. Born in 701 A.D., Li Po led a remarkable life that took numerous strange and <u>bizarre</u> twists and turns. His family's pleas to stay went <u>unheeded</u> and, at the age of nineteen, he left home for good. He was greatly interested in Taoism, a spiritual and philosophical system that rejects all <u>dogma</u> and stresses the importance of serenity and an open mind. Wandering over much of China, his clothes ragged and in <u>tatters</u>, Li Po was by turns a court poet, a hermit, a political prisoner, and an exile. Major themes in his poetry include the passage of time, the joys of nature, and the consolations of both friendship and solitude.

When he was in his forties, Li Po crossed paths with a younger writer. Tu Fu was also to become a celebrated poet. It is thought that the younger man fell almost <u>instantaneously</u> under the spell of Li Po. The older writer immediately assumed the role of Tu Fu's mentor.

By this time, Li Po was so admired in China that he was popularly referred to as a "banished immortal"—as if he were an <u>apparition</u> of a deity spending time on earth while in exile from heaven.

Like a <u>rumbling</u> waterfall crashing noisily to the ground, Li Po's poetry has inspired generations of readers with its romantic force and imaginative power. Perhaps the most famous story about the poet concerns his death. It is told that Li Po was sitting in a boat on the river when he tried to seize the moon's reflection in the water. He lost his balance and the boat capsized. Swept into the river's whirling <u>eddies</u>, the poet drowned.

1. Underline the word in this sentence that helps define <u>bizarre</u>. What is a synonym for **bizarre**?

2. Circle the words in this sentence that give a clue to the meaning of <u>unheeded</u>. Use the word **unheeded** in an original sentence.

3. Underline the words in this sentence that help explain the meaning of <u>dogma</u>. Define **dogma** in your own words.

4. Underline the word in this sentence that gives a clue to the meaning of <u>tatters</u>. Use **tatters** in an original sentence.

5. Circle the word in the next sentence that helps define <u>instantaneously</u>. What is an antonym for **instantaneously**?

6. Underline the words in this sentence that hint at the meaning of <u>apparition</u>. Define **apparition** in your own words.

7. Underline the word in this sentence that gives a clue to the meaning of <u>rumbling</u>. Use **rumbling** in an original sentence.

8. Circle the words in this sentence that hint at the meaning of <u>eddies</u>. Use **eddies** in an original sentence.

Imagist Poets
Literary Analysis: Imagist Poetry

The **Imagists** were American poets who became prominent between 1909 and 1918. The major objectives of the Imagist poets were (1) to use everyday language, choosing exact words and avoiding near-exact words, (2) to avoid clichés, (3) to create new rhythms and avoid the old, (4) to exercise absolute freedom in the choice of subjects, (5) to present concrete images, (6) to work toward concentrated language, avoiding anything extra, and (7) to suggest rather than to state directly.

DIRECTIONS: *Read each poem or excerpt. Then answer the question.*

1. "Name three concrete images in this poem.

    so much depends / upon / a red wheel / barrow / glazed with rain / water / beside the white / chickens.

    _____

    _____

    _____

2. List five words in this excerpt that can be seen as exact.

    Among the rain / and lights / I saw the figure 5 / in gold / on a red / fire truck

    _____

    _____

    _____

    _____

3. Which of the objectives of the Imagist poets do you think are achieved in this excerpt? Explain.

    I have eaten / the plums / that were in / the icebox / and which / you were probably / saving / for breakfast

    _____

    _____

    _____

    _____

    _____

    _____

    _____

    _____

    _____

25

Name _____ Date _____

Reading Stategy: Engage Your Senses

One way to enjoy, appreciate, and understand what you read is to engage your senses. Imagine yourself actually seeing, smelling, hearing, tasting, or touching the images presented by the writer. Put yourself at the scene mentally, and experience the images in your mind's eye.

DIRECTIONS: *Use this graphic organizer to help yourself engage your senses as you read these poems. From each poem, choose images that appeal to the senses. Write the image in the corresponding box or boxes. Remember that many images can be appreciated by more than one sense.*

	See	Hear	Touch	Smell	Taste
"The River-Merchant's Wife: A Letter"					
"In a Station of the Metro"					
"The Red Wheelbarrow"					
"The Great Figure"					
"This Is Just to Say"					
"Pear Tree"					
"Heat"					

Imagist Poets
Vocabulary Builder

Forms of *appear*

The following words are based on the verb *appear,* meaning "to come into sight or into being" or "to become understood."

apparent	appearance	apparition

A. DIRECTIONS: *Rewrite each sentence by replacing the italicized word or words with one of the words in the box.*

1. The *seeming* cause of the accident was a drunk driver.

   _____

2. The *ghostly face* in the hallway mirror made the movie audience scream.

   _____

3. The glamorous young star knew that her *showing* at the charity event was important.

   _____

   _____

Using the Word List

apparition	voluminous	dogma

B. DIRECTIONS: *Fill in each blank with the word from the Word List that fits best.*

1. The professor carried on a(n) _____ correspondence with the author whose biography he was writing.

2. Don't accept as _____ the following rules about writing poetry; your own ideas may be just as good.

3. The grieving widow thought she saw a(n) _____ of her late husband standing in the moonlit garden.

Unit 5 Resources: Disillusion, Defiance, and Discontent
27

Name _____ Date _____

Imagist Poets
Grammar and Style: Concrete and Abstract Nouns

A **concrete noun** names a physical thing that can be perceived with one or more of the five senses. An **abstract noun** names something that cannot be seen, heard, smelled, tasted, or touched. An abstract noun can be a quality, a characteristic, or an idea. Some examples of abstract nouns are *beauty, strength, courage,* and *justice.* The following excerpt is from the poem "The River-Merchant's Wife: A Letter." The concrete noun is underlined, and the two abstract nouns are in italics.

Two small <u>people</u>, without *dislike* or *suspicion.*

A. PRACTICE: *Underline the concrete nouns in the lines of poetry that follow. Circle the abstract nouns.*

1. "I played about the front gate, pulling flowers."
2. "The leaves fall early this autumn, in wind."
3. "The apparition of these faces in the crowd; / Petals on a wet, black bough."
4. "a red wheel / barrow / glazed with rain / water / beside the white / chickens."
5. "Silver dust / lifted from the earth / higher than my arms reach"
6. "O wind, rend open the heat . . . rend it to tatters."

B. Writing Application: *Below is a list of abstract nouns. On each line, write a sentence that includes the abstract noun as well as at least one concrete noun. One sentence has already been written for you.*

1. strength _____The movers lifted the huge piano with a strength I found incredible._____
2. beauty _____
3. love _____
4. courage _____
5. future _____
6. success _____
7. kindness _____
8. justice _____
9. fear _____
10. talent _____

Name _____ Date _____

Imagist Poets
Support for Writing

As you prepare to write a **review of a manuscript** by an imagist poet, take notes on one of the poems in this selection. Use the graphic organizer to show why as an editor you will or will not accept the poem for publication.

Review of [poem title by poem author]

What is strong in the poem	What is weak in the poem	Why I would/would not publish the poem

On a separate page, write your draft of a letter to the poet, telling him or her why you are or are not going to publish the poem. When you revise, replace vague words with specific descriptions.

Name _____ Date _____

Listening and Speaking

As you work with a group of classmates to prepare for an **informal debate** about the value of Williams's poem "The Red Wheelbarrow," follow these tips:

- Find examples to support a position that the poem is either "poetic" or "anti-poetic."
- Decide which position you will argue.
- Strengthen your position by thinking about what the other side will say and building an argument against it.

When you present your position, speak clearly and specifically about why you believe the poem to be a good one or a bad one.

Research and Technology

As you collect or create graphics to **illustrate** one of the Imagist poems, use the Internet or books in the library. Keep a list of possible graphics in the chart below. Use graphic arts software to create an illustration that goes with the poem.

Art work used: Web sites?	Color? Black and white?	How to set words of poem with artwork?

Rough sketch of how final product will look

Read and display the finished product to your classmates, and then add your illustration to a classroom display.

Imagist Poets
Enrichment: Music

Ezra Pound in "A Few Don'ts by an Imagiste" says that the art of poetry "has exact parallels in music." Imagiste poets used repetition of sounds, and a variety of rhythms to create a musical quality in their poems.

A. DIRECTIONS: *Draw on your knowledge about poetry and music to fill in the following chart. Compare how poetry and music both use rhythm and emotional content to create a mood or to communicate a feeling. Select individual pieces of music that reflect the mood and the musical rhythms of each of the poems. You may consider any and all types of music, including classical, folk, rock, and jazz.*

Poem	Music
"The River-Merchant's Wife: A Letter"	
"In a Station of the Metro"	
"The Red Wheelbarrow"	
"The Great Figure"	
"This is Just to Say"	
"Pear Tree"	
"Heat"	

B. DIRECTIONS: *On the lines provided, explain in what ways the music you have selected reflects the moods and musical rhythms of the poems.*

_____

_____

_____

_____

_____

_____

_____

_____

Imagist Poets
Selection Test A

Critical Reading *Identify the letter of the choice that best answers the question.*

____ 1. For whom is the poet writing "A Few Don'ts by an Imagiste"?
A. for musicians
B. for painters
C. for writers of poetry
D. for writers of prose

____ 2. In "A Few Don'ts by an Imagiste," why does the poet say poetry should be written as though it is music?
A. because Imagist poems are written by people who can't write music
B. because Imagist poets use many adjectives, just like musicians
C. because Imagist poems are unlike all other forms of art except music
D. because Imagist poems are complicated, like music

____ 3. In "The River-Merchant's Wife: A Letter," what image does the poet use to show that much time has passed since the husband first left?
A. He used bamboo stilts.
B. Monkeys make noise in the trees.
C. The butterflies are yellow.
D. The moss by the gate has grown deep.

____ 4. In "The River-Merchant's Wife: A Letter," what growth does the wife describe in the letter?
A. her remembrance of her childhood
B. her growing love for her husband
C. her shyness when she first married
D. her trip up to the lookout

____ 5. In "The River-Merchant's Wife: A Letter," what is suggested by the wife's memory of hair that "was still cut straight across" her forehead?
A. It refers to her knowledge of hairstyles.
B. It refers to the hairstyle she has now.
C. It refers to her hairstyle as a bride.
D. It refers to her childhood hairstyle.

____ 6. To what does the poet compare his experience in the metro in "In a Station of the Metro"?

    A. to walking through a crowd in a train

    B. to meeting ghosts in a rainy forest

    C. to picking flowers in a rainstorm

    D. to trying to find someone in a crowd

____ 7. In "The Red Wheelbarrow," which of the following conveys an image of something concrete that you could feel or see?

    A. so much

    B. depends

    C. upon

    D. wheelbarrow

____ 8. To which sense do the clanging gongs and howling sirens appeal in "The Great Figure"?

    A. sight

    B. smell

    C. touch

    D. sound

____ 9. To which senses do the images of sweet, cold plums appeal in "This is Just to Say"?

    A. smell and sight

    B. taste and touch

    C. sound and touch

    D. sound and smell

____ 10. What is the main image conveyed by the silver "mass" in "Pear Tree"?

    A. a speaker touching a pear tree

    B. the blossoms on a pear tree

    C. the height of a pear tree

    D. people standing under a pear tree

Vocabulary and Grammar

____ 11. Which word best replaces *voluminous* in this sentence: "The writer made *voluminous* notes that took up pages and pages"?

    A. confused

    B. many

    C. few

    D. loving

____ **12.** Which of the following phrases shows a concrete noun that can be felt or seen?
  A. feeling lonely
  B. higher than the sky
  C. two people
  D. dislike and disgust

Essay

13. In "A Few Don'ts by an Imagiste," Pound says, "Don't imagine that a thing will 'go' in verse just because it's too dull to go in prose." What do you think he means by this "Don't"? Does he believe it is easier to write good poetry than good prose? Or does he believe that a writer should not confuse the two? Write a brief essay to give your ideas.

14. "The Red Wheelbarrow" describes a red wheelbarrow near some white chickens. The wheelbarrow is covered in rainwater. To what sense does this poem mainly appeal? Where do you think this poem takes place? What are some other images you might add to the poem? Write a brief essay to address these questions.

Name _____ Date _____

Critical Reading *Identify the letter of the choice that best completes the statement or answers the question.*

____ 1. In Pound's "The River-Merchant's Wife: A Letter," why does the young wife wish to meet her husband at Cho-fu-Sa?
   A. She is frightened of being alone.
   B. She is bored with her life at home.
   C. She misses her husband terribly.
   D. She is eager to see the goods he has bought in his travels.

____ 2. Which idea is represented by the description of the two children in the first stanza of "The River-Merchant's Wife: A Letter"?
   A. ignorance
   B. innocence
   C. mortality
   D. romance

____ 3. Which of the following senses is *not* appealed to by the following line from Ezra Pound's "The River-Merchant's Wife: A Letter"?
   I played about the front gate, pulling flowers.
   A. sight
   B. smell
   C. taste
   D. touch

____ 4. Which of the following statements best communicates the meaning of "In a Station of the Metro"?
   A. Human contact in the city is as vulnerable and fleeting as a petal in a rainstorm.
   B. People rush around so fast in cities that they disappear as quickly as they appear.
   C. To a person with a very good imagination, petals on a branch can look like faces.
   D. In the darkness of a subway station, faces can suddenly look like flower petals.

____ 5. What mood is evoked by the imagery in "In a Station of the Metro"?
   A. confusion
   B. despair
   C. joy
   D. wistfulness

____ 6. William Carlos Williams wrote poetry that evokes emotions and ideas through its presentation of
   A. abstract objects.
   B. things.
   C. simple ideas.
   D. complex ideas.

___ 7. The influence of Imagism in "The Red Wheelbarrow" is most clearly reflected in the
   A. emotions suggested in the poem.
   B. use of musical rhythms.
   C. simplicity of the images and language.
   D. lack of rhyme.

___ 8. Which of the following statements best describes the image Williams creates in his poem "The Red Wheelbarrow"?
   A. The image has a single, specific meaning that the author conveys successfully.
   B. The image is open to interpretation based on the individual reader's emotional and intellectual response.
   C. The image has a meaning that can't be expressed in prose.
   D. The image closely resembles a painting.

___ 9. Which of the senses are engaged by Williams's poem, "This Is Just to Say"?
   A. sight and hearing
   B. sight and taste
   C. sight, hearing, and taste
   D. sight, taste, and touch

___ 10. Which detail best conveys H. D.'s spiritual feelings about the pear tree?
   A. "no flower ever parted silver/from such rare silver"
   B. "higher than my arms reach/you front us with great mass"
   C. "no flower ever opened/so staunch a white leaf"
   D. "bring summer and ripe fruits/in their purple hearts"

___ 11. Which statement best summarizes the theme of "Pear Tree"?
   A. The pear tree is so beautiful that it hardly seems real.
   B. The blossoming pear tree symbolizes the coming of summer.
   C. The beauty of the pear tree symbolizes the enormous gap between humans and nature.
   D. The pear tree embodies both celestial and earthly beauty.

___ 12. To which senses does the imagery in "Pear Tree" appeal most strongly?
   A. hearing and smell
   B. sight and touch
   C. sight and hearing
   D. taste and touch

___ 13. In "Heat," the lines "O wind, rend open the heat,/cut apart the heat,/rend it to tatters" allow the reader to imagine the heat as a
   A. comforting blanket.
   B. delicate veil.
   C. heavy curtain.
   D. swinging door.

____ 14. By creating an image of the wind as a plow, H. D. suggests that the wind can
   A. generate cooler temperatures.
   B. blow the heat away.
   C. break up the heat.
   D. bring the rain.

Vocabulary and Grammar

____ 15. Which of the following words is closest in meaning to the italicized word in the following sentence?

   It is better to present one Image in a lifetime than to produce *voluminous* works.

   A. plentiful
   B. large
   C. insightful
   D. precise

____ 16. Which of the following words is closest in meaning to the word *apparition*?
   A. disappearance
   B. mistiness
   C. beauty
   D. phantom

____ 17. An abstract noun *cannot* name
   A. a quality such as value.
   B. a characteristic such as intelligence.
   C. an idea such as freedom.
   D. a particular flower.

Essay

18. The poems of William Carlos Williams emphasize what he called "the here and now"—the exact moment of an experience rather than its meaning or implications. Do you think this is a simplistic way of looking at life, or do you think it has some value? Explain your ideas in an essay.

19. Imagism as a poetic movement flourished for less than a decade. In his later years, William Carlos Williams said, "We have been looking for too big, too spectacular a divergence from the old. . . . It was a natural blunder from the excess of our own feelings." Write an essay in which you express your opinion of Williams's statement. Base your essay upon his three poems in this unit—"The Red Wheelbarrow," "The Great Figure," and "This Is Just to Say"— that were written under the influence of Imagism.

20. Imagist poets tried to create vivid, precise images that produce a sudden moment of illumination. They excluded all but the essential details needed to create an emotional response. Ezra Pound's fourteen-word poem "In a Station of the Metro" is a classic work of Imagism. It began as a thirty-line poem based on Pound's observation of a group of beautiful faces as he stepped off a subway train in Paris. Write an essay in which you speculate on what Pound might have included in his original, longer description of the incident. Use the content of "In a Station of the Metro" as your point of departure.

Study these words from the selection. Then, complete the activities.

Word List A

catering [KAYT uhr ing] *v.* attending to the wants or needs of
   I want to get it myself, so please stop <u>catering</u> to me.

imperceptible [im per SEPT uh buhl] *adj.* very small or slight; difficult to observe
   Judy speaks with a foreign accent, although it is virtually <u>imperceptible</u>.

insincere [in sin SEER] *adj.* not sincere; hypocritical
   Laurie knew that her boyfriend was <u>insincere</u> because he couldn't look her in the eye.

involuntarily [in vahl uhn TER uh lee] *adv.* unintentionally; against one's will
   The baby <u>involuntarily</u> kicked his mother when she bent over him.

irrelevant [i REL uh vuhnt] *adj.* unrelated to the matter
   The teacher doesn't have time to respond to <u>irrelevant</u> questions.

justified [JUST uh fyd] *v.* proved to be right or correct; validated
   Cassie <u>justified</u> her anger by remarking that her friends forgot to call her.

obnoxious [ahb NOK shuhs] *adj.* very unpleasant; objectionable; offensive
   We thought that Keith's loud, unruly behavior at the party was <u>obnoxious</u>.

veranda [vuh RAN duh] *n.* porch or balcony along the side of a building
   Since it was too hot inside the house, we ate supper outside on the <u>veranda</u>.

Word List B

contemptuously [kahn TEMP choo uhs lee] *adv.* scornfully
   My Great-aunt Harriet views young people <u>contemptuously</u>, believing them to be lazy.

exaggeration [eg zaj uh RAY shuhn] *n.* act of making something more noticeable than usual
   Stephanie recognized that the sales pitch for the new car was an <u>exaggeration</u>.

haughty [HAW tee] *adj.* proud; arrogant; disdainful
   Mr. Simon made it clear that he was a <u>haughty</u> aristocrat.

poignant [POI nyuhnt] *adj.* sharply painful to the feelings
   Robert's <u>poignant</u> speech brought tears to my eyes.

precariously [pree KAYR ee uhs lee] *adv.* in a dangerous, unstable manner
   Arnie set the vase <u>precariously</u> balanced on a narrow shelf.

recede [ree SEED] *v.* to move backward; to become fainter or more distant
   The memory of this bad day will eventually <u>recede</u>.

transcended [tran SEND uhd] *v.* went beyond or over
   Shakespeare's plays <u>transcended</u> the Elizabethan Age, and they are still popular today.

unconsciously [un KAHN shuhs lee] *adv.* in a manner without awareness or feeling
   Eve <u>unconsciously</u> bites her fingernails when she is nervous.

"Winter Dreams" by F. Scott Fitzgerald
Vocabulary Warm-up Exercises

Exercise A *Fill in the blanks, using each word from Word List A only once.*

"Chez Matisse" was the best French restaurant in town. Its owner and principal chef, André Latour, had been [1] _____ to a well-heeled gourmet crowd for over twenty years. André insisted on elegant, courteous service, and he could grow irritated or even [2] _____ with his staff if they were slack. For others, a slight decline in service might be [3] _____, but not for André. He considered no detail unrelated or [4] _____. Every aspect of his customers' dining experience fully [5] _____ his personal attention. One evening, the mayor came to dinner, together with a large group of guests. They sat outside on the [6] _____. After the main course, André stopped by their table. "I hope you don't think I am [7] _____, André," said the mayor, "but you are a marvel!" André [8] _____ shrugged his shoulders and smiled slightly. "It is my profession, Your Honor," he replied.

Exercise B *Revise each sentence so that the underlined vocabulary word is logical.*

Example: Tim had such <u>dexterity</u> that he had trouble handling the ball.
Tim had such <u>dexterity</u> that he had no trouble handling the ball.

1. We appreciated it when Ronnie greeted us so <u>contemptuously</u>.
_____

2. Sam was fond of <u>exaggeration</u> and used understatement in many anecdotes he told.
_____

3. Mel's <u>haughty</u> expression signaled that he had a humble outlook on life.
_____

4. The story was so <u>poignant</u> that it failed to move us.
_____

5. The vase wouldn't fall over because it was balanced so <u>precariously</u> on the shelf.
_____

6. As the tide began to <u>recede</u>, we moved farther on the beach to avoid getting wet.
_____

7. That writer's works <u>transcended</u> her times and have failed to appeal to modern readers.
_____

8. Tricia was <u>unconsciously</u> pleased by the music and spent a lot of time analyzing it.
_____

"Winter Dreams" by F. Scott Fitzgerald
Reading Warm-up A

Read the following passage. Pay special attention to the underlined words. Then, read it again, and complete the activities. Use a separate sheet of paper for your written answers.

F. Scott Fitzgerald's most famous novel, *The Great Gatsby*, is now regarded as an American classic. Jay Gatsby, the book's central character, is a fascinating figure. On one level, he is offensive and even <u>obnoxious</u>. It is implied, for example, that he has made his vast fortune in shady, maybe even illegal, business deals. Gatsby's showy, extravagant parties reveal him as somewhat <u>insincere</u> and hypocritical. He is no more interested in the crowds of socialites and exploiters he invites to his mansion than they are interested in him. Gatsby is <u>catering</u> to his guests as a means of impressing Daisy Buchanan, the lost love he hopes to win back. This goal, in Gatsby's mind, has <u>justified</u> all the attention and expense he lavishes on the partygoers congregating regularly on his splendid <u>veranda</u> and manicured lawns.

During much of *The Great Gatsby*, Fitzgerald strongly criticizes the shallowness and moral bankruptcy of American life in the Jazz Age. Yet it is not <u>irrelevant</u> to note that, at the same time, Fitzgerald's novel combines satire and irony with a profound streak of humanity. Slowly and almost <u>imperceptibly</u>, for example, Gatsby himself becomes a somewhat sympathetic figure. We begin to see him as a victim of his own illusions. He is <u>involuntarily</u> struggling in a trap that he has misidentified as the American Dream. Toward the end of the book, Gatsby's funeral is attended only by his father and one former guest. It is impossible not to feel sorry for him.

1. Underline the words in this and the next sentence that give a clue to the meaning of <u>obnoxious</u>. Use the word *obnoxious* in a sentence.

2. Circle the words in this sentence that hint at the meaning of <u>insincere</u>. What are two antonyms for *insincere*?

3. Underline the words in this sentence that give a clue to the meaning of <u>catering</u>. Use *catering* in a sentence.

4. Underline the words in this sentence that hint at the meaning of <u>justified</u>. What is a synonym for *justified* in this context?

5. Circle the words in this sentence that offer a clue to the meaning of <u>veranda</u>. Write a sentence describing a real or imaginary *veranda*.

6. Underline the words in this sentence that give a clue to the meaning of <u>irrelevant</u>. What is an antonym for *irrelevant*?

7. Circle the words in this sentence that give a clue to the meaning of the word <u>imperceptibly</u>. What is an antonym for *imperceptibly*?

8. Underline the word in this sentence that gives a clue to the meaning of <u>involuntarily</u>. What is a synonym for the word *involuntarily*?

"**Winter Dreams**" by F. Scott Fitzgerald
Reading Warm-up B

Read the following passage. Pay special attention to the underlined words. Then, read it again, and complete the activities. Use a separate sheet of paper for your written answers.

For a long time, the only way Joshua could deal with his crush on Nicolette Peters was to write about it in his notebook. In reality, he had no chance with her—she was beautiful and rich, a <u>haughty</u> figure who looked down on everyone else at school. When she passed Joshua in the hall, she would stare <u>contemptuously</u> straight ahead in scorn, as if he wasn't there.

In his journal, however, Joshua's fantasies took over, and all the differences between him and Nicolette would <u>recede</u> into the background. He would become a different person: older, not a student but a businessman with all the money in the world. They would go on safari together, or travel to Paris, or go hang-gliding in Montana, the two of them perched <u>precariously</u> a thousand feet above the ground. To impress someone like Nicolette Peters—to win her heart—would require money. Joshua didn't realize it, but <u>unconsciously</u> he had made an equation between money and love. In all the stories he wrote about his future with Nicolette, it was always through material wealth that they <u>transcended</u> the gulf between them. When he thought of Nicolette, he thought of champagne and yachts, of lavish hotels, and of how much she would admire him for being able to afford these splendors.

Then one day, he saw Nicolette at a fast-food restaurant, of all places. She had just spilled a chocolate milkshake all over herself, and she caught him looking, and she yelled at him to get away from her. She looked so ordinary—not to mention angry—that suddenly his fantasies of her seemed like a ridiculous <u>exaggeration</u>. He could hardly look at his journal after that, for it had become a lost dream, a <u>poignant</u> reminder of feelings he no longer had.

1. Underline the words in this sentence that hint at the meaning of <u>haughty</u>. What is a synonym for *haughty*?

2. Circle the words in this sentence that hint at the meaning of the word <u>contemptuously</u>. What are two antonyms for the word *contemptuously*?

3. Underline the words in this sentence that hint at the meaning of <u>recede</u>. Use *recede* in an original sentence.

4. Underline the words in this sentence that hint at the meaning of <u>precariously</u>. What is an antonym for *precariously*?

5. Circle the words in this sentence that hint at the meaning of <u>unconsciously</u>. Use *unconsciously* in a sentence of your own.

6. Circle the words in this sentence that give good clues to the meaning of <u>transcended</u>. What is a synonym for *transcended*?

7. Underline the words in this sentence that hint at the meaning of <u>exaggeration</u>. What is an antonym for *exaggeration*?

8. Underline the words in this sentence that hint at the meaning of <u>poignant</u>. What is a synonym for *poignant*?

Name _____   Date _____

"Winter Dreams" by F. Scott Fitzgerald
Literary Analysis: Characterization

To emphasize a character's personality traits, a writer often may build into the story deliberate contrasts and comparisons with other characters. Fitzgerald uses this technique as he develops the character of Judy in "Winter Dreams."

Answer the following questions, citing details from the story to support your answers.

1. In contrast to Judy's "glittering" personality, what kind of personality does Irene have?

   _____

   _____

   _____

2. In which ways is Judy like her father?

   _____

   _____

   _____

3. In one passage, Fitzgerald characterizes Judy's house. What is the house like, and how is it different from Judy?

   _____

   _____

   _____

4. Fitzgerald's two main characters are not "one-sided." Both of them have qualities that seem contradictory, but each is a totally believable human being. Judy, for example, is both a flighty, insensitive flirt and a forlorn, confused young woman. Now consider the character of Dexter. What is the contrast between his attitude toward Judy and his attitude toward his career? How do these contrasting traits make him seem believable?

   _____

   _____

   _____

   _____

   _____

Name _____ Date _____

"Winter Dreams" by F. Scott Fitzgerald
Reading Strategy: Draw Conclusions About Characters

When you read a story, you can **draw conclusions about characters** by combining information from the story with your personal knowledge of human behavior. To draw conclusions, you often need to read between the lines to infer emotions and motivations that are not directly stated.

DIRECTIONS: *Read each excerpt from "Winter Dreams." Then answer the question that follows.*

1. As so frequently would be the case in the future, Dexter was unconsciously dictated to by his winter dreams.
   Does Dexter always plan his moves carefully and then follow them, or does he sometimes behave impetuously?

   _____

2. "You hit me in the stomach!" declared Mr. Hedrick wildly. / "Did I?" [Judy] approached the group of men. "I'm sorry. I yelled 'Fore!'" / ". . . Here I am! I'd have gone on the green except that I hit something."
   How does Judy probably feel about hitting Mr. Hedrick?

   _____

3. [Judy] wore a blue silk afternoon dress, and [Dexter] was disappointed at first that she had not put on something more elaborate.
   What does Judy's behavior towards Dexter on their first date reveal about her?

   _____

4. [Dexter] had been born in Keeble, a Minnesota village fifty miles farther north, and he always gave Keeble as his home instead of Black Bear Village. Country towns were well enough to come from if they weren't inconveniently in sight and used as footstools by fashionable lakes.
   How does Dexter probably feel about his background?

   _____

5. There was a pause. Then [Judy] smiled and the corners of her mouth drooped and an almost imperceptible sway brought her closer to [Dexter], looking up into his eyes.
   How does Judy use her physical attractiveness to her advantage?

   _____

"**Winter Dreams**" by F. Scott Fitzgerald
Vocabulary Builder

Using the Root -somn-

A. DIRECTIONS: *The word* somnolent *combines the adjective-forming suffix* -ent, *which means "that has, says, or does," and the word root* -somn-, *which means "sleep." The word* somnolent, *therefore, means "sleepy." Using the information following each word and what you know about the word root* -somn-, *write the word that best completes each sentence.*

insomnia (in = "not")   somnambulate (ambulare = "to walk")
somniferous (ferre = "to bring")   somniloquy (loqui = "to speak")

1. Whenever Becky would _____, her dog followed her cautiously.
2. Barry often found that a warm glass of milk was a _____ bedtime treat.
3. Corinne was so worried about the test that she had _____.
4. Kurt's habit of _____ embarrassed him when he said too much one night.

Using the Word List

fallowness	preposterous	fortuitous	sinuous
mundane	poignant	pugilistic	somnolent

B. DIRECTIONS: *In each blank, write the letter of the choice that is closest in meaning to the word in italics.*

___ 1. a *mundane* activity
   A. marvelous
   B. commonplace
   C. wavy
   D. sneaky

___ 2. a *preposterous* idea
   A. on purpose
   B. perfect
   C. unusual
   D. ridiculous

___ 3. the field's *fallowness*
   A. inactivity
   B. foulness
   C. shallowness
   D. following

___ 4. a *pugilistic* attitude
   A. pug-nosed
   B. piglike
   C. calm
   D. like a boxer

___ 5. a *poignant* moment
   A. picky
   B. painful
   C. poor
   D. wealthy

___ 6. a *fortuitous* event
   A. unlucky
   B. fifth
   C. chance
   D. lazy

___ 7. a *somnolent* mood
   A. shaky
   B. lively
   C. sleepy
   D. thin

___ 8. a *sinuous* turn
   A. wavy
   B. tough
   C. straight
   D. right

"Winter Dreams" by F. Scott Fitzgerald
Grammar and Style: Dashes

Dashes are used to introduce information that either interrupts the flow of the text or requires the reader's immediate attention. Dashes may set off appositions, modifiers, or dramatic phrases. The frequent use of dashes in "Winter Dreams" reflects the jumbled emotions portrayed in the story.

A. PRACTICE: *The sentences below are from "Winter Dreams." Insert dashes where necessary by writing a ^ between the words where each dash should be.*

1. And one day it came to pass that Mr. Jones himself and not his ghost came up to Dexter with tears in his eyes. . . .

2. There was a general ungodliness in the way her lips twisted down at the corners when she smiled, and in the Heaven help us! in the almost passionate quality of her eyes.

3. He knew that if he moved forward a step his stare would be in her line of vision if he moved backward he would lose his full view of her face.

4. [His parents] persuaded Dexter several years later to pass up a business course at the State university his father, prospering now, would have paid his way for the precarious advantage of attending an older and more famous university in the East. . . .

B. Writing Application: *Combine each set of phrases or sentences into one sentence by using dashes.*

1. "That Judy Jones!" remarked Mr. Hedrick on the next tee, as they waited for her to play on ahead. They waited some moments.

_____

2. He had a rather priggish notion that he should know more about such things. He was the young and already fabulously successful Dexter Green.

_____

3. He loved her, and he would love her until the day he was too old for loving. But he could not have her.

_____

4. Early in that summer morning the sun rose slowly up into the hazy sky. The sun was reddish and swollen.

_____

"Winter Dreams" by F. Scott Fitzgerald
Support for Writing

Prepare to write a **character analysis** of Dexter Green by collecting information from the story in the graphic organizer below.

Dexter Green's Character

Dexter Green's Thoughts and Feelings	**Examples from story:**
Dexter Green's Appearance	**Examples from story:**
Dexter Green's Actions	**Examples from story:**
My Conclusions About Dexter Green's Character	**He is the kind of person who** _____ _____ _____ _____

On a separate page, open your character analysis with a main idea statement about Dexter's character. Then, provide evidence to support your conclusion. When you revise, add more examples from the story to back up your opinions.

"Winter Dreams" by F. Scott Fitzgerald
Support for Extend Your Learning

Listening and Speaking

As you think of songs that might remind Dexter of Judy, narrow down your list to one song to use as a **presentation** to the class. Use these tips:

- Think about the kind of music that would be most suitable—would a piece of modern music work? Or do you need to use music from the Jazz Age?
- Practice speaking about the characters for a while, then using the song to emphasize your points. Go back and forth a few times between playing the music and discussing their relationship.

When you make your presentation, talk about how people often respond when they hear music.

Research and Technology

As you research the lives and work of F. Scott and Zelda Fitzgerald, enter information into the chart below. Use the information to write a **report** that shows the connections between their relationship and his fiction.

What is the most interesting information you found about the relationship of F. Scott and Zelda Fitzgerald?	What is the most interesting information you found about F. Scott Fitzgerald's fiction?
What connection can you make between their lives together and his writing?	

Name _____ Date _____

"**Winter Dreams**" by F. Scott Fitzgerald
Enrichment: Film

DIRECTIONS: *Fitzgerald considered "Winter Dreams" a first draft for* The Great Gatsby, *a novel he wrote in 1925. Obtain and watch a copy of the film version of* The Great Gatsby. *As you watch the movie, consider the characters and plot in "Winter Dreams." In the space below, write comparisons of leading characters in, and the plots of, the story and the movie. Finally, discuss whether "Winter Dreams" could be a first draft of* The Great Gatsby. *Support your opinion with examples from both the story and the movie.*

Compare and Contrast

1. Dexter Green and Jay Gatsby: _____

_____

_____

_____

2. Judy Jones and Daisy Buchanan: _____

_____

_____

_____

3. Plot of "Winter Dreams" and plot of *The Great Gatsby*: _____

_____

_____

_____

_____

Analyze

4. Fitzgerald considered "Winter Dreams" a first draft for *The Great Gatsby*. In my opinion,

_____

_____

_____

_____

_____

_____

Name _____ Date _____

"**Winter Dreams**" by F. Scott Fitzgerald

Selection Test A

Critical Reading *Identify the letter of the choice that best answers the question.*

_____ 1. How is the character of Dexter revealed when he says, "There aren't any caddies here except me" in "Winter Dreams"?

    A. by the character's thoughts

    B. by the character's actions

    C. by the character's words

    D. by a description of the character

_____ 2. What effect does Judy's changing personality have on Dexter in "Winter Dreams"?

    A. It makes him forget about her.

    B. It makes him work harder.

    C. It makes him fascinated with her.

    D. It makes him think she is ill.

_____ 3. In "Winter Dreams," how is the character of Dexter revealed when the writer says that he was a favorite caddy?

    A. by the character's words

    B. by the character's thoughts

    C. by the character's actions

    D. by the writer's description

_____ 4. In "Winter Dreams," what conclusion can be drawn after Dexter sees Judy for the first time?

    A. Judy will learn to be a good golfer.

    B. Judy will be important to him.

    C. Judy will become his wife.

    D. Judy will ask Dexter to caddy.

_____ 5. In "Winter Dreams," what conclusion can be drawn about Judy based on her behavior toward the men on the golf course?

    A. She doesn't care whom she hurts.

    B. She wants to improve her golf game.

    C. She takes responsibility for herself.

    D. She hopes to meet Dexter again.

Unit 5 Resources: Disillusion, Defiance, and Discontent

_____ 6. In "Winter Dreams," how does Judy appear when she refuses to marry a poor man?

A. She seems friendly.

B. She seems small-minded.

C. She seems religious.

D. She seems unhappy.

_____ 7. Why does Dexter quit his caddying job in "Winter Dreams"?

A. He is thinking about Judy.

B. He is going to study instead.

C. He wants to be wealthy.

D. He is bored by the work.

_____ 8. What is a theme of "Winter Dreams"?

A. Life without dreams is unfulfilling.

B. Physical beauty is unimportant.

C. Dreams can be disappointing.

D. Living for love is all important.

_____ 9. Why does Dexter become engaged to Irene Scheerer in "Winter Dreams"?

A. He wants to share in her wealth.

B. He wants a more steady life.

C. He no longer loves Judy Jones.

D. He wants to make Judy jealous.

_____ 10. In "Winter Dreams," what conclusion can be drawn about Dexter as he weeps at the end of the story?

A. He has a difficult time with grief.

B. He has lost the dreams he once had.

C. He wishes he had never met Judy.

D. He does not want to grow old.

Vocabulary and Grammar

_____ 11. Which word best replaces *poignant* in this sentence: "The author's description was so *poignant* that the reader cried"?

A. pretty

B. hopeful

C. painful

D. fancy

___ **12.** In which sentence are dashes used correctly?

    A. Judy, a beautiful woman—influenced Dexter's decisions.

    B. Dexter—a caddy—first met Judy at the golf course.

    C. Dexter hated the spring—but loved—the fall.

    D. Dexter was engaged—to Irene, but he called it off.

Essay

13. In "Winter Dreams," why do you think Dexter is so angry at the end of the story, when Devlin describes Judy as no longer very attractive? What does this picture of Judy say about Dexter and the way he has lived his life? Write a brief essay that explains what Dexter wanted to believe about Judy and how he has been disappointed.

14. In "Winter Dreams," the author says that Dexter "wanted the glittering things themselves." How does this description explain Dexter's attraction to Judy? What conclusions can you draw about why Dexter weeps at the end of the story? Write a brief essay to answer these questions.

"Winter Dreams" by F. Scott Fitzgerald
Selection Test B

Critical Reading *Identify the letter of the choice that best completes the statement or answers the question.*

____ 1. Why is the following passage a particularly telling characterization?

When, as Judy's head lay against his shoulder that first night, she whispered, "I don't know what's the matter with me. Last night I thought I was in love with a man and tonight I think I'm in love with you—" it seemed to him a beautiful and romantic thing to say. It was the exquisite excitability that for the moment he controlled and owned.

   A. It reveals the basic thrust of both Judy's and Dexter's feelings.
   B. It explains why Dexter is so drawn to Judy.
   C. It shows how young both Judy and Dexter really are.
   D. It illustrates the fact that Dexter has lost touch with reality.

____ 2. Judy's alternating indifference and attention to Dexter have the effect of
   A. making him feel confused about what he wants.
   B. ultimately strengthening his resolve to resist her.
   C. making her even more desirable to him.
   D. helping him learn that hard work is the best way to deaden painful feelings.

____ 3. When Dexter Green first meets Judy Jones, she is about to beat her nurse. The reader learns that Dexter believes Judy may be justified in beating the nurse. What does this tell the reader?
   A. Judy is a moral child.
   B. Dexter is enthralled by Judy.
   C. Judy is unusually weak for a girl.
   D. Dexter has no sense of right and wrong.

____ 4. Upon his second encounter with Judy Jones, when she hits Mr. Hedrick with a golf ball, Dexter Green is overwhelmed by her _____.
   A. sincerity
   B. intelligence
   C. bad manners
   D. beauty

____ 5. Who is the most important person to Judy Jones as a young woman?
   A. her father
   B. Dexter Green
   C. the next man she meets
   D. herself

____ 6. Which character trait does Dexter establish when he quits his caddying job?
   A. abandoning his commitments
   B. choosing paths that will lead to success
   C. seeking unattainable goals
   D. letting his obsession with Judy control his decisions

_____ 7. Fitzgerald first reveals Dexter's reverence for the ideals of high society by
  A. describing his dreams as a teenager.
  B. commenting that Dexter reached out for the best.
  C. revealing Dexter's thoughts about the men for whom he caddies.
  D. describing his first reaction to Judy Jones.

_____ 8. Why is Judy Jones's beauty important to her character?
  A. She was such an ugly child.
  B. She uses it to get what she wants.
  C. It gives a contrast to her humbleness.
  D. It allows her to move into a higher social circle.

_____ 9. Why does Dexter Green quit seeing Irene Scheerer?
  A. Dexter decides to become engaged to Judy Jones instead.
  B. Irene's parents strongly object to Dexter, so she breaks the engagement.
  C. Irene tells Dexter she is in love with a man from New York.
  D. Dexter decides that, although pleasant, Irene is too boring for him.

_____ 10. After Judy Jones hits Mr. Hedrick with a golf ball, the reader learns "[h]er glance fell casually on each of the men—then scanned the fairway for her ball." From this, the reader can conclude that Judy Jones was
  A. ashamed that she had hit Mr. Hedrick and did not want him to look her in the eye.
  B. embarrassed about being such a bad golfer.
  C. concerned more about where her shot lay than about Mr. Hedrick.
  D. overwhelmed by Dexter Green and did not want him to figure that out.

_____ 11. Which of the following statements best describes the theme of "Winter Dreams"?
  A. Those whose lives are based on the pursuit of illusions are doomed to disappointment.
  B. A person without dreams or illusions cannot live a full life.
  C. Love that is based on physical beauty cannot be as satisfying as love based on inner character.
  D. The pursuit of material satisfaction interferes with the pursuit of emotional satisfaction.

_____ 12. Dexter Green probably becomes engaged to Irene Scheerer because of his
  A. strong love for Irene.
  B. jealous fit over Judy Jones.
  C. desire for stability.
  D. desire for Irene's inheritance.

_____ 13. Why does Fitzgerald choose not to provide a physical description of Dexter?
  A. Dexter's appearance is important only to the point that Judy is attracted to him.
  B. Dexter's lack of physical characteristics makes him more puzzling and enigmatic.
  C. Judy's beauty is emphasized by the lack of physical details about Dexter.
  D. The story is about Dexter's personality and his emotional and mental traits.

Vocabulary and Grammar

____ 14. Which of the following would a "*pugilistic* youth" be most likely to do?
   A. serenade a woman with a love song
   B. be one of the best dancers at a ball
   C. start a fight with another boy
   D. be the richest student in his class

____ 15. Which word is closest in meaning to the italicized word in the following phrase?

   the great white bulk of the Mortimer Joneses' house, *somnolent*, gorgeous, drenched with the splendor of the damp moonlight

   A. drowsy
   B. enormous
   C. radiant
   D. proud

____ 16. What image does Fitzgerald portray when he says Judy Jones was "swimming to the floating surfboard with a sinuous crawl"?
   A. Judy swims noisily.
   B. Judy swims quickly.
   C. Judy swims sleepily.
   D. Judy swims gracefully.

____ 17. In which of the following excerpts do the dashes interrupt what someone is saying?
   A. "'The best—caddy I ever saw,' shouted Mr. Mortimer Jones over a drink that afternoon."
   B. ". . . in the way her lips twisted down at the corners when she smiled, and the—Heaven help us!—in the almost passionate quality of her eyes."
   C. "The smile again—radiant, blatantly artificial—convincing."
   D. "When he was twenty-three Mr. Hart—one of the gray-haired men who like to say 'Now there's a boy'—gave him a guest card . . ."

Essay

18. In real life, people have contradictory attributes—particularly in their desires and needs—making them complete and complicated human beings. When, like real people, fictional characters possess contradictory attributes, a story is more believable and successful. Choose one of the story's main characters—Dexter Green or Judy Jones—and write an essay describing his or her attributes. How are the character's wants and needs contradictory? Would the character be as convincing without contradictory attributes?

19. Many of Fitzgerald's stories embody the author's fascination with and growing distrust of America's wealthy society in the 1920's. Choose two characters from "Winter Dreams"—one who seems to share the author's fascination and one who might represent the wealthy society he distrusts. Write an essay explaining how Fitzgerald's fascination and distrust are manifested in the two characters. How do the characters interact? What does this interaction show about Fitzgerald's fascination and distrust? Support your analysis with details from the story.

Vocabulary Warm-up Word Lists

Study these words from the selection. Then, complete the activities.

Word List A

boosted [BOOST uhd] *v.* raised; lifted up
Lisa <u>boosted</u> her son up onto her shoulder.

clamped [KLAMPD] *v.* fastened; gripped
Hilary <u>clamped</u> the lid of her suitcase shut.

embankment [em BANK muhnt] *n.* mound of earth raised to hold back water
We enjoyed the view of the river from the <u>embankment</u>.

flick [FLIK] *v.* to twitch or flutter
Abigail likes to <u>flick</u> her skirt when she dances.

fraction [FRAK shuhn] *n.* small part of a whole
If you move over a <u>fraction</u>, we'll all have more room on the bench.

plodding [PLAHD ing] *adj.* moving or walking heavily; trudging
<u>Plodding</u> up that long hill, the horses will soon become tired.

skidded [SKID uhd] *v.* slid sideways
Our car <u>skidded</u> on the ice.

trench [TRENCH] *n.* ditch
Martha dug a <u>trench</u> to hold the water that was dripping from the roof.

Word List B

armored [AR muhrd] *adj.* protected by a defensive covering
Military vehicles are usually <u>armored</u>.

dispersed [dis PERSD] *v.* scattered
The children blew on the dandelions and <u>dispersed</u> the seeds.

parapet [PAR uh pet] *n.* wall or edge of a roof or balcony
Expecting to be besieged, the soldiers took up a position on the castle's <u>parapet</u>.

passive [PAS iv] *adj.* inactive; offering little or no resistance
Tim is so <u>passive</u> about his job that it seems as if he doesn't really care.

peered [PEERD] *v.* looked intently; gazed; stared
The two boys <u>peered</u> through the window, trying to see inside the abandoned shed.

quartz [KWAHRTS] *n.* type of hard, crystallized rock
That shiny figurine is made out of <u>quartz</u>.

swerved [SWERVD] *v.* turned suddenly to the side
Driving late at night, Becky <u>swerved</u> so she wouldn't run over the raccoon.

waggling [WAG ling] *adj.* moving shakily; wobbling
The <u>waggling</u> wings of the bees show the direction of a food source at the hive.

Name _____ Date _____

"The Turtle" *from* **The Grapes of Wrath** by John Steinbeck
Vocabulary Warm-up Exercises

Exercise A *Fill in the blanks, using each word from Word List A only once.*

On Saturday morning, David [1] _____ the combination lock shut to tether his bike to a small tree. Soon he was [2] _____ slowly along the riverbank, binoculars in hand. Bird watching was his favorite hobby, and this morning he was looking for kingfishers. He knew that these fish-eating birds nest in a burrow they dig into a(n) [3] _____ beside a watercourse. The nesting chamber lies at the end of a [4] _____ or tunnel that may be as long as 10 feet. The tunnel's width, as small as 2 inches, is only a small [5] _____ of its length. This small opening makes kingfisher burrows hard to spot. David [6] _____ his chances of a sighting by watching for any kind of movement. If a kingfisher chanced to [7] _____ its brightly-colored feathers near the ground, there was a good chance its nest was nearby. Finally, he saw a flash of bright blue about thirty feet down-stream. A ringed kingfisher! The bird [8] _____ to a halt, looked directly at David, and then disappeared in an instant.

Exercise B *Decide whether each statement below is true or false. Circle* T *or* F, *and explain your answer.*

1. It is often difficult to resist or fight against an <u>armored</u> vehicle.
   T / F _____

2. When immigrants arrived in America, they often <u>dispersed</u> to different cities.
   T / F _____

3. A <u>parapet</u> is usually constructed very close to the ground.
   T / F _____

4. If your reactions to a crisis are <u>passive</u>, you take rapid and effective action.
   T / F _____

5. Someone who has <u>peered</u> into a telescope lens has likely stared intently.
   T / F _____

6. <u>Quartz</u> is a type of precious metal.
   T / F _____

7. If a car <u>swerved</u> suddenly, it made a rapid turn.
   T / F _____

8. Insects <u>waggling</u> their wings can be described as motionless.
   T / F _____

"The Turtle" *from* **The Grapes of Wrath** by John Steinbeck
Reading Warm-up A

Read the following passage. Pay special attention to the underlined words. Then, read it again, and complete the activities. Use a separate sheet of paper for your written answers.

When you think about it, turtles are amazing animals. Part of an ancient order of reptiles, the Chelonia turtles have many distinctive qualities. First and foremost is their hard shell, which is <u>clamped</u> on a turtle's back to protect the vital organs of its body. The shell has doubtless <u>boosted</u> or at least improved many turtles' chances of survival. In fact, this species outlives all other vertebrate creatures, including man. There is one record of a turtle surviving in the wild for 138 years.

Turtles are found all over the world. Land turtles are usually found close to water, for example, on a riverside <u>embankment</u> or near a <u>trench</u> that has been dug to serve as a canal or artificial watercourse. Land turtles are among the slowest-moving creatures in nature. One species, for example, has been clocked <u>plodding</u> along at one-third of a mile per hour!

A large <u>fraction</u> of turtle species are aquatic or sea turtles. Even these creatures, however, lay their eggs on land. Female green turtles, for example, crawl up the beach when it is time to lay eggs. At a point above high tide, they <u>flick</u> all four flippers rapidly to dig a nest in the sand. The female carefully deposits the eggs in the hole, covers it completely, and destroys all traces of the nest locations by flinging sand around with her front flippers. This process, which takes a few hours, is fascinating to watch. At many beaches throughout the world, tourists who have happened on the scene have often <u>skidded</u> to a halt and gazed at the mother turtles in fascination.

1. Underline the words in this sentence that give a clue to the meaning of <u>clamped</u>. What is an antonym for *clamped*?

2. Circle the words in this sentence that give a clue to the meaning of <u>boosted</u>. What are two synonyms for *boosted*?

3. Circle the word that offers a clue to the meaning of <u>embankment</u> here. Use the word *embankment* in an original sentence.

4. Circle the words in this sentence that offer clues to the meaning of <u>trench</u>. What is a synonym for *trench*?

5. Underline the words in this and the previous sentence that hint at the meaning of <u>plodding</u> here. What is a synonym for *plodding*?

6. Underline the words in this sentence that give a clue to the meaning of <u>fraction</u>. What is a synonym for *fraction*?

7. Circle the word in this sentence that gives a clue to the meaning of <u>flick</u>. Use the word *flick* in an original sentence.

8. What clue can you find in this sentence to the meaning of <u>skidded</u>?

Name _____ Date _____

Read the following passage. Pay special attention to the underlined words. Then, read it again, and complete the activities. Use a separate sheet of paper for your written answers.

One of John Steinbeck's most famous novels, *The Grapes of Wrath,* was inspired by a natural disaster of the early 1930s, the Dust Bowl. The term "Dust Bowl" refers to a geographical area as well as to an event. Until 1915 or so, the grasslands in this part of the Great Plains supported mainly cattle. After World War I, though, agricultural interests underline(swerved) suddenly, and millions of acres were plowed under to grow wheat. If farmers could have underline(peered) into the future and seen the consequences of this change, they would probably not have altered the area's ecology so dramatically.

Even in normal times, the Dust Bowl receives less than 20 inches of rainfall a year. Under a blistering sun, the flat prairie land shimmers, as if it were made of underline(quartz). Sometimes the only living creatures seem to be beetles, underline(waggling) their limbs to and fro as they move slowly in the intense heat.

Beginning in the early 1930s, a severe drought, combined with poor land management practices over the past decade, led to extreme conditions. Previously, the area's topsoil, underline(armored) with the water-retaining roots of native grasses, was stable. Now, heavy spring gusts underline(dispersed) the unprotected soil with such force that the dust storms were called "black blizzards." If you stood high up on a underline(parapet) during these storms, you could see the wind-blown dust being carried for huge distances. Some storms, in fact, blew all the way across the country to the East Coast.

The dust storms were a catastrophe for the area's farmers. They had no choice but to bow to the overwhelming forces of nature. underline(Passive) in the face of such a disaster, many of them went bankrupt, lost their farms, and were forced to move.

1. Underline the words that give a clue to the meaning of underline(swerved). Write a sentence of your own using the word *swerved*.

2. Circle the words in this sentence that give a clue to the meaning of the word underline(peered). What is a synonym for *peered*?

3. Underline the words in this sentence that hint at the meaning of underline(quartz).

4. Underline the words in this sentence that give a clue to the meaning of underline(waggling). What is a synonym for *waggling*?

5. Circle the words in this sentence and the next that give a clue to the meaning of underline(armored). Use a word meaning the opposite of *armored* in a sentence of your own.

6. Underline the word in this sentence that hints at the meaning of the word underline(dispersed). What are two antonyms of *dispersed*?

7. Circle the words in this sentence that hint at the meaning of underline(parapet).

8. Circle the words in this sentence that hint at the meaning of the word underline(passive). Use a word meaning the opposite of *passive* in an original sentence.

Name _____ Date _____

"The Turtle" *from* The Grapes of Wrath by John Steinbeck
Literary Analysis: Theme

The **theme** of a work of art is its central insight into life. An author's theme is shown through story events, characters, and even story details. Strong determination to survive is a theme of *The Grapes of Wrath*. The Joad family travels from its home of many generations in Oklahoma to California, where it hopes to establish a new farm. This short chapter, "The Turtle," mirrors that theme; the turtle, like the Joads, travels toward an unknown goal, determined to survive despite all obstacles.

DIRECTIONS: *Identify details in "The Turtle" that might be connected to the theme of survival. Explain how each detail relates to the story of the Joads or to the theme of survival in general.*

1. Story detail:

   _____

   _____

   How it connects to theme:

   _____

   _____

   _____

   _____

2. Story detail:

   _____

   _____

   How it connects to theme:

   _____

   _____

   _____

   _____

3. Story detail:

   _____

   _____

   How it connects to theme:

   _____

   _____

   _____

   _____

Name _____ Date _____

"The Turtle" *from* The Grapes of Wrath by John Steinbeck
Reading Strategy: Find Clues to Theme

Highly descriptive language and complex syntax can make it difficult to grasp an author's theme, or central message about life. Breaking down a long, difficult sentence into meaningful sections—and restating the sections in your own words—can help you to understand that sentence and gain clues to the theme. When you run across unfamiliar words, use context clues to help define them. Defining individual words will provide you with clues to the theme. Look at this example from "The Turtle."

Steinbeck's Version

Pushing hind legs strained and slipped, boosting the shell along, and the horny head protruded as far as the neck could stretch.

Broken Down and Rephrased

The back legs strained and slipped as they pushed up the hill. / The back legs boosted the shell along. / The horny head stuck out as far as it could.

Unfamiliar word: *Protrude* means "to stick out" because the neck is stretching as far out as possible.

DIRECTIONS: *Use this graphic organizer to help you break down long sentences and define unfamiliar words in "The Turtle." Each time you come across a difficult sentence, write sections of the sentences in the top row of boxes and restate the sections in your own words below. Write down any difficult words, and use context clues to define them. A sample has been done for you.*

Difficult Words				
Now the going was easy,	and all the legs worked,	and the shell boosted along,	waggling from side to side.	(The turtle moved from side to side as it walked.)
(It was easy to move across the highway.)	(All four legs moved.)	(The turtle moved along.)	(moving from side to side)	

Difficult Words			

"The Turtle" *from* **The Grapes of Wrath** by John Steinbeck
Vocabulary Builder

Using the Prefix *pro-*

A. DIRECTIONS: *In the following words, the prefix* pro- *means "forward." More information about the origin of several words containing* pro- *is given below. Use the words to complete the sentences.*

> project (L. *jacere* means "to throw")
>
> procrastinate (L. *cras* means "tomorrow")
>
> promote (L. *movere* means "to move")

1. Rather than finishing his homework on Saturday, Bob decided to _____ and do it on Sunday instead.

2. After Juanita had worked as an assistant manager for two years, her boss decided to _____ her to manager.

3. The slide machine used light to _____ an image onto a large screen.

Using the Word List

embankment	protruded

B. DIRECTIONS: *Underline the better definition for the italicized word in each sentence or phrase.*

1. The highway department built an *embankment* to hold the new interstate. (raised structure, tunnel)

2. A flagpole *protruded* from a column next to the front door of the house. (thrust forward, glistened)

Name _____ Date _____

Grammar and Style: Parallel Structure

Writers use **parallel structure** to express similar ideas in similar grammatical form. The following example from "The Turtle" uses parallel prepositional phrases beginning with *into* and parallel verb forms followed by the word *in.*

> A red ant ran *into the shell, into the soft skin inside the shell,* and suddenly head and legs *snapped in,* and the armored tail *clamped in sideways.*

A. PRACTICE: *The following sentence is from "The Turtle." Underline the parallel verbs that are followed by the same word.*

> For a long moment the turtle lay still, and then the neck crept out and the old humorous frowning eyes looked about and the legs and tail came out.

B. Writing Application: *Rewrite the following sentences so that they have two parallel verbs. Make sure the words that follow the verbs are parallel as well.*

1. The apples were dipped in caramel before chocolate was placed on them.

   _____

   _____

2. The faster train arrived in Seattle before the slower train got to Portland.

   _____

   _____

3. A caterpillar changes into a chrysalis before it becomes a butterfly.

   _____

   _____

4. Marcy's younger sister swung on the swing set before climbing on the monkey bars.

   _____

   _____

5. At night, you should turn on a light before you watch television.

   _____

   _____

6. On the standardized test, Jamie wrote with a pen even though he was told to use a pencil.

   _____

   _____

Name _____ Date _____

"The Turtle" *from* The Grapes of Wrath by John Steinbeck
Support for Writing

Prepare to write a **historical context essay** to compare the events of "The Turtle" with the lives of people during the Depression. Enter your research on the Depression in the chart below, comparing it with information in "The Turtle."

The Great Depression as Reflected in "The Turtle"

Basic Effects of Depression on American Farmers	Summary of Turtle Story	Conclusion About How the Depression and the Turtle Story Connect

On a separate page, introduce your essay with a main idea statement that compares "The Turtle" with the lives of ordinary American farmers during the Depression. Then, support your opinion with information from your research and the story. When you revise, be sure to include historical context. Provide citations for the source of your information.

"The Turtle" *from* **The Grapes of Wrath** by John Steinbeck
Support for Extend Your Learning

Listening and Speaking

Prepare to **interview** someone who lived through the Great Depression. After you have made up your questions, follow these instructions:

- Come to the interview with a tape recorder.
- Request your subject's permission to record the conversation.
- Take notes as reminders of what your subject discussed.

When you present the results of your interview to the class, provide both an introduction and a conclusion.

Research and Technology

Work with a partner to turn "The Turtle" into a **cartoon strip.** How many panels will you use? Which characters from the story will you picture? How can you put the story into a few panels and still convey the message?

1.	2.	3.
4.	**5.**	**6.**

Use graphic arts software to put your drawings into cartoon form.

"The Turtle" *from* The Grapes of Wrath by John Steinbeck
Enrichment: Survival

John Steinbeck uses the story about the turtle crossing the road as a fable for the rest of the novel. The turtle represents the Joads in their life journey. In the story, Steinbeck reveals certain physical characteristics and survival skills possessed by the turtle. Consider how similar human characteristics and skills would serve a person well in the workplace.

DIRECTIONS: *Examine the photo of the turtle and list in the table's left column the physical characteristics that Steinbeck includes in his description. Also add to the left column any survival skills Steinbeck describes. Then fill in the rest of the table.*

Physical Characteristics or Survival Skill	How It Protects the Turtle	How It Would Serve a Person in the Workplace

"The Turtle" *from* **The Grapes of Wrath** by John Steinbeck
Selection Test A

Critical Reading *Identify the letter of the choice that best answers the question.*

_____ 1. In "The Turtle" from *The Grapes of Wrath*, where does the turtle live that is like the climate of the people suffering from the Oklahoma drought?
   A. in a climate that is cold and wet
   B. in a climate that is cold and dry
   C. in a climate that is hot and dry
   D. in a climate that is hot and wet

_____ 2. What is the "life" that waits to wake up and grow in many places in "The Turtle" from *The Grapes of Wrath*?
   A. animals asleep for the winter
   B. Seeds waiting to be spread all over
   C. people asleep at the wheel of a car
   D. insects living under the soil

_____ 3. In "The Turtle" from *The Grapes of Wrath*, how is the turtle's struggle for survival shown?
   A. He opens his horny beak.
   B. He keeps on going, no matter what happens.
   C. He moves to the side of a road.
   D. He toe nails slip in the dust.

_____ 4. In a literary work, what is a theme?
   A. a statement about life
   B. a repeated musical idea
   C. a description of a character
   D. a mood or atmosphere

_____ 5. What theme about life is important in "The Turtle" from *The Grapes of Wrath*?
   A. the hugeness of the desert
   B. the effect of humans on animals
   C. the struggle for survival
   D. the importance of laughter

____ 6. In "The Turtle" from *The Grapes of Wrath*, how will the turtle's journey help plants spread and grow?

A. He carries ants inside his shell.

B. He carries oat seeds with him.

C. He drives grasshoppers ahead of him.

D. He scares a driver into slowing down.

____ 7. In "The Turtle" from *The Grapes of Wrath*, how does the sedan driver help the turtle stay alive?

A. She feeds the turtle.

B. She builds a home for the turtle.

C. She gives the turtle away.

D. She avoids hitting the turtle.

____ 8. In "The Turtle" from *The Grapes of Wrath*, how do the sedan driver and truck driver provide important clues to the theme?

A. They have the ability to either help or prevent survival.

B. They are people who cannot help themselves.

C. They are people who are helping the turtle.

D. They are people looking for new opportunities.

____ 9. In "The Turtle" from *The Grapes of Wrath*, how does the stem of the wild oat seeds use the turtle to carry it to a place where it can grow?

A. It travels next to the turtle.

B. It wraps around the turtle's leg.

C. It lies on the ground.

D. It sticks to the driver's truck.

____ 10. How does "The Turtle" from *The Grapes of Wrath* connect to the story of the main part of the book, in which a family travels to California to find a better life?

A. The turtle does not want to go anywhere.

B. The turtle also takes a long journey.

C. The turtle has many responsibilities.

D. The turtle warms itself in the sun.

Vocabulary and Grammar

_____ 11. Which answer best replaces *protruded* in this sentence: "The turtle's head *protruded* from his shell so I could see it"?

A. flipped over

B. pushed out

C. went behind

D. sat under

_____ 12. Which passage shows parallel construction that contains similar ideas in a similar grammatical form?

A. For a moment he stopped.

B. The desert was dry, brown, and hot.

C. The truck went back to the road.

D. The car swung to the right.

ESSAY

13. "The Turtle" describes the struggle for survival of a turtle. The turtle also carries seeds that will grow in a new place. If the truck driver had hit the turtle, the life of the turtle and the seeds it carried would end. What do you think Steinbeck is saying about the value of animal and plant life? Write a brief essay to give your opinions.

14. In *The Grapes of Wrath,* the Joad parents and their children travel across the country in a truck, trying to find a new place to live and work. In what way could their situation be compared to the turtle in the story and what he is doing? Write a brief essay to compare the Joads in their travels in their truck with the turtle and his travels in his shell.

"The Turtle" *from* **The Grapes of Wrath** by John Steinbeck
Selection Test B

Critical Reading *Identify the letter of the choice that best completes the statement or answers the question.*

____ 1. After the sedan driver saw the turtle, she swerved to
   A. avoid the turtle.
   B. hit the turtle.
   C. avoid the truck.
   D. dislodge a wild oat head.

____ 2. Which of the following words best describes the setting of the story?
   A. wet
   B. dry
   C. cold
   D. urban

____ 3. What did the turtle carry across the road?
   A. an ant
   B. a grasshopper
   C. a tiddly-wink
   D. wild oat seeds

____ 4. What theme might the head of wild oats in the story represent?
   A. reproduction
   B. revenge
   C. hardship
   D. the importance of family

____ 5. When you run across an unfamiliar word in a sentence, where can you find context clues to help define it?
   A. a dictionary
   B. a thesaurus
   C. on the previous page
   D. in the text around the word

____ 6. An author's theme is rarely
   A. directly stated.
   B. indirectly stated.
   C. within a story.
   D. shown through story details.

____ 7. A theme is best described as
   A. a detailed fable.
   B. a game played with a small disk.
   C. an insight into life.
   D. a story with long sentences.

_____ 8. Which of the following excerpts is related to the central theme of the story?
A. "The sun lay on the grass and warmed it . . ."
B. "The hind feet kicked his shell along, and it scraped on the grass, and on the gravel."
C. "As though they worked independently the hind legs pushed the shell against the wall."
D. "And as the turtle crawled on down the embankment, its shell dragged dirt over the seeds."

_____ 9. In *The Grapes of Wrath*, the Joads encounter kind people as well as people who make their lives more difficult. Which character in the turtle story might represent people who help the Joads?
A. the sedan driver
B. the truck driver
C. the ant
D. the turtle

_____ 10. In *The Grapes of Wrath*, the Joads encounter kind people as well as people who make their lives more difficult. Which character in the turtle story might represent people who make the Joads' lives more difficult?
A. the sedan driver
B. the truck driver
C. the ant
D. the turtle

_____ 11. From the sentence, "His front wheel struck the edge of the shell, flipped the turtle like a tiddlywink, spun it like a coin, and rolled it off the highway," you can figure out that a tiddlywink is something that _____.
A. rolls
B. spins
C. flips
D. strikes edges

_____ 12. From the phrase, "and the grass heads were heavy with oat beards to catch on a dog's coat, and foxtails to tangle in a horse's fetlocks," you can figure out that a fetlock is
A. part of a fox.
B. part of a horse.
C. a type of grass.
D. a type of dog.

Vocabulary and Grammar

_____ 13. The expression of similar ideas in similar grammatical form is called
A. perpendicular structure.
B. perpendicular themes.
C. parallel structure.
D. parallel themes.

Name _____ Date _____

___ 14. In the following line, what are the parallel phrases?

[A]nts and ant lions to set traps for them, grasshoppers to jump into the air . . .

A. to set—to jump
B. to set traps for—to jump into
C. ants—ant lions
D. ants—grasshoppers

___ 15. The word *protruded* means
A. pulled back.
B. thrust forward.
C. in favor of.
D. interrupted.

___ 16. Where would you expect to find an embankment?
A. inside a turtle shell
B. on a truck
C. next to a lake
D. under a lake

___ 17. In the word *protruded*, the prefix *pro-* means _____.
A. against
B. without
C. thrust
D. forward

Essay

18. To anthropomorphize means to give human form or personality to things that are not human. Write an essay in which you show how Steinbeck anthropomorphizes the turtle. What human characteristics does he give the turtle? What effect does such humanizing have on the reader?

19. The novels and stories of John Steinbeck often have characters who face hardships. Decide whether "The Turtle" is an example of such a story. Write an essay explaining your position. How would you characterize the events of the turtle's life in the story? Does it matter that the turtle is not human? Support your position with details from the story.

20. Although this selection from *The Grapes of Wrath* is entitled "The Turtle," it might just as appropriately have been called "The Seeds." Write an essay in which you agree or disagree with this statement. What is the relationship between the turtle and seeds in the story? Include evidence to support your position.

Vocabulary Warm-up Word Lists

Study these words from the selections. Then, complete the activities.

Word List A

community [kuh MYOON uh tee] *n.* all the people living in a particular district or area
   Cindy is devoted to the <u>community</u> and takes part in many civic activities.

dues [DOOZ] *n.* membership fees in an organization or club
   Because of rising costs, the club will increase its membership <u>dues</u> next year.

folk [FOHK] *n.* people in general
   The <u>folk</u> of that region enjoy oral storytelling.

interfered [in ter FEERD] *v.* came in or between for some purpose
   Dennis was unhappy when his boss <u>interfered</u> with his vacation plans.

official [uh FISH uhl] *adj.* holding an office or position of authority; formal
   Part of the mayor's <u>official</u> duties was to welcome distinguished visitors to the city.

scolds [SKOHLDZ] *v.* strongly criticizes; reproaches; rebukes
   The teacher often <u>scolds</u> her students when they don't do their homework.

statistics [stuh TIS tiks] *n.* information or facts in numerical form
   Debaters often use reasons, examples, and <u>statistics</u> to support their arguments.

yanks [YANKS] *v.* pulls hard or suddenly
   The paratrooper <u>yanks</u> on the cord to release the parachute.

Word List B

absurd [uhb SERD] *adj.* utterly illogical; ridiculous
   Theo gave an <u>absurd</u> explanation when asked why he was late.

content [kuhn TENT] *adj.* happy; satisfied
   Ira was <u>content</u> with all the provisions of the sales contract.

installment plan [in STAHL muhnt plan] *n.* system of payments at regular intervals
   Grandma bought her first fridge on the <u>installment plan</u>, paying $30 a month.

phonograph [FOH nuh graf] *n.* record player
   Years ago, the <u>phonograph</u> was standard for musical entertainment.

psychology [sy KAHL uh jee] *n.* study of the human mind and motivations
   Many writers often exhibit a strong interest in their characters' <u>psychology</u>.

reaped [REEPD] *v.* harvested
   Bad weather caused most farmers to be disappointed when they <u>reaped</u> the crops.

sensible [SEN suh buhl] *adj.* aware of; in tune with; responsive to
   As club president, Jack was <u>sensible</u> to the hopes and aspirations of all the members.

union [YOON yuhn] *n.* labor group organized for collective bargaining
   Forming a <u>union</u> could help improve workers' conditions at the factory.

Poems by E. E. Cummings and W. H. Auden
Vocabulary Warm-up Exercises

Exercise A *Fill in the blanks, using each word from Word List A only once.*

Susan was convinced that her [1] _____ needed a civic and cultural center. From research on the Internet, she found [2] _____ proving that such centers helped build public spirit and pride. Hoping for [3] _____ backing for her plan, she got an appointment to see the mayor. As she sat down in his office, he frowned and pretended to [4] _____ her. "Do you really think that the local [5] _____ will back a project like this? It sounds as if you're planning some sort of private club, with members paying [6] _____ to sit around and listen to fancy piano music!" Susan knew he was joking and promptly [7] _____ her folder of notes out of her briefcase. "Now listen, Joe, you said you'd give me a fair hearing," she said. "It'll all be paid for by private donations. Nothing will [8] _____ with your promise to the voters not to raise taxes."

Exercise B *Revise each sentence so that the underlined vocabulary word is logical. Be sure to keep the vocabulary word in your revision.*

Example: Because his plea was so <u>eloquent</u>, we turned down his request.
Because his plea was so <u>eloquent</u>, we agreed to his request.

1. Their argument was so <u>absurd</u> that we were compelled to take it seriously.
   _____

2. His scowling, frowning face showed that he felt <u>content</u> with our proposal.
   _____

3. Louise decided to use the <u>installment plan</u> and paid the full price of the TV at once.
   _____

4. Steve purchased a <u>phonograph</u> so that he could carefully edit his digital pictures.
   _____

5. If you wish to study the history of rock formations, take a course in <u>psychology</u>.
   _____

6. Fred <u>reaped</u> the harvest by distributing tiny seeds into the furrows of the field.
   _____

7. Evan was <u>sensible</u> to our point of view, avoiding any contact or discussion with us.
   _____

8. Jane thought she would join a <u>union</u> to negotiate better with the factory's labor force.
   _____

Name _____   Date _____

Poems by E. E. Cummings and W. H. Auden
Reading Warm-up A

Read the following passage. Pay special attention to the underlined words. Then, read it again, and complete the activities. Use a separate sheet of paper for your written answers.

One afternoon, Alan takes a bike ride that brings him to an old cemetery in the woods. When he walks through the gates, he's surprised by how far it extends, like a neighborhood or <u>community</u> of headstones. Toward the front, giant stone monuments tower above him, announcing the importance of those buried there. A marble angel spreads its wings, and the inscription on one stone seems designed to make Alan afraid. "Vengeance is mine, and I will repay," it <u>scolds</u>.

As he walks farther into the cemetery, Alan enters a wide expanse of World War II graves, less fancy, just row after row of ordinary stones with <u>statistics</u> on them: dates of birth and death. These dull, <u>official</u> stones seem to have been mass-produced in a factory. They make Alan think about how many soldiers must have died in the war and how little we know about them now. Unlike those monuments with the stone angels, there are the graves of common <u>folk</u>, ordinary people like Alan himself. He wonders what his own stone will say, or his father's. Most of the people Alan knows will never have the money for fancy headstones. They pay their union <u>dues</u> to protect their jobs and struggle to send their kids to college.

When he goes back towards the gate, Alan notices a very old stone that has started to lean towards the ground. It's so worn by age that he can't even read the inscription on it. He bends down and tries to <u>yank</u> it back into place with his hands, but it won't budge. He worries that eventually the stone will crumble into nothing, but then he decides that maybe it belongs the way it is, leaning. Maybe he shouldn't have <u>interfered</u>, trying to alter the past.

1. Underline the words that give a clue to the meaning of <u>community</u>. Use the word *community* in an original sentence.

2. Circle the words in this sentence and the previous sentence that give a clue to the meaning of <u>scolds</u>. Use a word meaning the opposite of *scolds* in an original sentence.

3. Underline the words in this sentence that give a clue to the meaning of <u>statistics</u>. What type of reference book would likely contain *statistics*?

4. What is a synonym for <u>official</u>? What is an antonym for the word *official*?

5. Circle the words in this sentence that offer a clue to the meaning of <u>folk</u>. Use the word *folk* in an original sentence.

6. Underline the words in this sentence that give clues to the meaning of <u>dues</u>. What is a synonym for *dues*?

7. Underline the words in this sentence that hint at the meaning of <u>yank</u>. What is a synonym for *yank*?

8. Underline the words in this sentence that hint at the meaning of <u>interfered</u>. What is a synonym for *interfered*?

Name _____   Date _____

Poems by E. E. Cummings and W. H. Auden
Reading Warm-up B

Read the following passage. Pay special attention to the underlined words. Then, read it again, and complete the activities. Use a separate sheet of paper for your written answers.

Probably the best-known feature of E. E. Cummings's poetry is the author's eccentric use of punctuation and capitalization. This aspect of his verse, which seemed irrational or even <u>absurd</u> to some critics at first, <u>reaped</u> Cummings a lot of attention. However, the recognition he gained from this aspect of his style was probably not as important to Cummings as the fact that people seemed genuinely <u>content</u> and pleased when they read his verse.

<u>Sensible</u> to the dangers of conformity and complacency, Cummings was always the individualist. In some of his work, he satirizes the humdrum hollowness of a materialistic society. During Cummings's career, a new consumer economy was developing in America. Credit was suddenly available to millions of consumers, who rushed to buy appliances, such as a dishwasher, a refrigerator, or a <u>phonograph</u>. People paid for such purchases over time on the <u>installment plan</u>, reducing their debt by a little every month.

For Cummings, the race to gain more and more material things was not the product of a healthy mindset or <u>psychology</u>. Instead, in his poetry, he upheld the values of ordinary, common people. An anonymous laborer who worked hard and belonged to a <u>union</u> might be a hero for Cummings. Someone like "anyone" in "anyone lived in a pretty how town" is celebrated by Cummings as an authentic embodiment of the American Dream.

Cummings's experiments with punctuation and capitalization, then, were a means to an end. He wanted to capture readers' attention humorously in order to communicate serious themes about the meaning of human existence and the dignity (or lack of it) of human behavior. His poetry remains as relevant in our day as it was in his—perhaps even more so.

1. Underline the words in this sentence that hint at the meaning of <u>absurd</u>. Use a word meaning the opposite of *absurd* in an original sentence.

2. Circle the words in this sentence and the next that hint at the meaning of <u>reaped</u>. Is this word used literally or figuratively here?

3. Underline the words in this sentence that hint at the meaning of <u>content</u>. What are two antonyms for *content*?

4. Underline the words in this sentence that hint at the meaning of <u>sensible</u>. What is a synonym for *sensible*?

5. Circle the words in this sentence that hint at the meaning of <u>phonograph</u>.

6. Circle the words in this sentence that give a good clue to the meaning of <u>installment plan</u>.

7. Underline the words in this sentence that hint at the meaning of <u>psychology</u>. Write an original sentence using the word *psychology*.

8. Circle the words in this sentence that hint at the meaning of <u>union</u>. Why might workers join a *union*?

Unit 5 Resources: Disillusion, Defiance, and Discontent
© Pearson Education, Inc., publishing as Pearson Prentice Hall. All rights reserved.
75

"old age sticks" and **"anyone lived in a pretty how town"** by E. E. Cummings
"The Unknown Citizen" by W. H. Auden
Literary Analysis: Satire

Satire uses the elements of sarcasm and humor to make readers aware of the problems of society. It has great potential as a tool with which to effect social change. Advertisers have recognized the power of this tool, and many advertising campaigns have used satire to promote some ideas and ridicule others, particularly in the area of public service. For example, one anti-smoking campaign featured a series of posters with a caption that read "Smoking Makes You Attractive" but with photographs of smokers who looked disheveled or sick.

Think about how you might plan advertising for each of the following public service campaigns. On the lines below each one, write the satirical slogan you would present; then write two or three sentences in which you explain how you would present the slogan to enhance its satirical value and how you hope the slogan would be effective.

1. A campaign to educate drivers about the importance of obeying traffic signs.

_____

_____

_____

_____

_____

2. A campaign to encourage everyone to have an annual physical checkup.

_____

_____

_____

_____

_____

3. A campaign to get people to stop littering public beaches.

_____

_____

_____

_____

_____

4. A campaign to warn teens about the dangers of drug abuse.

_____

_____

_____

_____

_____

"old age sticks" and **"anyone lived in a pretty how town"** by E. E. Cummings
"The Unknown Citizen" by W. H. Auden
Reading Strategy: Relate Structure to Meaning

You can often relate a poem's **structure**—the way it is put together in words, lines, and stanzas—to its **meaning**—the central ideas the poet wants you to take away. For example, the poems of Cummings often break the rules of syntax—the way in which words, phrases, and clauses are arranged to form sentences—to reinforce a message of personal individuality or of the individual person trying to break loose from conventional boundaries or patterns. Both "anyone lived in a how town" and "old age sticks" present patterns or cycles of living that each generation relives in turn (although they try to do otherwise). The regular structure of the stanzas of both poems reinforces the concept of patterns.

DIRECTIONS: *For each of the following passages from the three poems, do the following: First, write the meaning of the passage. Secondly, write how one or more of the following structural elements reinforce that meaning:* **stanzas, rhymes, rhythm, syntax, capitalization, punctuation.**

1. when by now and tree by leaf
   she laughed his joy she cried his grief
   bird by snow and stir by still
   anyone's any was all to he

   _____

   _____

2. old age sticks
   up Keep
   Off
   signs)&

   youth yanks them
   down (old)
   age
   cries No

   Tres)&(pas)
   youth laughs
   (sing
   old age

   _____

   _____

3. Both Producers Research and High-Grade Living declare
   He was fully sensible to the advantages of the Installment Plan
   And had everything necessary to the Modern Man.
   A phonograph, a radio, a car and a frigidaire.

   _____

   _____

"old age sticks" and **"anyone lived in a pretty how town"** by E. E. Cummings
"The Unknown Citizen" by W. H. Auden
Vocabulary Builder

Using the Root -*psych*-

Psyche is a mythological figure. Her name is the same as the Greek word for "breath" or "soul."
The Greek root -*psych*-, which forms the basis of several English words, means "mind" or "soul."

A. DIRECTIONS: *Use each word formed from the root -psych- to fill the appropriate blanks in the sentences. Then, without using a dictionary, define each word based on its context in the sentence and what you know about the meanings of its roots.*

psychopath (-*path*- = "suffering, disease")   psychokinesis (-*kinesis*- = "motion")   psychotherapy

1. In the science fiction movie, the heroine was able to make objects leap across the room by her powers of _____.

   _____

2. Two years of _____ helped Samantha get over her fears and work more effectively at her job.

   _____

3. The strange notes left at the crime scenes suggested to police that the criminal was a _____.

   _____

Using the Word List

statistics   psychology

B. DIRECTIONS: *Each sentence has a blank space indicating that a word has been omitted. Choose the lettered word that best completes the meaning of the sentence and write the word in the blank.*

1. A knowledge of _____ is important for people who work in teaching, marketing, and sports.
   A. psychosis   **B.** psychiatry   **C.** psychodrama   **D.** psychology

2. Baseball _____ such as batting averages and earned-run averages help management to evaluate the players' performance.
   A. plays   **B.** statistics   **C.** riddles   **D.** negotiations

"old age sticks" and **"anyone lived in a pretty how town"** by E. E. Cummings
"The Unknown Citizen" by W. H. Auden
Grammar and Style: Parentheses

Parentheses, ( ), are generally used to enclose extra information. They are used for slightly different purposes than commas and dashes. Use commas to set off material that is especially closely connected to the rest of a sentence. Use dashes to emphasize the information being set off and to show that the material is of great importance. You should use parentheses when the material is unimportant and interruptive in nature, such as the nonessential bit of information in the following sentence.

E. E. Cummings (I think) uses punctuation sparingly.

A. PRACTICE: *Complete each sentence by adding parentheses where necessary.*

1. E. E. Cummings' poetic style is at least in my opinion unusual.

2. He began writing poetry so I've read after World War I.

3. You and probably most other people can sometimes recognize a Cummings poem by its un conventional use of punctuation and grammar.

4. I like his poems because of a playfulness if that's the right word that makes the poems fun to read.

5. W. H. Auden is a more traditional poet you'd have to say than E. E. Cummings.

6. He doesn't if you'll pardon the expression throw grammar and punctuation to the wind.

7. Auden was born in England if I'm not mistaken and came to America in 1939, just before the outbreak of World War II.

8. Prior to leaving England, he and I'm glad of this spoke out against the rise of Nazism in Germany.

B. Writing Application: *Write a review of one of the three poems in this grouping. Give your personal opinions of the style and message of the poem you choose. In your review, include at least three expressions that are set off by parentheses.*

_____

_____

_____

_____

_____

_____

"old age sticks" and **"anyone lived in a pretty how town"** by E. E. Cummings
"The Unknown Citizen" by W. H. Auden

Support for Writing

As you prepare for a poetry reading of works by Cummings and Auden, gather information for an **introduction** that compares and contrasts the work of both poets.

The poetry of E. E. Cummings and W. H. Auden

How are the poems of E. E. Cummings and W. H. Auden alike in theme or structure? _____ _____ _____
How are the poems of E. E. Cummings and W. H. Auden different in theme or structure? _____ _____ _____
Background on E. E. Cummings: _____ _____ _____
Background on W. H. Auden: _____ _____ _____

On a separate page, write a draft of your introduction to the poetry reading. Give concrete examples from the poems to support the opinions you give. When you revise your work, be sure your details support your main points.

"old age sticks" and **"anyone lived in a pretty how town"** by E. E. Cummings
"The Unknown Citizen" by W. H. Auden
Support for Extend Your Learning

Listening and Speaking

Hold a **poetry reading** with your classmates and listen to tapes or CDs of the poetry of E. E. Cummings and W. H. Auden. Discuss the poems afterwards and choose a personal favorite to read to the group. As you read, follow these tips:

- Match your tone to the tone of the poem.
- Speak so you can be heard.
- Emphasize words and phrases in the poem, based on its meaning.

After everyone has heard the poems, ask whether listeners have changed their opinions of any of the poems.

Research and Technology

To prepare a **written report** on totalitarian governments in Europe after World War I, do research in the library and on the Internet. Enter your information below.

Country	Who the leader was	How the leader gained power	How did government restrict people's actions or speech
Germany			
Italy			
U.S.S.R.			

Put your findings together in a report that compares and contrasts how freedom was limited in these three nations. Use spreadsheets in your report.

Name _____ Date _____

"old age sticks" and **"anyone lived in a pretty how town"** by E. E. Cummings
"The Unknown Citizen" by W. H. Auden
Enrichment: Art

The paintings *Remember Now the Days of Thy Youth* and *Turret Lathe Operator* that accompany "old age sticks" and "The Unknown Citizen" provide striking visual commentaries on these two poems.

DIRECTIONS: *Study the paintings and think about them in relation to the poetry. Then answer the following questions. If you need more space for your answer, use the back of this page or another sheet of paper.*

1. Describe the colors used in each painting. How are they appropriate to the subjects of the paintings? Do you think the colors fit the poems they accompany? Why or why not?

   _____
   _____
   _____
   _____

2. How does the theme of each painting relate to the theme of the poem it accompanies?

   _____
   _____
   _____
   _____

3. What features of the painting *Remember Now the Days of Thy Youth* might make it an appropriate illustration for "anyone lived in a pretty how town"?

   _____
   _____
   _____

4. Why might the title of Grant Wood's *Turret Lathe Operator* make you think of Auden's "The Unknown Citizen"?

   _____
   _____
   _____

5. What features of these paintings, such as use of shadow and light, arrangement of elements, and depiction of human figures, relate to the themes of the poems they accompany?

   _____
   _____
   _____

"old age sticks" and **"anyone lived in a pretty how town"** by E. E. Cummings
"The Unknown Citizen" by W. H. Auden
Selection Test A

Critical Reading *Identify the letter of the choice that best answers the question.*

_____ 1. What is one possible way to interpret the phrase "old age sticks"?
  A. Older people hang out together.
  B. Older people stick up signs.
  C. Older people are stuck in a rut.
  D. Older people are all the same.

_____ 2. Which of these statements captures the theme of "old age sticks"?
  A. Older people have all the answers.
  B. Older people don't listen to anyone.
  C. Old age ends the freedom of youth.
  D. Old age and youth should cooperate.

_____ 3. In "old age sticks," how does the poet show the ways in which old age tries to control youth?
  A. by capitalizing words such as *Keep Off*
  B. by putting single words on two lines
  C. by showing youth singing and laughing
  D. by enclosing some words in parentheses

_____ 4. In "anyone lived in a pretty how town," whom does the poet mean by "anyone"?
  A. people who live in towns
  B. all ordinary people
  C. a person named "anyone"
  D. himself

_____ 5. In "anyone lived in a pretty how town," how does the poet show the passage of time?
  A. by showing people laughing and crying
  B. by describing men, women, and children
  C. by showing people dancing and singing
  D. by naming changing seasons and weather

_____ 6. Whom is the poet making fun of in "anyone lived in a little how town"?
  A. people who live in small towns
  B. people who don't know how to laugh
  C. people who live boring lives
  D. people who never leave home

_____ 7. In "The Unknown Citizen," what is Auden making fun of?

    A. the need for people to die during wartime

    B. the need for everyone to be the same

    C. the need for people to struggle for freedom

    D. the need for people to get involved in politics

_____ 8. In "The Unknown Citizen," what characteristics of the citizen are not known by the state?

    A. how he felt about his life

    B. that he paid his Union dues

    C. how much he drank

    D. what things he owned

_____ 9. What characteristic of society does the poet make fun of in "The Unknown Citizen"?

    A. its focus on making people happy

    B. its focus on asking important questions

    C. its focus on living as an individual

    D. its focus on being the same as everyone

_____ 10. What is a central theme of "The Unknown Citizen"?

    A. Society rewards people who take risks.

    B. Society encourages people to act boldly.

    C. Society respects people who fight wars.

    D. Society rewards people who fit in.

Vocabulary and Grammar

_____ 11. Which word best replaces *psychology* in this sentence: "Those who study *psychology* agree that everyone's brain needs a certain amount of sleep"?

    A. the science of the mind

    B. the science of nature

    C. the science of the stars

    D. the science of the earth

_____ **12.** Which of the following sentences uses parentheses correctly?

  A. Although E. E. Cummings's poems use an unusual form (they generally express traditional ideas).

  B. W. H. Auden won the Pulitzer Prize in 1948 for *The Age of Anxiety* (a long narrative poem).

  C. E. E. Cummings was a skillful poet (who used his poems to challenge other beliefs).

  D. W. H. Auden's concerns included individuality, poverty, (and the responsibilities of the artist).

Essay

13. In "old age sticks," the poet ends by saying that "youth goes right on growing old." What do you think the poet is trying to suggest? What warning for young people might be in the line? Write a brief essay to give your opinion about the meaning of the final stanza.

14. In the final two lines of "The Unknown Citizen," the poet writes that the question of whether the citizen was "free" or "happy" is foolish, because the people who control society would have known if anything was wrong. Is it a foolish question? Does the citizen in this poem have feelings? Write a brief essay to address these questions.

"old age sticks" and **"anyone lived in a pretty how town"** by E. E. Cummings
"The Unknown Citizen" by W. H. Auden

Selection Test B

Critical Reading *Identify the letter of the choice that best completes the statement or answers the question.*

_____ 1. In the following line from "anyone lived in a pretty how town," why does Cummings alter normal word order?

(with up so floating many bells down)

A. to convey a sense of social optimism
B. to emphasize the number of church bells
C. to reflect the breakdown of social order
D. to imitate the motion of bells ringing

_____ 2. In "anyone lived in a pretty how town," Cummings begins the word "anyone" with a lowercase letter in order to

A. suggest the character's common humanity.
B. emphasize the character's deceptive nature.
C. call attention to the character.
D. show contempt for the character.

_____ 3. What is the theme of "anyone lived in a pretty how town"?

A. Ordinary people can achieve great things.
B. Loneliness and lack of love can kill people.
C. True humanity is squelched by conventional society.
D. Creativity triumphs over small-mindedness.

_____ 4. In "anyone lived in a pretty how town," what group is Cummings satirizing in the line, "they sowed their isn't they reaped their same"?

A. anyone and noone
B. people who live quiet, productive lives
C. people who live safe, conforming lives
D. the citizens of the pretty how town

_____ 5. Why does Cummings break up the word "growing" in the last two lines of "old age sticks"?

A. to imitate the faltering speech of old people
B. to emphasize the grumbly nature of old people
C. to preserve the sticklike shape of the poem
D. to emphasize the gradual nature of aging

_____ 6. Which statement summarizes the theme of "old age sticks"?

A. Young people are the hope of the future.
B. Young people and old people should work together.
C. Age diminishes the free spirit of youth.
D. Old people deserve respect from the young.

____ 7. In "old age sticks," what is the group that is the subject of the last stanza doing there?
   A. They are yanking down signs.
   B. They are dying.
   C. They are getting old.
   D. They are sticking up signs.

____ 8. In "The Unknown Citizen," Auden directs his satire against what he sees as too great an emphasis on
   A. independence and freedom.
   B. obedience and conformity.
   C. creativity and initiative.
   D. originality and eccentricity.

____ 9. A central theme of "The Unknown Citizen" is that modern society
   A. encourages people to think on their own.
   B. rewards people for behaving morally.
   C. discourages people from acting boldly.
   D. pressures people to report on their neighbors.

____ 10. In "The Unknown Citizen," what is Auden's attitude toward the modern version or sense of the word "saint"?
   A. He condemns it because it implies someone who condones insincerity.
   B. He applauds it because it implies someone who never does anything wrong.
   C. He despises it because it implies someone who never takes risks.
   D. He approves of it because it implies someone who chooses the heroic.

____ 11. What pair of questions does Auden call "absurd" in "The Unknown Citizen"?
   A. Was he kind? Was he happy?
   B. Was he rich? Was he poor?
   C. Was he free? Was he rich?
   D. Was he free? Was he happy?

____ 12. Which line from "The Unknown Citizen" is the best example of the way Auden uses elements of structure to affect the meaning of his poem?
   A. "But satisfied his employers, Fudge Motors Inc."
   B. "A phonograph, a radio, a car and a frigidaire."
   C. "He was fully sensible to the advantages of the Installment Plan"
   D. "He was married and added five children to the population."

____ 13. In "The Unknown Citizen," whom did the citizen serve "in everything he did"?
   A. his employers, Fudge Motors Inc.
   B. the Greater Community
   C. public opinion
   D. the state

____ 14. Which quotation from "The Unknown Citizen" is the clearest example of satirical writing?
    A. "Except for the War till the day he retired / He worked in a factory and never got fired, . . ."
    B. "And his Health-card shows he was once in hospital but left it cured."
    C. "He was married and added five children to the population."
    D. "Our researchers into Public Opinion are content / That he held the proper opinions for the time of year. . . ."

Vocabulary and Grammar

____ 15. Which word best expresses the subject matter of "old age sticks"?
    A. prohibitions
    B. satire
    C. psychosis
    D. youth

____ 16. What might Social Psychology workers have been especially concerned about in their reports on the unknown citizen?
    A. his emotions and attitudes
    B. his physical fitness
    C. his productivity on the job
    D. the number of children he had

____ 17. In which passage does E. E. Cummings make the most unconventional use of parentheses?
    A. "children guessed(but only a few / and down they forgot as up they grew / autumn winter spring summer) / that noone love him more by more"
    B. "youth yanks them / down(old/age/cries No/Tres)&(pas)"
    C. "Women and men(both dong and ding)"
    D. "one day anyone died i guess / (and noone stooped to kiss his face)"

Essay

18. In "The Unknown Citizen," Auden implies that the society treats the citizen as just another statistic. How do you think the citizen would feel about being treated this way? How might he want to be treated instead? Write an essay in which you answer these questions.

19. Poets, through their poems, sometimes reveal their personal concerns about the nature of society. This tells the reader something about the poet—his or her likes, dislikes, beliefs, fears, and hopes. A reader of "The Unknown Citizen" can form a reasonably accurate picture of what the poet dislikes and, by inference, what he admires. Write an essay in which you speculate on the kind of person and the kind of society that Auden respects. Support your opinion with evidence from the poem.

20. It has been said that in "anyone lived in a pretty how town," E. E. Cummings focuses on the eternal rhythms of life, the seasons of nature, and the cycle of human rituals that are universally connected with childhood, adulthood, and death. In an essay, discuss Cummings's focus. What elements in the poem support this statement about his focus?

Unit 5: Disillusion, Defiance, and Discontent
Benchmark Test 7

MULTIPLE CHOICE

Literary Analysis and Reading Skills *Read the selection. Then, answer the questions that follow.*

Well, thish-yer Smiley had rat-tarriers, and chicken cocks, and tomcats and all them kind of things till you couldn't rest, and you couldn't fetch nothing for him to bet on but he'd match you. He ketched a frog one day and took him home, and said he cal'lated to educate him; and so he never done nothing for three months but set in his back yard and learn that frog to jump. And you bet you he *did* learn him, too. He'd give him a little punch behind, and the next minute you'd see that frog whirling in the air like a doughnut—see him turn one summerset, or maybe a couple if he got a good start, and come down flat-footed and all right, like a cat. He got him up so in the matter of ketching flies, and kep' him in practice so constant, that he'd nail a fly every time as fur as he could see him. Smiley said all a frog wanted was education and he could do 'most anything—and I believe him.

from "The Celebrated Jumping Frog of Calaveras County" by Mark Twain

1. Which of these is revealed about the character of Smiley, based on the narrator's description of him?
   A. Smiley can communicate with animals.
   B. Smiley is an easy-going person.
   C. Smiley enjoys betting.
   D. Smiley loves to train animals.

2. The reader learns about Smiley through indirect characterization. Which of these best defines the term *indirect characterization* as it is used in this selection?
   A. Smiley's traits are revealed by what another character says about him.
   B. Smiley's traits are revealed by what the author directly says about him.
   C. Smiley's traits are revealed mainly by what he says to other characters.
   D. Smiley's traits are revealed through describing his own thoughts.

3. Which conclusion is most likely, based on the information in the selection?
   A. Smiley intends to use the frog for betting.
   B. Smiley intends to sell the frog at a county fair.
   C. The narrator is not a character in the story.
   D. The narrator does not approve of what Smiley is doing.

4. Which strategy would best help a reader clarify the details in this selection?
   A. looking up *ketched* in a dictionary
   B. rereading to understand the dialect
   C. reading other stories by the author
   D. researching the behavior of frogs

5. Which of these best describes stories such as the excerpt from "The Celebrated Jumping Frog of Calaveras County"?
   A. symbols
   B. fables
   C. allusions
   D. satire

6. Which of these can most directly reveal the theme of a literary work?
   A. an author's collective works
   B. critical reviews of the work
   C. characters' comments and actions
   D. the author's background

Read the selection. Then, answer the questions that follow.

In this excerpt from "Old Ironsides," the poet protests the destruction of a historic battleship. The poem helped save the ship, which is now a national memorial.

> Her decks, once red with heroes' blood,
> Where knelt the vanquished foe,
> When winds were hurrying o'er the flood,
> And waves were white below,
> No more shall feel the victor's tread,
> Or know the conquered knee—
> The harpies of the shore shall pluck
> The eagle of the sea!
>
> Oh, better that her shattered hulk
> Should sink beneath the wave;
> Her thunders shook the mighty deep,
> And there should be her grave;
> Nail to the mast her holy flag,
> Set every threadbare sail,
> And give her to the god of storms,
> The lightning and the gale!

from "Old Ironsides"
by Oliver Wendell Holmes

7. Who is the speaker in the selection?
   A. the ship
   B. a sailor
   C. a fictional character
   D. the poet

8. Which lines from the poem best express the poet's strong feelings that the ship should not be destroyed?
   A. lines 1 and 2
   B. lines 9 and 10
   C. lines 5 and 6
   D. lines 13 and 14

9. Which of these would most likely help you fully appreciate the selection?
   A. reading other works by the poet
   B. reading other poems about battleships
   C. listening to the poem's musicality
   D. summarizing the poem's message

10. Through the poet's use of imagery, what does he invite the reader to do?
    A. engage the senses of sight and sound
    B. appreciate the lure of the sea
    C. oppose warfare at sea
    D. mourn the loss of a great ship

11. Which of these is a clue to the theme of the selection?
    A. images of heroes in battle with their enemies
    B. images of the ship being torn apart and sunk by storms
    C. the use of rhythm and rhyme in the poem
    D. the poet's use of punctuation marks in the poem

12. Which of these is a characteristic of imagist poems?
    A. references to historical or literary events that are meaningful
    B. people, places, or things that represent something beyond themselves
    C. use of the common themes of life and death
    D. use of a limited number of words that appeal to the senses to evoke emotion

13. Which of these is often true of poetry?
    A. Images in a poem appeal to all the senses.
    B. The theme of a poem is intentionally hidden.
    C. The speaker in a poem is a nonhuman entity.
    D. A poem's structure and meaning are related.

14. Which of these is a characteristic of a dramatic monologue?
    A. A character addresses the reader.
    B. The listener is silent.
    C. The author addresses the reader.
    D. It occurs only in a drama.

Vocabulary

15. Based on your knowledge of the root *-pose-*, what is the meaning of *composed* in the following sentence?

    Taylor composed himself before the race by taking long, deep breaths.

    A. calmed
    B. rested
    C. convinced
    D. trained

16. What is the definition of *orchestrated* in the following sentence?

    The library's directors orchestrated the move to the new facility.

    A. convened a committee
    B. arranged music
    C. voted in opposition to
    D. organized and directed

17. Based on your knowledge of the prefix *di-*, what is the meaning of *divulge* in the following sentence?

    The investigators pressured the journalist to divulge the source of her information.

    A. question
    B. approach
    C. reveal
    D. deny

18. What is the definition of *apparently* in the following sentence?

    The untouched food on the table suggested that Dave had apparently left in a hurry.

    A. in a mysterious manner
    B. in a manner that is not understood
    C. in a manner that seems clear
    D. in a hasty manner

19. Based on your knowledge of the root *-somn-*, what is the meaning of *somnambulist* in the following sentence?

    Having awakened two nights in a row in her kitchen, Lilly began to suspect that she was a somnambulist.

    A. person who walks while asleep
    B. person who is extremely tired
    C. person who suffers a memory loss
    D. person who daydreams often

20. What is the meaning of *procession* in the following sentence, based on your knowledge of the prefix *pro-*?

   A procession of circus performers approached the huge tent from the nearby trailers.

   A. collection
   B. parade
   C. gathering
   D. committee

21. Based on your knowledge of the root *-psych-*, what is the definition of *psychosis* in the following sentence?

   The lead actor was praised for his portrayal of a patient recovering from psychosis.

   A. a type of skin disorder
   B. a type of mental illness
   C. a lung ailment
   D. a heart condition

Grammar

22. What is the noun clause in the following sentence?

   Progress, not perfection, is what counts in trying to break old habits.

   A. what counts in trying to break old habits
   B. progress, not perfection
   C. what counts
   D. trying to break old habits

23. What is the reflexive pronoun in the following sentence?

   He and I will make ourselves breakfast before meeting them at the trailhead.

   A. he
   B. I
   C. ourselves
   D. them

24. What is the adjectival modifier in the following sentence?

   Her impressions of college were formed from vivid stories that she heard from her older siblings.

   A. impressions of college
   B. vivid
   C. that she heard from her older siblings
   D. older

25. Which word in the following sentence is an abstract noun?

On the side of the tea package was a quote from Thoreau about finding success.

   A. side
   B. package
   C. quote
   D. success

26. Where should you insert a dash in the following sentence?

The rolling hills, the sparkling river, the crisp air all these made it a splendid outing.

   A. between the comma after *river* and *the*
   B. between *these* and *made*
   C. between *air* and *all*
   D. between *all* and *these*

27. What is the best way to repair the faulty parallel structure in the following sentence?

Twain's writing is strong, vigorous, and with an authentic quality.

   A. Twain's writing is strong, is vigorous, and has an authentic quality.
   B. Twain's writing is strong and vigorous, and it has an authentic quality.
   C. Twain's writing has a strong quality, is vigorous, and has an authentic quality.
   D. Twain's writing is strong, vigorous, and authentic.

28. What word or words should you enclose in parentheses in the following sentence?

My neighbor the one on the left makes cheese from goats' milk.

   A. the one on the left
   B. my neighbor
   C. from goat's milk
   D. the one

ESSAY

29. Think of a character from a favorite fairy tale. Write a character analysis of that character. Remember to include interactions and relationships with other characters as insights into the character's personality.

30. Write a thorough character analysis of one of the characters you read about in this unit. Begin with a general statement about the character. Remember to include interactions and relationships with other characters as insights into the character's personality. Explain how the character changes in the course of the literary work.

31. Suppose that you are a teenager living in colonial times. Write an essay in which you tell about a typical day in your life. Provide details about your home and about your family activities. Tell whether you go to school. Describe the clothes you wear. Mention details about your social life. Remember to include as much historical context in your essay as possible.

Name _____ Date _____

MULTIPLE CHOICE

Read the selection. Then, answer the questions that follow.

Being overweight can often lead to depression, heart disease, and diabetes. If you want to lose weight, most doctors will tell you to eat less, exercise more, and drink lots of water. Government guidelines also provide practical advice. For example, they suggest starting the day with a healthy breakfast and then, over the course of the day, consuming five to seven servings of fruit and vegetables.

Certainly, reducing food portions will help you to drop unwanted pounds. So will keeping serving dishes off the dinner table. Studies show that when we see food on our plates or in nearby serving dishes, we keep eating until the food is gone, even when we're no longer hungry.

Of course, some fad diets gain popularity by promising that followers will never have to restrain themselves as long as they follow the diet's limited food plans. One such diet says that you can eat as much as you want, as long as you eat only grapefruit! Such food plans often lead to bingeing. If dieters feel cheated and deprived by the lack of rich foods, they may have a temporary lapse and load up on fatty snacks. If you want to slim down, change your eating habits to healthy foods, get lots of exercise and sleep, use common sense, and regard any "miracle" diet with suspicion.

1. According to the selection, what is one disease that may occur if someone is overweight?
   A. tuberculosis
   B. diabetes
   C. pneumonia
   D. lung cancer

2. Which statement most accurately reflects government guidelines for losing weight?
   A. Reduce the amount of dairy products you eat each day.
   B. Eat large amounts of protein, such as red meat, each day.
   C. Increase your portions of such foods as pasta, bread, and other carbohydrates.
   D. Increase your portions of such foods as apples, strawberries, beans, and broccoli.

3. Why might it be a good idea to keep serving dishes off the dinner table?
   A. People tend to finish all the food they see on the table, whether they are hungry or not.
   B. If the serving dishes are not in sight, people will forget that they are hungry.
   C. It is impolite to put serving dishes on the table when someone is trying to lose weight.
   D. If the serving dishes are nearby, people may add butter and other seasonings to the food.

4. Based on this selection, what is a "fad diet"?
   A. a weight-loss diet suggested by one's family doctor
   B. a weight-loss diet that is extremely popular for a while
   C. a weight-loss diet that always works
   D. a weight-loss diet that prevents bingeing

5. According to the selection, what false promise do many fad diets make to their followers?
   - A. You can eat anything you want, in any size portion.
   - B. You do not have to restrain yourself as long as you follow our food plan.
   - C. You will lose 20 pounds in a week.
   - D. You will look and feel much better if you avoid eating too much grapefruit.

6. According to the selection, what do fad diets often lead to?
   - A. depression
   - B. sleeplessness
   - C. common sense
   - D. bingeing

7. Why should people regard "miracle" diets with suspicion?
   - A. They often include fatty snacks.
   - B. They rely too heavily on getting plenty of exercise and sleep.
   - C. They rarely work because dieters feel cheated and may load up on fatty snacks.
   - D. They rarely work because dieters sometimes forget to take serving dishes off the table.

Read the selection. Then, answer the questions that follow.

A doctor who practiced medicine on the American frontier during the nineteenth century had to identify illnesses, perform minor surgeries, bandage wounds, set broken bones, deliver babies, and relieve pain. He or she was expected to be available for these tasks at any time of day or night. When summoned by a patient, the doctor had to rush to the sick person's bedside, usually on horseback. Then, he or she often would have to perform medical procedures in terrible conditions.

Imagine traveling by horseback through a blizzard to a person's home in order to amputate a limb or deliver a baby. There is no electricity, so you work by the light of a lantern. Because you are operating in someone's bedroom, it is harder to maintain sanitary conditions. Rooms are drafty, ceilings are leaky, and there is no clean running water.

In return for providing medical services, doctors on the frontier were paid very little. His or her fees were rarely paid in cash. A chicken, a stack of firewood, or a bushel of beans might be used as payment instead.

Many of the physicians practicing on the frontier had very little formal training in medicine. Most had served as apprentices, gaining skills as they assisted experienced doctors. However, many "doctors" merely carried a bag of instruments and a how-to book. Perhaps among their most useful medical tools were confidence and good luck.

8. According to the selection, what were the normal working hours for frontier doctors?
   - A. They usually worked from 8 AM to 5 PM.
   - B. They usually worked in twelve-hour shifts.
   - C. They were expected to be available from noon to midnight.
   - D. They were expected to be available 24 hours a day.

9. According to the selection, where did most frontier doctors practice medicine?
   - A. in a hospital
   - B. in an office
   - C. in the patient's bedroom
   - D. in the patient's kitchen

10. Which of the following is a "terrible condition" that frontier doctors often had to work under?
   A. lack of bandages
   B. lack of electricity
   C. lack of confidence
   D. lack of patients

11. What is the most important reason that lack of clean running water presented a problem for frontier doctors?
   A. The patients were often thirsty.
   B. The doctors had to set people's broken bones.
   C. The operating conditions were very unsanitary.
   D. The only source of heat was from fireplaces.

12. Based on the selection, what statement is true about frontier doctors?
   A. There were very few female doctors on the frontier.
   B. Their hours were long and difficult, but they were paid well.
   C. Most of them received medical training at a college or university.
   D. Most gained their training by working as apprentices.

13. What is the most probable reason that patients paid their doctors with items such as chickens or a stack of firewood?
   A. These were materials that doctors particularly wanted.
   B. People generally did not have cash, so they paid for services with the goods that they had.
   C. Paper money and coins did not exist during the frontier era.
   D. Doctors did not want to carry cash because they were afraid of being robbed.

14. What facts in the selection support the statement *Perhaps among their most useful medical tools were confidence and good luck?*
   A. Frontier doctors had to perform many different tasks, such as amputating limbs and delivering babies.
   B. Frontier doctors did not have modern equipment such as x-rays and ultrasound.
   C. Although frontier doctors had very little training, they had to try to solve serious medical problems.
   D. Frontier doctors often had to travel through blizzards in the middle of the night, on horseback.

15. What is the most probable reason that a frontier doctor carried a how-to book?
   A. to find the homes of various patients
   B. to follow directions while doing medical procedures
   C. to figure out how much of a fee to charge for certain procedures
   D. to follow directions regarding sanitary procedures

Vocabulary Warm-up Word Lists

Study these words from the selection. Then, complete the activities.

Word List A

falter [FAWL tuhr] *v.* to hesitate or pause
Amy did not <u>falter</u> in her dedication to the cause of equality for women's sports teams.

grandeur [GRAND yoor] *n.* splendor; magnificence
The <u>grandeur</u> of the richly decorated opera house was breathtaking.

lordly [LOHRD lee] *adj.* noble; grand
The queen's private secretary had elegant, polished manners and a <u>lordly</u> bearing.

meager [MEE guhr] *adj.* lean; inadequate
Jamie was not pleased with the <u>meager</u> portion of steak that was served to him.

paralyzed [PAR uh lyzd] *adj.* unable to move or act
Utterly confused, Alicia just stood there, as if she were <u>paralyzed</u>.

peril [PER il] *n.* great danger
If you don't ski well, a difficult mountain poses considerable <u>peril</u>.

perplexity [per PLEKS uh tee] *n.* confusion; bafflement; puzzlement
That complicated project has left Susan in a state of <u>perplexity</u>.

stammering [STAM uhr ing] *adj.* struggling to get words out; stuttering
<u>Stammering</u> in anxiety, the messenger could hardly get his words out.

Word List B

converging [kuhn VERJ ing] *adj.* joining together; meeting
To get to Harry's place, you take a right turn where three roads are <u>converging</u>.

receding [ree SEED ing] *adj.* moving backward; becoming more distant
<u>Receding</u> when you leave the city, the sound of traffic becomes ever more faint.

sullen [SUL uhn] *adj.* gloomy; bad-tempered
Meg is a <u>sullen</u> child and rarely smiles.

tempo [TEM poh] *n.* pace; rate of activity
I like the spirited, rapid <u>tempo</u> of this musical piece.

timorous [TIM uhr uhs] *adj.* fearful
We adopted a small, <u>timorous</u> kitten.

tragedy [TRAJ uh dee] *n.* play or story with an unhappy or disastrous ending
Lydia told us about the <u>tragedy</u> of her son's disappearance.

visage [VIZ uhj] *n.* face; countenance; appearance
None of us is really ready for the gray <u>visage</u> of winter.

vista [VIS ta] *n.* broad, scenic view or overlook
Go to the memorial park sometime, because the <u>vista</u> at sunset is truly spectacular.

Name _____ Date _____

"The Far and the Near" by Thomas Wolfe
Vocabulary Warm-up Exercises

Exercise A *Fill in the blanks, using each word from Word List A only once.*

Medieval life in Europe was dominated by the feudal system. In this system,

[1] _____ nobles, such as barons, allowed those in more

[2] _____ circumstances, called vassals, to farm the land. In return, a

noble's vassals promised to serve him loyally. They had to take up arms if necessary to

defend a lord who was in danger or [3] _____. A noble's importance and

[4] _____ increased with the number of vassals he could summon to his

aid. If a vassal should hesitate or [5] _____, he might be severely warned

or even punished. One can imagine the puzzlement or [6] _____ of a

peasant, standing almost [7] _____ with fear in front of an angry noble-

man and [8] _____ his excuses. It is safe to assume that most excuses

would have been in vain.

Exercise B *Decide whether each statement below is true or false. Circle* T *or* F, *and explain your answer.*

1. Streams that are <u>converging</u> separate from a common source and go their own way.
   T / F _____

2. The water level in a <u>receding</u> tide gradually diminishes.
   T / F _____

3. A <u>sullen</u> companion on a long plane ride is usually good company.
   T / F _____

4. An orchestra conductor decides on the <u>tempo</u> at which the music will be played.
   T / F _____

5. If you are <u>timorous</u>, you are not easily frightened.
   T / F _____

6. In drama, you can expect a <u>tragedy</u> to end with the death or destruction of the main character.
   T / F _____

7. A person's <u>visage</u> often offers a good clue to the emotions he or she is feeling.
   T / F _____

8. On a clear day, the <u>vista</u> from a mountaintop can often be spectacular.
   T / F _____

Name _____ Date _____

"The Far and the Near" by Thomas Wolfe
Reading Warm-up A

Read the following passage. Pay special attention to the underlined words. Then, read it again, and complete the activities. Use a separate sheet of paper for your written answers.

The credit for inventing the first railroad locomotive belongs to a British engineer named George Stephenson. Born in 1781, Stephenson first became interested in railroad engines when he saw a machine called a "steam boiler on wheels" constructed by John Blenkinsop. This contraption, with three sets of wheels, had been built to haul coal out of the mines. With three sets of wheels, however, it would often <u>falter</u> and break down. Stephenson, thinking that the design could be improved, built a machine he called the Blucher. It was a <u>lordly</u> engine compared to Blenkinsop's. It could pull eight wagons carrying 30 tons of coal at a speed of 4 miles per hour. Although its hauling capacity may seem very <u>meager</u> today, for the year 1820, the engine possessed a certain <u>grandeur</u> as the most powerful machine of its time.

Stephenson's landmark challenge, however, came in the 1820s. Manchester and Liverpool invited him to build a 40-mile railroad to connect the two cities. Other engineers might have reacted with puzzlement, confusion, or <u>perplexity</u>, but not Stephenson. Taking the challenge in stride, in 1829 Stephenson had nearly completed the railway line. That year, he and his son Robert took part in a contest to build a new locomotive. Their entry, a steam engine they called the *Rocket*, won easily. Imagine how the spectators must have looked and felt on the day of the engine's first run. Standing stock still and almost <u>paralyzed</u> with wonder, they would probably have been <u>stammering</u> at each other, unable to get their words out. At a speed of 36 miles per hour, the *Rocket* might have seemed to pose great danger or <u>peril</u> to railroad passengers. There must have been something incredibly exciting, though, about the capacity to move so fast in an age of horse-drawn carriages!

1. Underline the words that give a clue to the meaning of <u>falter</u>. What is a synonym for *falter*?

2. Circle the words in this and the next sentence that give a clue to the meaning of <u>lordly</u>. Use the word *lordly* in an original sentence.

3. Underline the words in this and the previous sentence that give a clue to the meaning of <u>meager</u>. What is an antonym for *meager*?

4. What is a synonym for <u>grandeur</u>? What is an antonym for the word *grandeur*?

5. Circle the words in this sentence that offer a clue to the meaning of <u>perplexity</u>. Use a word meaning the opposite of *perplexity* in a sentence of your own.

6. Underline the words in this sentence that give clues to the meaning of <u>paralyzed</u>. Is *paralyzed* used literally or figuratively here?

7. Underline the words that hint at the meaning of <u>stammering</u>. What is a synonym of the word *stammering*?

8. Underline the words in this sentence that give a clue to the meaning of <u>peril</u>. Use a word meaning the opposite of *peril* in an original sentence.

"The Far and the Near" by Thomas Wolfe
Reading Warm-up B

Read the following passage. Pay special attention to the underlined words. Then, read it again, and complete the activities. Use a separate sheet of paper for your written answers.

Tracey boarded the train in Boston with a <u>sullen</u> frown, depressed at the idea of spending three whole days traveling across the country. Compared to the flash and speed of air travel, a train seemed like an old person, winding its careful way over the land, slow and <u>timorous</u>. Her mother argued, though, that the train would give Tracey a better sense of the places she was traveling through.

"At least once in your life, you should experience how vast the country really is," her mother insisted.

So now Tracey sat down in her compartment next to an old woman whose foggy eyes and wrinkled <u>visage</u> seemed to confirm everything she feared. The journey would indeed be dull, from the passengers to the painfully slow <u>tempo</u> of the train's movement. Before long, the old woman had fallen asleep and Tracey was left to silently contemplate the passing <u>vista</u> outside her window.

How dull it all seemed: towns and houses appearing and then <u>receding</u> into the distance, all of them the same. If her mother meant her to have an interesting experience, did she really think that sitting still for three days would fit the bill? Occasionally the train would pull into a station, and Tracey would watch the complicated network of different tracks <u>converging</u> like streams into a single river. Eventually, she began to see something beautiful in the idea of a railroad. She saw how much work had gone into building it, laying tracks that connected the entire country.

By lunchtime, seated in the dining car, Tracey had decided that the train had its advantages. Sitting in the comfortable booth, ordering from a menu, she thought is was not such a <u>tragedy</u> to be traveling in this old-fashioned way.

1. Underline the words in this sentence that hint at the meaning of <u>sullen</u>. What are two synonyms for **sullen**?

2. Circle the word in this sentence that hints at the meaning of <u>timorous</u>. Use a word meaning the opposite of **timorous** in a sentence of your own.

3. Underline the words in this sentence that hint at the meaning of <u>visage</u>. What is a synonym for **visage**?

4. Underline the words in this sentence that hint at the meaning of <u>tempo</u>. What is a synonym for **tempo**?

5. Circle the words in this sentence that hint at the meaning of <u>vista</u>. Use the word **vista** in an original sentence.

6. Circle the words in this sentence that give a good clue to the meaning of <u>receding</u>. Use a word meaning the opposite of **receding** in a sentence of your own.

7. Underline the words in this sentence that hint at the meaning of <u>converging</u>. What is an antonym for **converging**?

8. Underline the words in this and the previous sentence that hint at the meaning of <u>tragedy</u>. Does a **tragedy** have a happy ending or a sad ending?

"The Far and the Near" by Thomas Wolfe
Literary Analysis: Climax and Anticlimax

Most short stories have plots based on the following structure: exposition, rising action, climax, falling action, resolution. The **climax** is the high point of a story. If a story is very compelling, the reader may feel anxious to know what will happen to the characters and may feel a sense of relief upon reaching the climax. When a story has an **anticlimax,** the author builds up the reader's expectations for a grand finale only to deflate them with an ending that may seem disappointing or trivial.

DIRECTIONS: *Read each passage from "The Far and the Near." Then answer the questions that follow.*

1. Every day for more than twenty years, as the train had approached this house, the engineer had blown on the whistle, and every day, as soon as she heard this signal, a woman had appeared on the back porch of the little house and waved to him. At first she had a small child clinging to her skirts, and now this child had grown to full womanhood, and every day she, too, came with her mother to the porch and waved.

   Based on this passage, what kind of impression do you think that the woman has made on the engineer? What might the engineer expect her personality to be like?

   _____

   _____

   _____

2. He knew at once that the woman who stood there looking at him with a mistrustful eye was the same woman who had waved to him so many thousand times. But her face was harsh and pinched and meager; the flesh sagged wearily in sallow folds, and the small eyes peered at him with timid suspicion and uneasy doubt.

   How is this passage anticlimactic when paired with the passages above? What expectations does it disappoint?

   _____

   _____

   _____

"The Far and the Near" by Thomas Wolfe
Reading Strategy: Predict

The beginning and middle of a short story often contain clues about the story's outcome or about what will happen next. You can use these clues to **predict** what might happen. Some stories contain clues that foreshadow their endings or indicate what will actually happen. However, other stories have surprise endings.

DIRECTIONS: *Read each passage from "The Far and the Near." Then write a one-sentence prediction based on the passage.*

1. The engineer had grown old and gray in service. He had driven his great train, loaded with its weight of lives, across the land ten thousand times.

   _____

   _____

   _____

2. But no matter what peril or tragedy he had known, the vision of the little house and the women waving to him with a brave free motion of the arm had become fixed in the mind of the engineer as something beautiful and enduring, something beyond all change and ruin, and something that would always be the same, no matter what mishap, grief or error might break the iron schedule of his days.

   _____

   _____

   _____

3. Everything was as strange to him as if he had never seen this town before.

   _____

   _____

   _____

4. But now that he had found it, now that he was here, why did his hand falter on the gate; why had the town, the road, the earth, the very entrance to this place he loved turned unfamiliar as the landscape of some ugly dream? Why did he now feel this sense of confusion, doubt and hopelessness?

   _____

   _____

   _____

5. . . . the door was opened, and a woman stood facing him.
   And instantly, with a sense of bitter loss and grief, he was sorry he had come.

   _____

   _____

   _____

Name _____ Date _____

"The Far and the Near" by Thomas Wolfe
Vocabulary Builder

Using the Root -temp-

A. DIRECTIONS: *The word* tempo *is based on the word root* -temp-, *which means "time." Using the information following each word and what you know about the word root* -temp-, *write the word that best completes each sentence.*

> temporary (-ary = "relating to")
> contemporary (con- = "with")
> extemporaneous (ex- = "from"; -ous = "characterized by")
> temporal (-al = "of")

1. Thomas Wolfe was a _____ of F. Scott Fitzgerald.
2. Janet's speech at the awards dinner was _____.
3. Looking for a job, Frank went to an agency that placed _____ help.
4. Lost in meditations about the eternal hereafter, James neglected _____ matters.

Using the Word List

tempo	sallow	sullen	timorous	visage

B. DIRECTIONS: *Complete each sentence with the best word from the list in the box.*

1. The angry woman looked dully at the engineer, her face a _____, suspicious mask.
2. With _____ expressions, the women looked fearfully at the engineer.
3. "His heart . . . saw the strange and unsuspected _____ of an earth which had always been within a stone's throw of him, and which he had never seen or known."
4. The woman did not look healthy; "the flesh sagged wearily in _____ folds, and the small eyes peered at him with timid suspicion and uneasy doubt."
5. After he retired, the engineer experienced a slowing in the _____ of his daily life.

Name _____ Date _____

"The Far and the Near" by Thomas Wolfe

Grammar and Style: Restrictive and Nonrestrictive Participial Phrases

A **participle** is a form of a verb that acts as an adjective. A **participial phrase** is a group of words beginning with a participle that acts as an adjective. A **restrictive participial phrase** is necessary to the meaning of the sentence and is *not* set off with commas. A **nonrestrictive participial phrase** is not necessary to the meaning and, therefore, *is* set off with commas.

Here is an example of a restrictive participial phrase from "The Far and the Near." The phrase is underlined.

. . . finally nothing could be heard but the solid clacking tempo of the wheels <u>receding into the drowsy stillness of the afternoon</u>.

In this case, the participial phrase describes the noun *tempo* and is necessary to the meaning of the sentence.

Here is an example of a nonrestrictive participial phrase:

He had driven his great train, <u>loaded with its weight of lives</u>, across the land ten thousand times.

In this case, the participial phrase describes the noun *train*, but it is not necessary to the meaning of the sentence.

A. PRACTICE: *Read the following sentences or sentence parts, and underline each participial phrase. Then identify whether it is restrictive or nonrestrictive.*

1. "To one side of the house there was a garden neatly patterned with plots of growing vegetables. . . ." _____

2. ". . . now, schooled by the qualities of faith and courage and humbleness that attended his labor, he had grown old." _____

3. "And finally, stammering a crude farewell, he departed." _____

B. Writing Application: *Write sentences in which you use participial phrases as directed.*

1. Use *swept* in a nonrestrictive participial phrase.

_____

2. Use *planted* in a restrictive participial phrase.

_____

3. Use *posing* in a nonrestrictive participial phrase.

_____

4. Use *written* in a restrictive participial phrase.

_____

"The Far and the Near" by Thomas Wolfe
Support for Writing

Prepare to write a **comparison-and-contrast essay** about "The Far and the Near" by entering information from the story into the graphic organizer below.

Engineer's view of things when he is far from little house:
Engineer's view of things when he is near little house:
What story says about how dreams affect our lives:

On a separate page, write a draft of your essay, using material from the chart. When you revise, be sure you have included the two points of view of the engineer, from both near and far. Then add your conclusion about how dreams can affect one's life.

"The Far and the Near" by Thomas Wolfe
Support for Extend Your Learning

Listening and Speaking

Prepare to **interview** someone who travels regularly by train. Create questions to ask your interview subject, including the following:

- How does the landscape look to him or her from the train?
- What was romantic or exciting about journeys that he or she has taken?
- In what way is rail travel different from traveling by car?

When you have completed your interview, share it with your classmates. Compare what you have learned with what they found out in their interviews.

Research and Technology

Do research with a small group for a **written report** on the history of the railroad industry in the United States. Enter information into the chart below.

Railroads in U.S. History

Major Railroad Lines	People's Attitudes toward Railroads (Early Years)
Effects of Railroad on U.S. Industry	Changes in Modern Railroad Use

When you prepare your report, include maps and other graphics that give a picture of railroad history and modern use of railroads.

Name _____ Date _____

Enrichment: Art

Grant Wood, a famous Midwestern painter, was a contemporary of Thomas Wolfe. Like Wolfe, Wood drew much of the material for his work from his own life. Look carefully at *Stone City, Iowa*, the painting by Wood that appears with the story. The women in Wolfe's story "The Far and the Near" might have lived in a town such as this one.

DIRECTIONS: *Refer to Wood's painting.* Stone City, Iowa *as you answer the following questions.*

1. What buildings did the artist include in this painting?
   _____

2. Referring to this painting, what do you think is the main occupation of people who live in this town?
   _____

3. What cargo might be carried by a train passing through the town in the painting?
   _____

4. How many people are depicted in the painting? Judging from this number, what can you surmise about life in this town?
   _____
   _____

5. Do you think that people in this town often meet strangers? Why or why not?
   _____
   _____

6. Explain why the people in this town might react positively to a visit from someone like the train engineer.
   _____
   _____

7. Explain why the people in this town might react negatively to a visit from someone like the train engineer.
   _____
   _____

"The Far and the Near" by Thomas Wolfe
Selection Test A

Critical Reading *Identify the letter of the choice that best answers the question.*

____ 1. In "The Far and the Near," why does the engineer find the little house so appealing day after day?
A. It is on a pretty land and well kept up.
B. It lasts through the changes in his life.
C. He would like to have a house like it.
D. Passing it tells him he is almost home.

____ 2. In "The Far and the Near," what prediction can you make as you read about the engineer's daily wave to the people in the little house?
A. The engineer will never see the house again.
B. The engineer will find out they are his family.
C. The engineer will become tired of waving every day.
D. The engineer will want to visit the family in the house.

____ 3. In "The Far and the Near," what does the engineer believe that leads to his disappointment?
A. He will move to the little house.
B. His life is connected to the women.
C. His children will meet the women.
D. His train is a powerful machine.

____ 4. In "The Far and the Near," what can the reader predict will happen after reading that the engineer's "sense of bewilderment and confusion grew" as he walks in the town?
A. The engineer will be unable to find the house with the women.
B. The engineer's will not find what he expects at the house.
C. The engineer will decide he wants to keep his job.
D. The engineer will believe he has come to the wrong town.

____ 5. In "The Far and the Near," how does the writer make the anticlimax shattering?
A. by describing the engineer's expectations
B. by describing the weather each day
C. by describing what the town looks like
D. by describing the countryside

____ 6. What might you predict as a reader when you learn that the engineer will visit the house in "The Far and the Near"?

A. that the women will want to meet the engineer

B. that the women will offer to sell the engineer their house

C. that the women will give the engineer a good meal

D. that the women will invite the engineer to live there

____ 7. Which of these sentences describes the theme of "The Far and the Near"?

A. A life of hard work is rewarded by happiness.

B. Travel helps you see the way other people live.

C. People who are hopeful are always happy.

D. As you get closer to people, you learn about them.

____ 8. In "The Far and the Near," why is the appearance of the woman at the door anticlimactic?

A. She is leaving to go visit someone.

B. She is not what the engineer expected.

C. She is a woman in a different house.

D. She does not invite him into their house.

____ 9. In "The Far and the Near," why is the engineer so disappointed at the end of the story?

A. The engineer is older than the women.

B. The engineer's expectations are not met.

C. The women do not know the engineer.

D. The engineer is a threat to their peace.

____ 10. In "The Far and the Near," what is the main image in the story?

A. the train whistle

B. the little house

C. the engineer

D. the station platform

____ 11. What do you think Wolfe meant to suggest by the title "The Far and the Near"?

A. The engineer is near the women's house but far from their lives.

B. The engineer confuses the distances between towns on his route.

C. The engineer's job keeps him far from, not near, his family.

D. The engineer dreams of things that will happen in the near future.

Vocabulary and Grammar

_____ **12.** Which answer best replaces *sullen* in this sentence: "The woman did not smile, acting *sullen* in his presence?

    A. happy and funny

    B. prompt and ready

    C. important and special

    D. quiet and unhappy

_____ **13.** Which sentence contains a **nonrestrictive** participial phrase that modifies a noun?

    A. He felt the tenderness a man might feel for his own children.

    B. He had driven his train, loaded with the weight of lives, across the land.

    C. It was all as unfamiliar and strange as though it was dream.

    D. His own voice sounded unreal to him as he tried to explain his presence.

Essay

14. In "The Far and the Near," what do you think the author is saying about the power of the imagination and of one's expectations? What does the engineer expect to happen when he meets the women of the little house? What really happens? What point is the author making? Write a brief essay to express your opinions.

15. In "The Far and the Near," the engineer begins to feel uncomfortable about his visit to the house when he leaves the train station. The writer says, "Everything was strange to him as if he had never seen this town before." Why does the writer introduce the idea of strangeness? What do you think the writer means to suggest in this sentence? Write a brief essay to address these questions.

"The Far and the Near" by Thomas Wolfe
Selection Test B

Critical Reading *Identify the letter of the choice that best completes the statement or answers the question.*

____ 1. Why does the little house give the engineer such "extraordinary happiness"?
    A. The house reminds him of his own wife and family.
    B. Seeing the house introduces variety into the boring routine of his job.
    C. The vision of the house does not change despite the changes in his life.
    D. The house is the only beautiful spot on an otherwise unremarkable route.

____ 2. Which of the following details from the story *best* illustrates the source of the engineer's later disillusionment?
    A. "To one side of the house there was a garden. . . ."
    B. "He had seen them in a thousand lights, a hundred weathers."
    C. "[H]e felt that he knew their lives completely, to every hour. . . ."
    D. "The whole place had an air of tidiness, thrift, and modest comfort."

____ 3. Which of the following details from the story foreshadows a climactic ending?
    A. ". . . a tidy little cottage of white boards, trimmed vividly with green blinds."
    B. "For a moment the progress of the engine could be marked by heavy bellowing puffs of smoke. . . ."
    C. "Every day for more than twenty years . . . a woman had appeared. . . ."
    D. "He felt for them . . . such tenderness as a man might feel for his own children. . . ."

____ 4. Based on this passage, what can you predict will happen later in the story?

    But no matter what peril or tragedy he had known, the vision of the little house and the women waving to him . . . became fixed in the mind of the engineer as something beautiful and enduring, something beyond all change and ruin, and something that would always be the same, no matter what mishap, grief or error might break the iron schedule of his days.

    A. The women will always wave at the engineer.
    B. The engineer will ask the women to stop waving.
    C. Something will happen to change the engineer's vision.
    D. The engineer will get tired of watching the women wave every day.

____ 5. Which of the following details is a clue predicting the ending of the story?
    A. "He had driven his great train, loaded with its weight of lives, across the land ten thousand times."
    B. "He had known all the grief, the joy, the peril and the labor such a man could know . . . and now . . . he had grown old."
    C. "It was all as unfamiliar, as disquieting as a city in a dream, and the perplexity of his spirit increased as he went on."
    D. "Yes, this was the house he sought, the place he had passed so many times, the destination he had longed for with such happiness."

_____ 6. Which of the following details does *not* help the reader predict the ending of the story?
   A. "Everything was as strange to him as if he had never seen this town before."
   B. "He knew at once that he had found the proper place."
   C. "Why did he now feel this sense of confusion, doubt and hopelessness?"
   D. "And instantly, with a sense of bitter loss and grief, he was sorry he had come."

_____ 7. Why is the story's ending anticlimactic?
   A. The women do not invite him into their house.
   B. The house is exactly the same as the engineer expected.
   C. The women don't understand why it is important to the engineer to visit them.
   D. The engineer isn't sure that these are the same women who were waving to him.

_____ 8. Which of the following effects do you think Wolfe is striving for by giving "The Far and the Near" this anticlimax?

   . . . suddenly he knew that he was an old man. His heart, which had been brave and confident when it looked along the familiar vista of the rails, was now sick with doubt and horror as it saw the strange and unsuspected visage of an earth which had always been within a stone's throw of him, and which he had never seen or known.

   A. laughter
   B. surprise
   C. shock
   D. insight

_____ 9. The engineer's expectations of the women are bound to be disappointing because
   A. they cannot be as wonderful as he has built them up to be.
   B. his expectations are based on illusions he created over twenty years.
   C. his life experience has been completely different from theirs.
   D. the women have no reason to consider the engineer friendly or trustworthy.

_____ 10. What is the theme of "The Far and the Near"?
   A. The imagination can be one of the most tragic human attributes.
   B. Travel often exposes people to the foolishness of their expectations.
   C. Unexpected gestures to strangers are bound to be misunderstood.
   D. Up close, things are rarely as perfect as they seem from afar.

_____ 11. What ultimate effect does the engineer's visit to the cottage have on him?
   A. It makes him suspicious of the people around him.
   B. It teaches him that life basically consists of a set of unrealistic illusions.
   C. It turns him into a bitter and cynical old man.
   D. It shatters his faith in the ultimate beauty and goodness of life.

_____ 12. What is the probable reason Wolfe titled this story "The Far and the Near"?
   A. What is near in some ways turns out to be far in others.
   B. The women are near the tracks, but the train travels very far.
   C. The engineer is near to the women but far from his own family.
   D. The engineer is near to other people but far from happiness.

____ 13. How might the title "The Far and the Near" apply to the women?
  A. They are far from the engineer but near to each other.
  B. They are far from the engineer in personality but near to him in age.
  C. They feel friendly toward the faraway train but afraid of the engineer when he is near.
  D. They wave to the train because it travels from a place that is near to one that is far.

Vocabulary and Grammar

____ 14. Which two words best express the imagery of the phrase in italics?
  But her face was harsh and pinched and meager; *the flesh sagged wearily in sallow folds*. . . .
  A. bright; clownish
  B. tired; friendly
  C. mean; angry
  D. wrinkled; sickly

____ 15. Which of the following words is closest in meaning to *visage*?
  A. appearance
  B. terror
  C. rocks
  D. opinion

____ 16. Which of the following words could be substituted for *tempo* without changing the meaning of the excerpt?
  . . . finally nothing could be heard but the solid clacking tempo of the wheels receding into the drowsy stillness of the afternoon.
  A. rhythm
  B. melody
  C. tune
  D. monotone

____ 17. In the following excerpt, of what is the italicized part an example?
  . . . finally nothing could be heard but the solid clacking tempo of the wheels *receding into the drowsy stillness of the afternoon*.
  A. an anticlimax
  B. a prediction
  C. a restrictive participial phrase
  D. a nonrestrictive participial phrase

Essay

18. In an essay, interpret the engineer's feelings and explain why he might have found the women and the house "beautiful and enduring." Use details from the story to explain why they were so important to him.

19. When the climax of a story is unexpectedly disappointing, ridiculous, or trivial, it is called an anticlimax. In an essay, discuss how the ending of "The Far and the Near" is anticlimactic; include details from the story.

Vocabulary Warm-up Word Lists

Study these words from the poems. Then, complete the activities.

Word List A

genuine [JEN yoo in] *adj.* authentic; real
Experts will have to decide if that painting is genuine or a fake.

meditation [med uh TAY shuhn] *n.* deep thinking or consideration
Rodin's famous sculpture, *The Thinker*, shows a seated thinker sunk in meditation.

mute [MYOOT] *adj.* silent
When questioned by the police, the suspect remained completely mute.

quest [KWEST] *n.* search; hunt; pursuit
Many epics focus on a hero who undergoes adventures during a dangerous quest.

script [SKRIPT] *n.* text of the words for a film, play, or broadcast
The director and producers made numerous changes in the script for the film.

suffice [suh FYS] *v.* to be adequate enough
Will twenty dollars suffice to pay the charges for mailing that large package?

valid [VAL id] *adj.* acceptable; well-grounded on principles or evidence
This coupon is valid for a free day's auto rental.

wilderness [WIL duhr nes] *n.* uncultivated, uninhabited region; wasteland
If you go hiking in the wilderness, you should take a compass and a short-wave radio.

Word List B

derivative [duh RIV uh tiv] *adj.* unoriginal; stale
Her paintings were derivative and did not display much evidence of original talent.

insatiable [in SAY shuh buhl] *adj.* unable to be satisfied; greedy
Karl had an insatiable appetite, and he always seemed hungry.

insolence [IN suh lens] *n.* rudeness; utter disrespect; insulting behavior
At the party, Sam was rude to the point of insolence.

medallions [muh DAL yuhnz] *n.* large, ornamental medals
The university created several decorative medallions for its 200th anniversary.

palpable [PAL puh buhl] *adj.* able to be touched, felt, or handled; tangible
When the boss announced a salary freeze, the air of discontent was almost palpable.

souvenir [SOO vuh neer] *n.* memento; keepsake
As a souvenir from Paris, Brenda bought a small replica of the Eiffel Tower.

triviality [triv ee AL uh tee] *n.* insignificant matter; extremely minor issue
The triviality of Ronda's argument was such that most people took no notice of it.

unintelligible [un in TEL uh juh buhl] *adj.* unable to be understood
Since we knew no Russian, our efforts to communicate in Moscow were unintelligible.

Poems by Wallace Stevens, Archibald MacLeish, and Marianne Moore
Vocabulary Warm-up Exercises

Exercise A *Fill in the blanks, using each word from Word List A only once.*

Nina sat deep in [1] _____, thinking about the film

[2] _____ she was writing. Set in medieval Japan, the storyline for the movie

was simple. A young Buddhist hero retreats to the uninhabited [3] _____

and wanders there for seven years in a(n) [4] _____ for enlightenment.

The hero has made a vow of silence, so he must remain [5] _____ during

the entire film. Nina wondered what kind of strategies would [6] _____

to make her film both interesting and entertaining. The storyline, she knew, had a(n)

[7] _____ basis in history. To portray a(n) [8] _____ hero

convincingly, though, an actor of exceptional talent would be needed to play the main role in

the film.

Exercise B *Revise each sentence so that the underlined vocabulary word is logical. Be sure to keep the vocabulary word in your revision.*

Example: Since the highway was so <u>congested</u>, we arrived home early.
  Since the highway was so <u>congested</u>, we arrived home late.

1. We felt those art works were <u>derivative</u>, displaying a lot of original talent.
   _____

2. Aldo had an <u>insatiable</u> appetite and ate only one meal a day.
   _____

3. We praised Randy for his <u>insolence</u> during the meeting.
   _____

4. The cotton <u>medallions</u> commemorating the anniversary were very attractive.
   _____

5. When we met Sally, the tension was <u>palpable</u> and we barely noticed it.
   _____

6. If you want to forget a journey or trip, you should buy a <u>souvenir</u>.
   _____

7. The <u>triviality</u> of her action was such that we took it very seriously.
   _____

8. The lecturer's accent made him <u>unintelligible</u>, and we understood the lecture clearly.
   _____

Poems by Wallace Stevens, Archibald MacLeish, and Marianne Moore
Reading Warm-up A

Read the following passage. Pay special attention to the underlined words. Then, read it again, and complete the activities. Use a separate sheet of paper for your written answers.

In a sense, all three poets in this grouping are on a quest or search to define the essence of poetry. For Wallace Stevens, a valid or acceptable poem must be the "finding of a satisfaction." Even the most ordinary actions, such as a man skating, can suffice as adequate for the subject of poetry. What is essential is that the speaker and the reader can discover a passion or energy in the actions that are described. Elsewhere, Stevens wrote that poetry acts like "a purging of the world's poverty and change and evil and death." For this poet, poetry acted as a type of antidote to the wilderness—the ugly or savage elements in human existence.

Archibald MacLeish believes that "a poem should not mean but be." For MacLeish, a poem was not a script or text for a theme or underlying message. Instead, it was a collection of concrete, vivid images. Marianne Moore, the third poet in this group, uses the simple title "Poetry" as the title for her meditation or considered treatment of the nature of poetry. She begins by pretending to dislike verse and even uses the word "contempt" in the second line of her poem. Nevertheless, she quickly makes an about-face. She declares that, after all, there is place for the genuine in poetry—a place for authentic and true feelings.

Hundreds of poets, in fact, have tried to define poetry and have scarcely been mute on this subject. Robert Frost said that poetry is "what gets lost in translation." The English poet Samuel Taylor Coleridge put it a little more simply when he wrote that poetry was "the best words in the best order." Finally, the American poet Elizabeth Bishop said that poetry was "hundreds of things coming together at the right moment."

1. Underline the words that give a clue to the meaning of quest. Use the word **quest** in a sentence of your own.

2. Circle the words in this sentence that give a clue to the meaning of valid. What are two antonyms for **valid**?

3. Underline the words in this sentence that give a clue to the meaning of suffice. What is an adjective formed from the verb **suffice**?

4. What is a synonym for wilderness? Use the word **wilderness** in a sentence of your own.

5. Circle the words in this sentence that offer a clue to the meaning of the word script. Use the word **script** in an original sentence.

6. Underline the words in this sentence that hint at the meaning of meditation. What is a synonym for **meditation**?

7. Underline the words in this sentence that hint at the meaning of genuine. Use a word meaning the opposite of **genuine** in a sentence of your own.

8. Underline the words in this sentence that give a clue to the meaning of mute. What is a synonym for **mute**?

Name _____ Date _____

Read the following passage. Pay special attention to the underlined words. Then, read it again, and complete the activities. Use a separate sheet of paper for your written answers.

For the last few months, inspired by the rap music he loved so much, Cyrus had been writing poem after poem. What started out as a simple hobby soon became an insatiable urge, and before long Cyrus had enough poems to fill five notebooks.

In October, he finally got up the nerve to enter a poetry slam, where thirty of the best young poets in the country would compete against each other for only three prizes. These prizes were gold medallions, like those from the Olympic Games, attached to silk ribbons that the winners got to wear around their necks.

Before he even entered the room, Cyrus felt nervous, but now the darkness and hush made the tension inside him even more palpable. He didn't know how he would manage to compete against so many other, more experienced poets. But as the competition began, he gained confidence by listening to what the others had to offer.

Some of the poems lacked originality. They were derivative, copying famous rap songs almost line-by-line. Other poems bored the audience with ordinary situations like going to school or riding the bus—they never rose above the level of triviality. The worst poems, though, tried to sound impressive by using big words. They got so carried away that the meaning was lost and they became unintelligible.

When Cyrus's turn came, he felt confident that he could win at least one of the three medals. He began reciting his best poem, an anti-war poem, raising his fist in anger, his voice full of insolence. When he finished, the audience remained in a stunned silence, and he knew he would be taking home one of the gold medals as a souvenir of his first victory.

1. Underline the word in this sentence that hints at the meaning of insatiable. What is a synonym for *insatiable*?

2. Circle the words in this sentence that hint at the meaning of medallions.

3. Underline the words in this sentence that hint at the meaning of palpable. Use *palpable* in an original sentence.

4. Circle the words in this and the previous sentence that hint at the meaning of derivative. Use a word meaning the opposite of *derivative* in a sentence of your own.

5. Underline the words in this and the previous sentence that hint at the meaning of triviality. What are two adjectives you could use to describe a *triviality*?

6. Circle the words in this sentence that hint at the meaning of unintelligible. Use a word meaning the opposite of *unintelligible* in a sentence of your own.

7. Circle the words in this sentence that give a good clue to the meaning of insolence. What are two antonyms for *insolence*?

8. Underline the words in this sentence that hint at the meaning of souvenir. What is a synonym for *souvenir*?

"Of Modern Poetry" and **"Anecdote of the Jar"** by Wallace Stevens
"Ars Poetica" by Archibald MacLeish
"Poetry" by Marianne Moore
Literary Analysis: Simile

A **simile** compares two unlike things using the word *like* or *as*. Through the use of similes, a poet arouses associations in the reader's mind that help communicate an emotion or idea. For example, in "Ars Poetica," Archibald MacLeish compares the wordlessness of a poem with the flight of birds. In the reader's mind, the simile evokes the qualities of birds in flight— soundlessness, grace, and a sense of soaring about the earth.

DIRECTIONS: *In the following lines from the poems, the poets use similes. Describe the associations each simile evokes in your mind. Then explain why you think the poet chose each simile.*

1. "It [the poem] has to be on that stage / And, like an insatiable actor, slowly and / With meditation, speak words. . ."

_____

_____

_____

_____

2. "A poem should be palpable and mute / As a globed fruit."

_____

_____

_____

_____

3. "a tree, the immovable critic twitching his skin like a / horse that feels a flea . . ."

_____

_____

_____

_____

"Of Modern Poetry" and **"Anecdote of the Jar"** by Wallace Stevens
"Ars Poetica" by Archibald MacLeish
"Poetry" by Marianne Moore

Reading Strategy: Paraphrase

Often a poem contains unexpected words and images, which can make it difficult to read and understand. To help make the poem clearer, you can **paraphrase** difficult lines, or restate them in your own words.

DIRECTIONS: *Read the following excerpts from the poems in this selection. Then paraphrase each excerpt, or rewrite in your own words, to make it easier to read and understand.*

1. Then the theatre was changed / To something else. Its past was a souvenir.

   _____

2. It has to face the men of the time and to meet / The women of the time.

   _____

3. wholly / Containing the mind, below which it cannot descend, / Beyond which it has no will to rise.

   _____

4. The jar was gray and bare. / It did not give of bird or bush, / Like nothing else in Tennessee.

   _____

5. A poem should be palpable and mute / As a globed fruit.

   _____

6. A poem should be motionless in time / As the moon climbs.

   _____

7. A poem should not mean / But be.

   _____

8. Reading it [poetry], however, with a perfect contempt for it, one / discovers in / it after all, a place for the genuine.

   _____

9. these things are important not because a / high-sounding interpretation can be put upon them but / because they are / useful.

   _____

10. and can present / for inspection, imaginary gardens with real toads in / them

    _____

Name _____ Date _____

Vocabulary Builder

Using the Root -satis-

A. DIRECTIONS: *In "Of Modern Poetry," Wallace Stevens uses the word* insatiable *to describe an actor who must constantly perform. The root of* insatiable *is -satis-, which means "enough." The prefixes for the three words below are defined in parentheses. For each word, write a sentence in which the meaning of* satis *is demonstrated clearly.*

1. *dissatisfy* (*dis-* = "fail," "refuse to") _____

2. *insatiable* (*in-* = "no, not") _____

3. *unsatisfactorily* (*un-* = "the opposite") _____

Using the Word List

suffice	insatiable	slovenly	dominion
palpable	derivative	literalists	

B. DIRECTIONS: *In the following excerpts from the poems, substitute the correct word from the Word List for the bracketed word or words and write it on the blank.*

1. "A poem should be [able to be handled] _____ and mute / As a globed fruit."

2. "It took [the power to rule] _____ everywhere."

3. "nor till the poets among us can be / [people who take words at their exact meaning] _____ of / the imagination"

4. "It made the [untidy] wilderness _____ / Surround that hill."

5. "It has to be on that stage / And, like an [unable to be satisfied] _____ actor, slowly and / Without meditation"

6. "When they become so [based on something else] _____ as to become / unintelligible"

7. "The poem of the mind in the act of finding / What will [be adequate]" _____.

"Of Modern Poetry" and **"Anecdote of the Jar"** by Wallace Stevens
"Ars Poetica" by Archibald MacLeish
"Poetry" by Marianne Moore

Grammar and Style: Subject Complements

A **subject complement** follows a linking verb and identifies or describes the subject. It can be a noun, a pronoun, or an adjective.

Here is an example of a subject complement from "Of Modern Poetry." The subject complement is underlined.

Its past was a <u>souvenir</u>.

In this case, the subject complement is a noun that identifies the subject.

Here is an example of a subject complement from "Anecdote of the Jar."

The jar was <u>round</u> upon the ground

In this case, the subject complement is an adjective that describes the subject.

A. PRACTICE: *Read the following excerpts from the poems and underline each subject complement. Then identify its use in the sentence: as a noun identifying the subject or as an adjective describing the subject.*

1. "The actor is / A metaphysician in the dark"
   _____

2. "The jar was gray . . ."
   _____

3. "A poem should be motionless . . ."
   _____

4. ". . . all these phenomena are important."
   _____

B. Writing Application: *Use each of these words as a subject complement in a sentence.*

1. instrument
   _____

2. emotional
   _____

3. wilderness
   _____

4. bird
   _____

5. moon
   _____

Name _____ Date _____

"Of Modern Poetry" and **"Anecdote of the Jar"** by Wallace Stevens
"Ars Poetica" by Archibald MacLeish
"Poetry" by Marianne Moore

Support for Writing

In order to **compare and contrast** the ideas in two of the poems in this selection, enter material into the chart below.

Ideas about Poetry in the works of _____

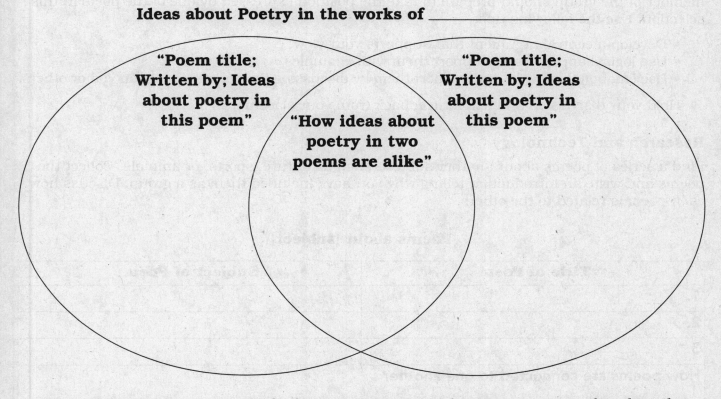

On a separate page, write a draft of your comparison and contrast essay to show how the ideas of the two poets are either similar or different. When you revise, add more examples from the poems to support your opinions.

"Of Modern Poetry" and **"Anecdote of the Jar"** by Wallace Stevens

"Art Poetica" by Archibald MacLeish

"Poetry" by Marianne Moore

Support for Extend Your Learning

Listening and Speaking

Work with a small group to prepare a **round-table discussion** called "What Is Poetry?" Each member of the group should prepare to take the position expressed by one of the poets in this selection. Use the following tips:

- Develop a central argument that supports your view.
- Use logical appeals, and support them with examples.
- Use emotional appeals, and support them by discussing the poem's impact on you or others.

Hold your discussion and ask for feedback from your classmates.

Research and Technology

Find a series of poems about another subject, such as nature, sports, or animals. Collect the poems and write an introduction telling why you have included them as a group. Discuss how each poem is related to the others.

Poems about [subject]

Title of Poem	Subject of Poem
1.	
2.	
3.	
How poems are connected to one another	

Share your collection with the class and then put it into the classroom library.

"Of Modern Poetry" and **"Anecdote of the Jar"** by Wallace Stevens
"Ars Poetica" by Archibald MacLeish
"Poetry" by Marianne Moore
Enrichment: Photography

Stevens, MacLeish, and Moore offer the reader interesting perspectives on how to recognize poetry. Stevens felt that the poet "helps people live their lives" by providing new ways to see the world.

DIRECTIONS: *Examine the photograph that appears with "Ars Poetica" in your textbook. How does the scene evoke a poem? What moods and ideas are conveyed in the illustration? Try to imagine what the poets Stevens, MacLeish, and Moore would have to say about this photograph. Write three different interpretations—one for each poet—in the space below. If possible, include quotations from their poetry to support your interpretations.*

As interpreted by Wallace Stevens:

1. _____

_____

_____

_____

_____

_____

As interpreted by Archibald MacLeish:

2. _____

_____

_____

_____

_____

_____

_____

As interpreted by Marianne Moore:

3. _____

_____

_____

_____

_____

_____

_____

_____

"Of Modern Poetry" and **"Anecdote of the Jar"** by Wallace Stevens
"Ars Poetica" by Archibald MacLeish
"Poetry" by Marianne Moore

Selection Test A

Critical Reading *Identify the letter of the choice that best answers the question.*

_____ 1. In "Of Modern Poetry," where does a poem begin, according to the poet?
A. on stage
B. in the ear
C. in the mind
D. in the heart

_____ 2. Which of these best paraphrases the passage from "Of Modern Poetry," in which the poet says that poems once "repeated what/ Was in the script"?
A. Old fashioned poetry is the best.
B. Poetry used to use the forms of the past.
C. Poems can be written as though they are plays.
D. Many plays have poetry in their scripts.

_____ 3. What responsibility does a modern poet have, according to "Of Modern Poetry"?
A. to write poems of love and war
B. to write poems of today's world
C. to write poems for staged readings
D. to write poems to be set to music

_____ 4. In "Of Modern Poetry," what is a poem compared to in the simile that says a poem must "speak words" to "an invisible audience"?
A. music
B. an actor
C. a stage
D. an ear

_____ 5. In "Anecdote of the Jar," what does the poet suggest by saying that the jar "did not give of bird or bush"?
A. It has been emptied of all its contents.
B. It supports no animal or plant life.
C. It stands out on the Tennessee hill.
D. It is more important than anything else.

_____ 6. To which sense does "Ars Poetica" appeal by suggesting that a poem should be as silent as a fruit or a stone?
A. smell
B. sound
C. sigh
D. taste

_____ 7. What quality of birds does the poet admire in the simile that says "A poem should be wordless / As the flight of birds" in "Ars Poetica"?
A. the birds' nests
B. the birds' speech
C. the birds' movement
D. the birds' friendship

_____ 8. How would you paraphrase the passage from "Ars Poetica" that says that a poet should limit himself or herself to writing "an empty doorway" instead of writing many words about grief?
A. A poet should write about empty doorways.
B. A poet should only use certain images to write about grief.
C. A poet should share a meaningful experience by using brief images.
D. A poet should write about grief to be a good poet.

_____ 9. In "Poetry," what does the poet suggest about how poetry affects critics, in the simile about "the immovable critic twitching his skin like a horse that feels a flea"?
A. Poetry annoys the critic.
B. The critic must sit still to write.
C. The critic is easily distracted.
D. The critic likes to write about animals.

_____ 10. Why does the poet tell her listeners in "Poetry" that she dislikes poetry?
A. to show that poetry is all about facts
B. to help teach them why it is useful
C. to explain why she likes critics
D. to convince them not to read it

_____ 11. Which of these is the best paraphrase of the passage from "Poetry" that suggests that "business documents and school-books" might be useful in understanding the world?
A. True poets must always fight against facts.
B. Business documents and school-books are not poetry.
C. Facts can be useful in the hands of a good poet.
D. Good poetry is never found in schoolbooks.

Unit 5 Resources: Disillusion, Defiance, and Discontent

Vocabulary and Grammar

____ 12. Which word best replaces *dominion* in this sentence: "The king had *dominion* over all the land around the castle"?
   A. belief
   B. speech
   C. control
   D. thought

____ 13. Which of the following passages contains a subject complement that follows a linking verb and a noun?
   A. He introduced me to his wife.
   B. His wife is a poet.
   C. She has written many poems.
   D. I have read her work.

Essay

14. Wallace Steven says in "Of Modern Poetry," that it has to "learn the speech of the place." What does he mean by "the place"— is he referring to a certain place, or the time during which poets live? How does he want poets to connect with the people who read their work? In a brief essay, respond to these questions.

15. In "Ars Poetica," MacLeish says, "A poem should not mean / But be." Is he criticizing other poets who use too many words to try to convey their feelings and thoughts? Is he encouraging poets to use brief images to capture their ideas? Write a brief essay to give your ideas.

"Of Modern Poetry" and **"Anecdote of the Jar"** by Wallace Stevens
"Ars Poetica" by Archibald MacLeish
"Poetry" by Marianne Moore
Selection Test B

Critical Reading *Identify the letter of the choice that best completes the statement or answers the question.*

____ 1. The central theme of "Of Modern Poetry" is that a modern poem must
  A. still be written in a traditional way.
  B. reflect the people of the time.
  C. use techniques such as similes and paraphrasing.
  D. draw from the past in order to speak to the people of the present.

____ 2. In "Anecdote of the Jar," which of the following might the jar most logically symbolize?
  A. the ambivalence that many people feel toward the wilderness
  B. the order that nature imposes on herself
  C. the carelessness of humans in dealing with nature
  D. the power that human civilization holds over nature

____ 3. Which of the following excerpts is a simile?
  A. "I placed a jar in Tennessee, / And round it was, upon a hill."
  B. "we cannot understand: the bat / holding on upside down . . ."
  C. "A poem should be wordless / As the flight of birds."
  D. "A poem should not mean / But be."

____ 4. The theme of "Ars Poetica" suggests that a poem should
  A. minimize the reader's tendency to react emotionally.
  B. strengthen the reader's intellectual grasp of life.
  C. appeal more to the senses than to the intellect.
  D. rely on lush imagery and elaborate diction.

____ 5. Which is the best way to paraphrase the following excerpt from "Ars Poetica"?
    A poem should be equal to:
    Not true.

  A. The lines of a poem should be equal in length—not true to real life.
  B. A poem should be equal to an object or emotion—not true to it.
  C. A poem should be true for some people but false for others.
  D. A poem's subject should usually be fairly represented, but not always.

____ 6. Which simile from MacLeish's "Ars Poetica" appeals primarily to the sense of sight?
  A. "palpable and mute / As a globed fruit"
  B. "motionless in time / As the moon climbs"
  C. "Dumb / As old medallions to the thumb"
  D. "Silent as the sleeve-worn stone"

_____ 7. What quality of poetry does the opening simile from "Ars Poetica" evoke?

> A poem should be palpable and mute
> As a globed fruit.

    A. complexity
    B. concreteness
    C. perfection
    D. lyricism

_____ 8. What does Moore suggest by the line "imaginary gardens with real toads in them"?
    A. The proper subject matter of poetry is folklore.
    B. Poetry can be used in scientific study.
    C. Poems fuse the real and the imagined.
    D. Poems convey only partial truths.

_____ 9. Which word best describes the speaker's tone in "Poetry" by Moore?
    A. brisk
    B. bitter
    C. stern
    D. insulting

_____ 10. Which is the best way to paraphrase the following excerpt from "Poetry"?

> Reading it, however, with a perfect contempt for it, one discovers in it after all, a place for the genuine.

    A. Poetry is more genuine when the poet dislikes writing.
    B. Even when one reads poetry disdainfully, one can find truth in it.
    C. Only people who hate poetry can find truth in it.
    D. Poetry that shows a contempt for the reader is truthful.

_____ 11. Which is the best way to paraphrase the following excerpt from "Poetry"?

> nor is it valid / to discriminate against "business documents and / schoolbooks"

    A. Nor should you criticize factual writing.
    B. Nor should you criticize writings that teach.
    C. Nor should you criticize writings that don't rhyme.
    D. Nor should you criticize all other styles of writing.

_____ 12. The message of "Poetry" is that
    A. poets should avoid obscuring the meaning in their poems.
    B. reading poetry is a waste of a person's time.
    C. real poetry is in business documents and schoolbooks.
    D. too much poetry is about unimportant subjects.

Vocabulary and Grammar

_____ 13. Which excerpt from "Ars Poetica" uses a subject complement?
    A. "A poem should be palpable and mute"
    B. "Memory by memory the mind—"
    C. "Not true."
    D. "The leaning grasses and two lights above the sea—"

_____ 14. When something is palpable, it is able to be _____.
   A. heard
   B. seen
   C. eaten
   D. touched

_____ 15. Which line from "Of Modern Poetry" uses a subject complement?
   A. "Its past was a souvenir."
   B. "In an emotion as of two people, as of two"
   C. "And, like an insatiable actor, slowly and"
   D. "Not to the play, but to itself, expressed"

_____ 16. Which of the following would an *insatiable* actor be most likely to do?
   A. choose a bit role in a play over a starring role
   B. need to rehearse lines over and over to remember them
   C. want to keep performing night after night
   D. be loud and presumptuous in his or her personal life

_____ 17. Which of the following is most nearly opposite in meaning to *slovenly*?
   A. attractive
   B. slim
   C. fast
   D. tidy

Essay

18. Poems are sometimes remembered for an unforgettable line or image. Marianne Moore's "Poetry," for example, contains the often quoted portrayal of good poetry: "imaginary gardens with real toads in them." Write an essay in which you identify and discuss memorable lines or images from at least one other poem in this selection. Include a discussion of Moore's "imaginary gardens" image, analyzing its effectiveness.

19. In "Ars Poetica," Archibald MacLeish writes several short couplets that give examples, ultimately supporting the idea that "A poem should not mean / But be." Which do you think is more effective in making the author's point to the audience: using examples, as in "Ars Poetica," or using a more direct approach, as in Wallace Stevens's "Of Modern Poetry"? Give details from the two poems to support your choice.

20. Wallace Stevens wrote that poetry "touches the sense of reality, it enhances the sense of reality, heightens it, intensifies it." Yet some readers feel that Stevens's poems convey a sense of *un*reality. Write an essay in which you state and support your opinion on whether Stevens's "Anecdote of the Jar" touches and enhances the reader's sense of reality. Use evidence from the poem to sustain your position.

Vocabulary Warm-up Word Lists

Study these words from the selections. Then, complete the activities.

Word List A

ceremonial [ser uh MOHN ee uhl] *adj.* formal
  With a <u>ceremonial</u> gesture, the butler led us into the living room of the mansion.

detached [dee TACHD] *adj.* disconnected; aloof; emotionally uninvolved
  <u>Detached</u> from that old set of friends, Marisa now goes her own way.

grave [GRAYV] *adj.* solemn; very serious
  Rarely smiling, Grandfather always has a <u>grave</u> look on his face.

illustrated [IL uhs trayt uhd] *adj.* provided with explanatory visual features
  Our high school yearbook, <u>illustrated</u> with cartoon drawings, is extremely appealing.

inclined [in KLYND] *v.* sloped; slanted; leaned
  The flooring of the old shed <u>inclined</u> and seemed about to give way.

invalid [IN vuh lid] *n.* person who is incapacitated by illness or disability
  Even though he's been sick for two weeks, Keith is not an <u>invalid</u>.

notion [NOH shuhn] *n.* vague idea, belief, or opinion
  In considering an academic focus, Heather has a <u>notion</u> that she'd like chemistry.

rigidity [ri JID uh tee] *n.* quality of being stiff and inflexible
  I think Katrina might enjoy new things if she weren't stuck in her <u>rigidity</u>.

Word List B

blurted [BLERT uhd] *v.* uttered suddenly
  During the test, Kate accidentally <u>blurted</u> out the answer to question #5.

citations [sy TAY shuhnz] *n.* honorable mentions for bravery in the armed forces
  Sam's superior officers recommended him for several <u>citations</u> for heroism.

illumined [il OO mind] *v.* gave light to; lit up
  The river was <u>illumined</u> by a full moon.

intent [in TENT] *adj.* engrossed; focused
  The successful art project kept the students <u>intent</u> for weeks on end.

limber [LIM buhr] *adj.* flexible
  Laura is exceedingly <u>limber</u> as a result of regular exercise.

loitered [LOY tuhrd] *v.* dawdled; proceeded slowly
  Not wanting to be the first to arrive, Paul <u>loitered</u> in the hallway.

lurched [LERCHD] *v.* staggered; rolled suddenly
  As soon as the rear wheels rolled out of the mud, the car <u>lurched</u> forward.

withered [WITH uhrd] *v.* shriveled; dried up
  After several days, the fresh-cut flowers <u>withered</u> in the vase.

Selections by Ernest Hemingway, Sherwood Anderson, and Eudora Welty
Vocabulary Warm-up Exercises

Exercise A *Fill in the blanks, using each word from Word List A only once.*

Soon after Glen took over as president of the board, he found that the hospital's
finances were in a(n) [1] _____ state of crisis. He could hardly remain
[2] _____ from the issue. If action weren't taken immediately, the hospital
itself would become a(n) [3] _____, as ill as any of its patients, and it
might even have to close its doors. This idea or [4] _____ was incredible.
For Glen's entire lifetime, the hospital had served the community. Although the job as
president had been described to him as largely symbolic and [5] _____,
Glen knew that he would have to take a hands-on approach. He called a meeting of the
board and used several [6] _____ charts to describe the grim financial
picture. Some board members [7] _____ to downplay the situation, but
Glen called on them to abandon their [8] _____ and come up with a
practical, creative plan to save the hospital.

Exercise B *Decide whether each statement below is true or false. Circle T or F, and explain
your answer.*

1. Someone who <u>blurted</u> out a statement probably said it suddenly and rapidly.
   T / F _____

2. <u>Citations</u> are normally issued in criticism for a soldier's conduct.
   T / F _____

3. If a fire <u>illumined</u> the room, it probably did not light up the dark shadows in the corners.
   T / F _____

4. If you are <u>intent</u> on an action, you probably have no interest in it.
   T / F _____

5. A gymnast who is <u>limber</u> has probably put in long hours of hard exercise.
   T / F _____

6. Teenagers who <u>loitered</u> on the way back from school reached their homes unusually
   early.
   T / F _____

7. A car that <u>lurched</u> into motion began to move slowly and smoothly.
   T / F _____

8. <u>Withered</u> flowers always look good in a vase on the living room table.
   T / F _____

Selections by Ernest Hemingway, Sherwood Anderson, and Eudora Welty
Reading Warm-up A

Read the following passage. Pay special attention to the underlined words. Then, read it again, and complete the activities. Use a separate sheet of paper for your written answers.

World War I greatly influenced literature of the early twentieth century. The war left a <u>grave</u> and lasting impression on the young Ernest Hemingway, for example. Hemingway was wounded during his service as a Red Cross ambulance driver. Like the characters in his story, "In Another Country," Hemingway spent time as an <u>invalid</u> at a hospital in Milan, Italy.

If you were a writer during this period, it was almost impossible to remain uninvolved or <u>detached</u> from the war. Wilfred Owen, a young British poet, began to write when he was still a schoolboy in his teens. In 1915, he enlisted in the British army and served as a soldier in France. In his poetry, Owen vividly described the horrors of poison gas attacks and trench warfare. Even a graphically <u>illustrated</u> magazine article could not begin to compare with Owen's portrait of the common soldier's everyday life and anguished feelings.

For Owen, the <u>notion</u> or idea that war was a glorious undertaking was far from the truth. Far from being a <u>ceremonial</u> or noble activity, warfare was a brutal, chaotic pursuit. It robbed the participants of their humanity on every level. Warfare, in Owen's eyes, arose out of the selfishness and <u>rigidity</u> with which nations pursued their nationalistic self-interest. Nations <u>inclined</u> toward waging war to increase their power and expand their territory. Such motives, Owen thought, had little to do with the ordinary citizen's well-being. In his poetry, he bitterly expressed his anger at the waste and cruelty of war, and he poured out his pity for warfare's victims.

1. Underline the words in this sentence that give a clue to the meaning of <u>grave</u>. Use the word *grave* as an adjective in an original sentence.

2. Circle the words in this and the previous sentence that give a clue to the meaning of <u>invalid</u>. Use the word *invalid* as a noun in an original sentence.

3. Underline the words in this sentence that give a clue to the meaning of <u>detached</u>. What is a synonym for *detached*?

4. Circle the words that offer a clue to the meaning of <u>illustrated</u> here. What is a noun formed from the word *illustrated*?

5. Circle the words in this sentence that offer clues to the meaning of <u>notion</u>. Use the word *notion* in an original sentence.

6. Underline the words in this sentence that give a clue to the meaning of <u>ceremonial</u>. What is an antonym for *ceremonial*?

7. Circle the words in this sentence that give a clue to the meaning of <u>rigidity</u>. Use a word meaning the opposite of *rigidity* in a sentence.

8. What clue can you find in this sentence to the meaning of <u>inclined</u>? What is a synonym for *inclined*?

Selections by Ernest Hemingway, Sherwood Anderson, and Eudora Welty
Reading Warm-up B

Read the following passage. Pay special attention to the underlined words. Then, read it again, and complete the activities. Use a separate sheet of paper for your written answers.

Tina loves ancient mythology, and, <u>intent</u> on learning everything she can about the subject, she spends hours at the local library reading up on all kinds of myths. One day, she <u>loitered</u> there for several hours after school, happily caught up in gathering information about the myth of the phoenix. When she came home just before dinner, she was so excited that she <u>blurted</u> out all the details to her parents and younger brothers as they ate.

"The phoenix was a fabulous bird invented by the ancient Egyptians," Tina explained as she <u>lurched</u> a bit awkwardly into her narration. "It was the size of an eagle, with brilliant scarlet and gold feathers, and it must have been terrifically beautiful. There was only one phoenix in existence at any single time, and each bird lived for over 500 years! I have no idea how any bird could keep its body <u>limber</u> and agile for that amount of time, but everyone agrees that the phoenix had an enormous lifespan.

"Here's the really neat part, though. When it came time for the phoenix to die, the bird dug a nest of dried-up, <u>withered</u> boughs and sweet-smelling spices. Then, it set the nest on fire and was consumed in the flames. As the fire <u>illumined</u> the surrounding area with brightness, a miracle occurred: a new phoenix mysteriously sprang from the flames!"

"What a story!" exclaimed Tina's father. "No wonder the phoenix has won <u>citations</u> as the symbol of immortality throughout the ages."

"You're right," said Tina. "I read that the Greeks and Romans borrowed the myth from the Egyptians. The story then continued on into the Middle Ages."

1. Underline the words that give a clue to the meaning of <u>intent</u>. Write a sentence of your own using the word *intent*.

2. Circle the words in this sentence that give a clue to the meaning of <u>loitered</u>. What are two antonyms for *loitered*?

3. Underline the words in this sentence that offer clues to the meaning of <u>blurted</u>.

4. Underline the words in this sentence that give a clue to the meaning of <u>lurched</u>. What is a synonym for *lurched*?

5. Circle the words in this sentence that give a clue to the meaning of <u>limber</u>. Use a word meaning the opposite of *limber* in a sentence of your own.

6. Underline the words in this sentence that hint at the meaning of <u>withered</u>. What are two antonyms for *withered*?

7. Circle the words in this sentence that hint at the meaning of <u>illumined</u>.

8. Circle the words in this sentence that hint at the meaning of the word <u>citations</u>. As used in this context, does the word *citations* have positive or negative connotations?

"In Another Country" by Ernest Hemingway
"The Corn Planting" by Sherwood Anderson
"A Worn Path" by Eudora Welty
Literary Analysis: Point of View

Much of what gives a story its unique tone and personality is point of view. A story's **point of view** is the perspective of its narrator. You can tell the point of view of a story by paying attention to the pronouns that refer to the character whose perspective is being presented.

Point of View	Pronouns
first person	*I, me, we, us*
second person	*you*
third person	*he, him, she, her, it, they, them*

A narrator who uses first-person point of view relates events that happened to him or her personally or that he or she witnessed firsthand. Second-person point of view is rarely used in short stories. Third-person point of view can be limited or omniscient. If a limited third-person point of view is used, an outside narrator relates events that happened from the perspective of one person. An omniscient, or all-knowing, third-person narrator can tell a story switching back and forth among the perspectives of different characters and can tell the reader information that a specific character in the story would be unlikely to know. Occasionally, narrators shift back and forth among different points of view in the course of one short story.

DIRECTIONS: *Read each passage and identify whether the point of view is first, second, or third person.*

1. Always, though, you crossed a bridge across a canal to enter the hospital. There was a choice of three bridges. On one of them a woman sold roasted chestnuts. It was warm, standing in front of her charcoal fire, and the chestnuts were warm afterward in your pocket. The hospital was very old and very beautiful, and you entered through a gate. . . .

   _____

2. The three with the medals were like hunting-hawks; and I was not a hawk, although I might seem a hawk to those who had never hunted; they, the three, knew better, and so we drifted apart.

   _____

3. Their one son, Will Hutchenson, was a small but remarkably strong boy. He came to our high school in town and pitched on our town baseball team. He was a fellow always cheerful, bright and alert, and a great favorite with all of us.

   _____

4. The path ran up a hill. "Seem like there is chains about my feet, time I get this far," she said, in the voice of argument old people keep to use with themselves. "Something always take a hold of me on this hill—pleads I should stay."

   _____

"In Another Country" by Ernest Hemingway
"The Corn Planting" by Sherwood Anderson
"A Worn Path" by Eudora Welty

Reading Strategy: Identify with Characters

Sherwood Anderson included in his writing some characters that are grotesques. Such characters have a one-track mind; they are controlled by a single emotion, concept, or goal.

DIRECTIONS: *On the lines after each of the following passages, identify an emotion, a concept, or a goal that the passage suggests. Then write one or two sentences to explain how the character might act if he or she were a grotesque, controlled by the way of thinking that you have identified.*

1. The major, who had been the great fencer, did not believe in bravery, and spent much time while we sat in the machines correcting my grammar. He had complimented me on how I spoke Italian, and we talked together very easily. One day I had said that Italian seemed such an easy language to me that I could not take a great interest in it; everything was so easy to say. "Ah yes," the major said. "Why, then, do you not take up the use of grammar?" So we took up the use of grammar, and soon Italian was such a difficult language that I was afraid to talk to him until I had the grammar straight in my mind.

   _____

   _____

   _____

   _____

   _____

2. Neither of the old people had ever been to the city and they were curious and eager. They wanted the drawings explained, and Hal said they were like two children wanting to know every little detail Hal could remember about their son's life in the big city. He was always at them to come there on a visit and they would spend hours talking of that.

   _____

   _____

   _____

   _____

   _____

"In Another Country" by Ernest Hemingway
"The Corn Planting" by Sherwood Anderson
"A Worn Path" by Eudora Welty
Vocabulary Builder

Using the Root -val-

A. DIRECTIONS: *The root -val- means "strength" or "value." Keeping that in mind, circle the letter of the one best answer in each of the following items.*

1. To *evaluate* students, teachers sometimes

   A. lecture.
   B. give tests.

   C. bring snacks.
   D. write on the chalkboard.

2. Which of the following objects would be most *valuable* to someone who wanted to sell it?

   A. a old pair of shoes
   B. a new refrigerator

   C. a ceramic cup
   D. a three-bedroom house

3. *Valiant* is most likely to be an accurate description of a

   A. bank teller.
   B. movie star.

   C. fire fighter.
   D. car salesperson.

4. A *valid* parking ticket is one that

   A. is legally binding.
   B. is not legally binding.

   C. has already been paid.
   D. is overdue for payment.

Using the Word List

invalided	grave	limber	obstinate

B. DIRECTIONS: *Fill in each blank with the appropriate word from the Word List.*

1. If the astronauts cannot produce more oxygen for the space station, their situation will be _____.

2. The mule, as _____ as ever, refused to move even one inch.

3. After breaking her leg, the dancer was _____ for the rest of the season.

4. Mickey knew that if he practiced every day, he would eventually be _____ enough to touch his toes.

"**In Another Country**" by Ernest Hemingway
"**The Corn Planting**" by Sherwood Anderson
"**A Worn Path**" by Eudora Welty

Grammar and Style: Punctuating Dialogue

Direct quotations, which report the exact words of a character, give life to prose. As you read stories that have dialogue, you can hear the words of the characters in your imagination, just as if you were standing there eavesdropping. In direct quotations, **punctuating dialogue** correctly is important. Direct quotations require quotation marks around the character's words. Commas set off the quotation from the rest of the sentence.

"Now comes the trial," said Phoenix.

Phoenix said, "I thank you for your trouble."

Except for the comma that introduces the quotation, periods and commas are placed inside the quotation marks. Question marks and exclamation marks are placed according to the logic of the sentence. If the character's words are a question or exclamation, the question mark or exclamation mark is placed *inside* the quotation marks. If the entire sentence is a question or exclamation, the question mark or exclamation mark is placed *outside* the quotation marks.

When a writer uses indirect quotations, reporting on what a character said without quoting the exact words, no quotation marks are necessary. Study these examples:

Character's words are a question or exclamation:

"How old are you, Granny?" he was saying.

She whispered, "Sic him!"

Entire sentence is a question or exclamation:

Did you wonder what the nurse meant when she said, "But it's an obstinate case"?

Indirect quotation:

The boys at first were very polite about my medals and asked me what I had done to get them.

A. PRACTICE: *Based on the punctuation, determine whether the character's words or the entire sentence is a question or exclamation. Write "character's words" or "entire sentence" in the blank.*

1. The major asked, "Will I play football, too?" _____

2. Did you hear the major reply, "No, I'm afraid not"? _____

3. "Speak grammatically!" the major shouted. _____

4. How horrible it was to hear the major admit, "I cannot resign myself"! _____

5. "Did you hear him say, "before the war, I played football." _____

"In Another Country" by Ernest Hemingway
"The Corn Planting" by Sherwood Anderson
"A Worn Path" by Eudora Welty
Support for Writing

Prepare to write a **memorial speech** about Will as though you are Hal Weyman in "The Corn Planting." Enter information about Will and his family in the graphic organizer below.

Will's strengths and talents	Will's importance to his family

How Will's dreams could best be expressed

Draft your memorial speech to give listeners a clear picture of who Will was and how he was important to his family. When you revise, be sure to use descriptive language. Add material about the dreams.

"In Another Country" by Ernest Hemingway
"The Corn Planting" by Sherwood Anderson
"A Worn Path" by Eudora Welty

Support for Extend Your Learning

Listening and Speaking

As you plan your **sequel** to "A Worn Path," think about what happens to Phoenix Jackson when she gets home. Use these questions as guidelines:

- Is Phoenix's grandson alive?
- Is anyone else present?
- What does Phoenix feel and do?
- How will your story end?

Read your story aloud to the class and ask for feedback. How does your sequel differ from those of your classmates?

Research and Technology

Research the role of Italy in World War I, as well as Hemingway's part in the war, on the Internet or in the library. Enter information below to use in a **research report** on your findings.

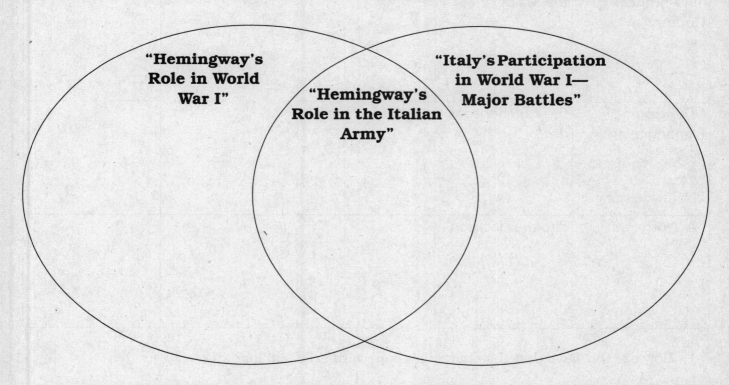

When you prepare your report, download maps and other graphics related to the historical period and use them in your presentation.

"In Another Country" by Ernest Hemingway
"The Corn Planting" by Sherwood Anderson
"A Worn Path" by Eudora Welty
Enrichment: Health

As you may know, people's physical and emotional health interact: One can affect the other. The characters in the stories in this section experience various challenges to their emotional health. They must adjust to the grief of physical injury or death. Think about how these characters cope with their grief. What actions do they take to help them cope?

DIRECTIONS: *Use the graphic organizer below to compare characters from these stories and how they approach grieving. In the third and fourth columns, write the reason for each character's grief and the ways he or she copes with it. In the fifth column, explain what each character still hopes for. Then answer the questions that follow.*

Story	Character	Reason for Grief	Ways of Coping	What the Character Hopes For
"In Another Country"	the Major			
"The Corn Planting"	the Hutchensons			
"A Worn Path"	Phoenix Jackson			

1. How are the ways that the characters cope with grief similar?

_____

_____

2. How do work and effort help the grief-stricken characters heal?

_____

_____

From the Author's Desk
Tim O'Brien Introduces "Ambush"

DIRECTIONS: *Use the space provided to answer the questions.*

1. What does Tim O'Brien mean when he says that "Ambush" is a short story that can stand "entirely on its own"?

   _____

   _____

2. According to O'Brien, is the story fiction or nonfiction? Briefly explain O'Brien's comments on "an invented character who has my name."

   _____

   _____

   _____

3. Fill in the chart below to compare and contrast the factual and the fictional elements and details in "Ambush" as O'Brien describes them.

   Factual Details   **Fictional Details**

   _____   _____

   _____   _____

   _____   _____

   _____   _____

4. Tim O'Brien says he will never know whether a bullet from his own weapon killed the young man, but that he is still responsible because he pulled the trigger. How do you evaluate O'Brien's statement? Do you agree or disagree? Briefly explain your answer.

   _____

   _____

   _____

   _____

   _____

5. According to O'Brien, what was his principal motivation or purpose in writing "Ambush"?

   _____

   _____

   _____

Name _____ Date _____

Tim O'Brien
Listening and Viewing

Segment 1: Meet Tim O'Brien
- What similarities can you find between writing fiction and performing magic?
- Why does Tim O'Brien care about truth in fiction writing?

_____

_____

_____

_____

Segment 2: Tim O'Brien Introduces "Ambush"
- Why did Tim O'Brien write the story "Ambush" in first-person and name the narrator "Tim O'Brien"?
- How do you think this influences the reader's interpretation of the story?

_____

_____

_____

_____

Segment 3: The Writing Process
- Do you agree with Tim O'Brien that revision is the most important step in the writing process?
- How does Tim O'Brien know when his story is finished?

_____

_____

_____

_____

Segment 4: The Rewards of Writing
- Why does Tim O'Brien believe that stories can be powerful forces in our lives?
- How do you think writing can help you be your "ideal self"?

_____

_____

_____

_____

"In Another Country" by Ernest Hemingway
"The Corn Planting" by Sherwood Anderson
"A Worn Path" by Eudora Welty
Selection Test A

Critical Reading *Identify the letter of the choice that best answers the question.*

_____ 1. In "In Another Country," why does the doctor tell the narrator he will be able to play football again?
  A. to warn him that his injury is bad
  B. to give him hope that he will recover
  C. to tell him to become a doctor
  D. to encourage him to help other soldiers

_____ 2. What part of this passage shows that "In Another Country" is written in the first person?
  The doctor came up to the machine where I was sitting and said: "What did you like best to do before the war? Did you practice a sport?"
  A. the mention of the machine
  B. the use of "I"
  C. the discussion about sports
  D. the doctor's question

_____ 3. How does the major feel about the doctor's advice in "In Another Country"?
  A. He respects it.
  B. He understands it.
  C. He does not believe it.
  D. He finds it amusing.

_____ 4. In addition to referring to the country of Italy, what is the other country in the title "In Another Country"?
  A. the city of Milan
  B. the outdoors, or nature
  C. a place where war occurs
  D. a book of photographs

_____ 5. Who is the person who knew Hal and Will and tells the story in "A Corn Planting"?
  A. Mr. Hutchenson
  B. Will Hutchenson
  C. Hal Waymon
  D. a narrator

____ 6. In "The Corn Planting," why do the Hutchensons go to the field after hearing of their son's death?

A. They do not want to be with Hal and the narrator.

B. They do not believe what they have been told.

C. They feel they must continue their planting.

D. They want to talk to each other about the funeral.

____ 7. In "A Worn Path," which word best describes Phoenix's character as she responds to challenges?

A. determined

B. angry

C. frightened

D. happy

____ 8. In "A Worn Path," who tells the story of Phoenix?

A. Phoenix

B. Phoenix's son

C. an outside narrator

D. a doctor

____ 9. In "A Worn Path," how would you describe Phoenix as she deals with the hunter?

A. truthful

B. tricky

C. friendly

D. funny

____ 10. In "A Worn Path," what tells the reader that Phoenix's life has been one of financial hardship?

A. She thinks a scarecrow is a ghost.

B. She takes a nickel from the ground.

C. She laughs at herself.

D. She speaks to a buzzard.

____ 11. What does the title refer to in the story "The Worn Path"?

A. the road Phoenix has to cross safely

B. the long and difficult path that is Phoenix's life

C. the path the hunter takes with his dogs

D. the path Phoenix takes through the corn

Vocabulary and Grammar

_____ **12.** Which word best replaces *obstinate* in this sentence: "Everyone could tell she was an *obstinate* woman who would not let anything get in her way"?
   A. entertaining
   B. fearful
   C. stubborn
   D. aging

_____ **13.** In which of the following sentences is the dialogue **correctly** punctuated with a comma and quotation marks?
   A. I bound to go to town, "mister," said Phoenix.
   B. "He cannot marry," he said angrily.
   C. "What will you do when the war is over if it is over? he asked me.
   D. Oh, that's just old Aunt Phoenix," she said.

Essay

14. In "In Another Country," the narrator says he feels separate from the other men who have been wounded in the war. Why do you think this is so? What are the differences between him and the others? Write a brief essay to address these questions.

15. In "A Worn Path," Phoenix's grandson could be either alive or dead. Write a brief essay that gives your opinion about her grandson's situation. Support your opinion with evidence from the story.

"In Another Country" by Ernest Hemingway
"The Corn Planting" by Sherwood Anderson
"A Worn Path" by Eudora Welty
Selection Test B

Critical Reading *Identify the letter of the choice that best completes the statement or answers the question.*

____ 1. When the narrator says the wounded soldiers "were all very polite and interested in what was the matter, and sat in the machines that were to make so much difference," he is being _____.
   A. ironic
   B. sympathetic
   C. objective
   D. observant

____ 2. Why does the major never miss a day with the machines?
   A. Self-discipline is important to him.
   B. It is his duty as an officer to become fit for service.
   C. His injury is improving rapidly.
   D. He wants to talk with the narrator.

____ 3. The major's attitude toward the doctor is best described as _____.
   A. amused
   B. furious
   C. indifferent
   D. determined

____ 4. Hemingway employs a direct, unadorned style of writing in order to
   A. remove all uncertainty about what he is trying to say.
   B. allow the reader to draw his or her own conclusions.
   C. deemphasize the importance of language.
   D. reduce the story to its essentials.

____ 5. Which of the following statements best describes the theme of "In Another Country"?
   A. Life is full of loneliness and loss.
   B. War makes all men brothers.
   C. Heroes are made, not born.
   D. For a brave man, anything is possible.

____ 6. "The Corn Planting" is told from a first-person point of view. You can tell this is so because
   A. an outside narrator tells the story.
   B. it is told by a minor character.
   C. the narrator refers to himself as "I."
   D. the narrator is the best character to tell the story.

_____ 7. A limited third-person point of view is one in which the story is told by
  A. an outside narrator with only one perspective.
  B. a narrator who seems to know everything about the story.
  C. a narrator who is not one of the main characters in the story.
  D. a narrator who refers to himself as "I."

_____ 8. What can you infer about Phoenix's personality from her reactions to the obstacles she encounters along the path?
  A. She is basically an optimistic and hopeful person.
  B. She is resilient and takes difficulties in stride.
  C. She feels more at home in the city than in the country.
  D. She has an unrealistic confidence in her strength.

_____ 9. Which of Phoenix's character traits come most into play in her interaction with the hunter?
  A. cunning and resolve
  B. bitterness and anger
  C. pride and courage
  D. guilt and shame

_____ 10. Which detail best supports the interpretation that Phoenix's grandson is dead?
  A. Phoenix expects him to be surprised by a paper windmill.
  B. Phoenix takes a long time to respond to the nurse's question about him.
  C. The nurse's records say he swallowed lye two to three years ago.
  D. The nurse asks Phoenix whether the boy is dead.

_____ 11. What point of view is used in the following passage?

  "You scarecrow," she said. Her face lighted. "I ought to be shut up for good," she said with laughter. "My senses is gone. I too old. I the oldest people I ever know. Dance, old scare-crow," she said, "while I dancing with you."

  A. first-person
  B. first-person limited
  C. third-person limited
  D. third-person by a main character

_____ 12. Which literary technique is most instrumental in conveying the story's ambiguity?
  A. limited third-person narration
  B. visual description
  C. foreshadowing
  D. indirect characterization

_____ 13. In what way does the title "A Worn Path" clearly represent the focus of the story?
  A. It symbolizes the great weariness Phoenix feels as she ages.
  B. It points to the gradual wearing away of Phoenix's vitality and wits.
  C. It illustrates the repetitiveness of an old person's life.
  D. It emphasizes Phoenix's sense of purpose and resolve.

Vocabulary and Grammar

_____ 14. Which of the following passages is punctuated correctly?
   A. "What will you do when the war is over if it is over"? he asked me.
   B. "What will you do when the war is over if it is over? he asked me."
   C. What will you do when the war is over if it is over? he asked me.
   D. "What will you do when the war is over if it is over?" he asked me.

_____ 15. When the narrator of "In Another Country" says that the major did not marry his wife until he was definitely *invalided* out of the war, he means that
   A. the major did not want to marry if he were at risk of dying in the war.
   B. the major did not marry his wife until he was about to leave for the war.
   C. the major was not allowed to marry while he was still fighting in the war.
   D. the major would have preferred going to war to marrying his wife.

_____ 16. Phoenix Jackson's cane is described as "limber as a buggy whip." This means that
   A. it belongs on a buggy.
   B. it is flexible.
   C. it is made of the same material as a buggy whip.
   D. Phoenix uses it on horses.

_____ 17. When the nurse in "A Worn Path" says that Phoenix's grandson is "an *obstinate* case," she means that
   A. the grandson is a spoiled, stubborn child.
   B. Phoenix is stubborn because she continues to make the trip.
   C. Phoenix should bring her grandson with her to see the doctor.
   D. the grandson never gets better because his throat will never heal.

Essay

18. Fiction writers may reveal the nature of a character mainly through his or her involvement with other characters. Hal in "The Corn Planting" is such a character. Write an essay describing Hal's character. What can you tell about his character from his involvement in the lives of the Hutchensons? What do we know about him outside of this involvement? Support your answer with details from the story.

19. Sometimes characters who are different on the surface and live quite different lives share similar outlooks and character traits. Write an essay comparing the major in "In Another Country" to Phoenix Jackson in "A Worn Path." How are their approaches to life similar? How are they different? Use examples from the stories to make your points.

20. In stories told from a first-person point of view, the reader learns only about the narrator's experiences and thoughts. How much the reader finds out depends on how closely involved the narrator is with the events of the story. Write an essay discussing the role of the first-person narrator in "In Another Country" and in "The Corn Planting." How do the narrators of these stories differ in their involvement? Why do you think the author of each story chose to tell it using a first-person narrator? Give evidence from the stories to support your answers.

Vocabulary Warm-up Word Lists

Study these words from the selections. Then, complete the activities.

Word List A

butcher [BUCH uhr] *n.* person who prepares and sells various cuts of meat
  At the supermarket, the <u>butcher</u> told me how to prepare lamb chops.

conductor [kahn DUK tuhr] *n.* ticket collector on a railroad train
  When I was little, I wanted to grow up to become a train <u>conductor</u>.

flinging [FLING ing] *adj.* throwing energetically or roughly
  The ocean waves pounded on the shoreline, <u>flinging</u> crowds of spray in all directions.

freight [FRAYT] *n.* cargo transported by ships, trains, or trucks
  The trucking industry is responsible for transporting most interstate <u>freight</u>.

husky [HUS kee] *adj.* muscular and strong; burly
  Doug is a <u>husky</u> youth who plays fullback on his high school football team.

luring [LOOR ing] *adj.* attracting
  Neon lights twinkled on the shop signs, <u>luring</u> customers to venture inside.

vivid [VIV id] *adj.* clear; graphic
  Many of Carl Sandburg's poems paint a <u>vivid</u> picture of everyday life in Chicago.

wicked [WIK uhd] *adj.* evil
  A <u>wicked</u> witch is one of the main characters in the movie *The Wizard of Oz*.

Word List B

bragging [BRAG ing] *adj.* boasting
  <u>Bragging</u> about his strength, the epic hero dared enemies to challenge him.

brawling [BRAWL ing] *adj.* fighting
  The <u>brawling</u> restaurant customers upset chairs and tables.

coarse [KORS] *adj.* rough; vulgar; not refined
  Cal's behavior is so <u>coarse</u> that few people invite him to parties anymore.

cunning [KUN ing] *adj.* crafty; wily; sly
  When it comes to getting her own way, Glenda is ingenious and <u>cunning</u>.

destiny [DES tuh nee] *n.* fate
  Little did young Abe Lincoln know that his <u>destiny</u> was to become president one day.

sneer [SNEER] *v.* to laugh mockingly
  Bruno <u>sneered</u> at our plan, calling it ridiculous.

toil [TOYL] *n.* hard work; heavy labor
  After each day's <u>toil</u> at the gardening center, Zach was exhausted.

wanton [WAHN tuhn] *adj.* unrestrained; immoral
  Their shameless, <u>wanton</u> behavior caused us to avoid them.

Poems by Carl Sandburg
Vocabulary Warm-up Exercises

Exercise A *Fill in the blanks, using each word from Word List A only once.*

Gary's uncle worked as a(n) [1] _____ at a specialty meat shop in a suburb of Chicago. He had told many [2] _____ tales about life in the big city, so Gary was excited as he boarded the train to make a weekend visit. As the train [3] _____ punched his ticket, Gary thought about how much he'd always loved trains. [4] _____ his heavy coat off into his seat, he decided to walk the length of the train. Peering in the baggage car window, he saw that his train was carrying quite a bit of [5] _____. You had to be [6] _____ and in very good shape, he reflected, to handle those big trunks. With Chicago [7] _____ him, Gary had arranged to spend a few extra days with his uncle. He hoped his teacher wouldn't think that his cutting school was [8] _____. After all, travel is educational.

Exercise B *Revise each sentence so that the underlined vocabulary word is logical. Be sure to keep the vocabulary word in your revision.*

Example: Because they are so <u>congenial</u>, no one invites them to parties.
Because they are so <u>congenial</u>, lots of people invite them to parties.

1. Carl, <u>bragging</u> about his ability at math, was very modest about his grades.

   _____

2. We found the children <u>brawling</u>, playing peacefully together.

   _____

3. The fabric of that shirt is <u>coarse</u>, extremely refined and silky to the touch.

   _____

4. When you go shopping, it is always advisable to trust a <u>cunning</u> salesperson.

   _____

5. A person's <u>destiny</u> often lies far back in the past.

   _____

6. I always enjoyed it when Jeremy would <u>sneer</u> at other people.

   _____

7. Yanick found that work at the factory was easy, amounting to endless <u>toil</u>.

   _____

8. Paul's considerate, responsible behavior struck us as almost <u>wanton</u>.

   _____

Name _____ Date _____

Poems by Carl Sandburg
Reading Warm-up A

Read the following passage. Pay special attention to the underlined words. Then, read it again, and complete the activities. Use a separate sheet of paper for your written answers.

Jacob's grandfather always loved to tell him about the old days in Chicago, where he'd worked as a policeman. Even now, at the age of seventy-nine, his grandfather was a big, <u>husky</u> man with huge wrists and forearms. They would watch baseball together on TV. Every inning or so his grandfather would start on another of his stories. He told them in such <u>vivid</u> language that Jacob could see the people and the action as if in a movie.

"Chicago was a tough, tough city back then, full of criminals and every other kind of <u>wicked</u> person," his grandfather said. "Did I ever tell you about Stanley and Ike and the railroad robbery?"

It turned out that Stanley was a <u>butcher</u> at the slaughterhouses, whose job was cutting up cattle into steaks. One day he came out of the shop, the doors <u>flinging</u> on their hinges from his mighty shove. He said that he'd had it—too much blood and guts for one lifetime. His friend Ike had come to meet him for a drink, and Ike raised his chin, his eyes <u>luring</u> Stanley away from the slaughterhouse.

Ike had a plan to make both of them rich. Because he worked as a <u>conductor</u> for the railroad, collecting tickets on the trains, he had access to the tracks. Ike told Stanley that he knew of a train arriving in town next week with a <u>freight</u> of copper wire. They could steal the wire and sell it for thousands of dollars.

"We caught up with them on the night of the robbery and arrested them both," said Jacob's grandfather. "You should have seen this big butcher, Stanley, crying like a baby. How he begged us to let him go."

1. Underline the words that give a clue to the meaning of <u>husky</u>. Use the word *husky* in a sentence of your own.

2. Circle the words in this sentence that give a clue to the meaning of <u>vivid</u>. Use a word meaning the opposite of *vivid* in an original sentence.

3. Underline the words in this sentence that give a clue to the meaning of <u>wicked</u>. What are two synonyms for *wicked*?

4. Circle the words in this sentence that give clues to the meaning of *butcher*.

5. Circle the words in this sentence that offer a clue to the meaning of <u>flinging</u>. What is an adjective you can use to describe the action of *flinging*?

6. Underline the words in this sentence that hint at the meaning of <u>luring</u>. What is an antonym for *luring*?

7. Underline the words in this sentence that hint at the meaning of <u>conductor</u>.

8. Underline the words in this sentence that give a clue to the meaning of the word <u>freight</u>. What is a synonym for *freight*?

Poems by Carl Sandburg
Reading Warm-up B

Read the following passage. Pay special attention to the underlined words. Then, read it again, and complete the activities. Use a separate sheet of paper for your written answers.

The American novelist Upton Sinclair was born in 1878, the same year as Carl Sandburg. Both writers devoted much of their attention to the city of Chicago, but Sinclair and Sandburg each had a separate, distinctive fate or <u>destiny</u>. Sandburg celebrated Chicago's raw energy: the <u>brawling</u> fights of the urban masses, as well as the <u>bragging</u> cockiness of a tough, industrial city on the move. Sinclair, by contrast, wrote about the rough, <u>coarse</u> lives of Chicago's working class, especially those who devoted long days of backbreaking <u>toil</u> in the Chicago stockyards.

Sinclair's most famous treatment of this topic was *The Jungle*, a novel he published at his own expense in 1906. Although it is technically fiction, this book is grounded vividly in fact. Sinclair brought a journalist's skill to describing the horrifying work conditions in the stockyards. Many of the workers were immigrants with almost no knowledge of English, and they were deceived and exploited by cruel, <u>cunning</u> foremen. These supervisors would openly <u>sneer</u> at the workers, mocking them for their poverty and ignorance. Sinclair showed that, even worse, there was an irresponsible and <u>wanton</u> disregard for public health and worker safety in the stockyards.

After *The Jungle* was published, it struck a nerve in American public opinion and became a best-seller. Sinclair had intended to awaken sympathy for the stockyard workers. The public, however, seized on a different issue: the health hazards from the impurities in low-quality, processed meats. Sinclair's novel soon led to the founding of the federal Food and Drug Administration, which was empowered to regulate the meatpacking industry. Surprised at his own success, Sinclair is supposed to have remarked, "I aimed at the public's heart and by accident I hit it in the stomach."

1. Underline the words in this sentence that hint at the meaning of <u>destiny</u>. Use the word *destiny* in an original sentence.

2. Circle the words in this sentence that hint at the meaning of <u>brawling</u>. How do people feel when they are *brawling*?

3. Underline the words in this sentence that hint at the meaning of <u>bragging</u>. Use *bragging* in an original sentence.

4. Underline the words in this sentence that hint at the meaning of <u>coarse</u>. What is an antonym for *coarse*?

5. Circle the words in this sentence that hint at the meaning of <u>toil</u>. What is a synonym for *toil*?

6. Circle the words in this sentence that give a good clue to the meaning of <u>cunning</u>. Are the connotations of *cunning* positive or negative?

7. Underline the words in this sentence that hint at the meaning of <u>sneer</u>.

8. Underline the words in this sentence that hint at the meaning of <u>wanton</u>. What are two antonyms for *wanton*?

"Chicago" and **"Grass"** by Carl Sandburg
Literary Analysis: Apostrophe

Apostrophe is the literary technique of directly addressing a person or thing as if that person or thing were present. This technique is frequently used in romantic poetry or funeral songs in which the speaker of the poem directly addresses the loved one, or death. For example, the clown in Shakespeare's play *Twelfth Night* addresses his love, "O mistress mine! where are you roaming?" *In Much Ado About Nothing*, a group of singers open a funeral song with, "Pardon, Goddess of the night, / Those that slew thy virgin knight;" / In a more modern example, the poet Sandburg is using apostrophe on lines such as this one from "Chicago":

Hog Butcher for the world, . . . They tell me you are wicked. . .

DIRECTIONS: *Read "Chicago." Then answer the questions below.*

1. List three clues that show that Sandburg is using apostrophe in this poem.

_____

_____

_____

_____

_____

_____

2. Who is being addressed in "Chicago"?

_____

_____

3. Suppose that the speaker of "Chicago" is responding to a previous conversation. What would that conversation have been like? Who would have participated in it?

_____

_____

_____

_____

_____

_____

4. How might the structure of this poem have been different if Sandburg had *not* used the technique of apostrophe?

_____

_____

_____

_____

_____

Name _____   Date _____

"**Chicago**" and "**Grass**" by Carl Sandburg
Reading Strategy: Respond

For poetry, to be effective, both writer and reader must do some work. The poet's job is to craft his or her message carefully, using tools such as images, rhyme, rhythm, and meter. The reader's job is to respond. As a reader, you can **respond** to a poem by visualizing the images, relating events in the poem to your own knowledge, and forming an opinion of the poem and its message. Your tools are your senses, your background knowledge, and your own gut feelings.

DIRECTIONS: *Use this graphic organizer to help you respond to passages from "Chicago" and "Grass." In the first column, write the passage. In the second column, note any senses that might help you respond in a sensory way to the image. In the third column, write down any background knowledge that you need in order to understand the passage. In the last column, write your opinion of the passage or your overall response to it. Do you agree with the passage? Do you disagree? What impression does the passage make on you? One passage has already been done for you.*

Passage	Senses	Background Knowledge	My Opinion or Response
"Under the smoke, dust all over his mouth, laughing with white teeth."	Sight—to imagine what the wonder looks like; Smell—to imagine the smell of the smoke; Touch—to imagine the feel of the dust on one's skin.	Chicago was an early center of industry in the United States. Someone who worked in a smoky, dusty environment might have worked in a factory.	It's unusual to see a worker laughing in the middle of hard physical labor and harsh working conditions.

"Chicago" and **"Grass"** by Carl Sandburg
Vocabulary Builder

Related Words: *brutal*

A. DIRECTIONS: *Knowing that the word* brutal *means "cruel," "crude," or "harsh," write the letter of the best description of the italicized word in each sentence.*

____ 1. An editor who criticizes a writer's work *brutally* is most likely to
  A. give the writer a physical beating.
  B. physically tear up the paper the work is written on.
  C. write unnecessarily severe comments about the work.
  D. suggest helpful changes in the writer's work.

____ 2. "The *brutalization* of prisoners of war" probably refers to
  A. beatings and torture.   C. censorship of letters.
  B. lack of clean water.   D. unfair imprisonment.

____ 3. Because her bus was a half hour late, Sarah growled her anger *brutishly.*
  A. charmingly   C. quietly
  B. harshly   D. whiningly

Using the Word List

brutal	wanton	cunning

B. DIRECTIONS: *Fill in each blank with a word from the Word List. Two words are used more than once.*

1. Stealthy and _____, the tiger crept through the grass.
2. Unable to find what she was looking for, Marisa began smashing the store's crystal with _____ abandon.
3. The temperature was bitterly cold, and the wind was _____.
4. The _____ reality was that Harold had no job, no money, and no place to live.
5. With a _____ disregard for Joseph's feelings, Darnell painted over the portrait that his friend had painstakingly rendered through months of effort.

"Chicago" and **"Grass"** by Carl Sandburg
Grammar and Style: Sentence Types

In English, there are four basic types of sentences: declarative, interrogative, imperative, and exclamatory. You can easily recognize interrogative and exclamatory sentences by their punctuation. **Interrogative sentences** end with a question mark because they ask a question, and **exclamatory sentences** end with an exclamation point because they express a strong emotion. **Declarative sentences** end with a period because they simply make a statement. **Imperative sentences**, however, may end with a period or an exclamation point. These sentences give commands or make requests, but they may also express a strong emotion.

Declarative Sentence:	They tell me you are wicked and I believe them. . . .
Interrogative Sentence:	Where are we now?
Imperative Sentence:	Shovel them under and let me work.
Exclamatory Sentence:	. . . under his wrist is the pulse, and under his ribs the heart of the people, laughing!

PRACTICE: *In the space next to each sentence, identify the type of sentence it is.*

1. "I turn once more to those who sneer at this my city. . . ." _____

2. "Come and show me another city with lifted head singing. . . ." _____

3. "What place is this?" _____

4. "And pile them high at Ypres and Verdun." _____

B. Writing Application: *Rewrite each of the following sentences to make it into another type of sentence. You may need to change the meaning of a sentence or the point of view from which it is written. For example, the declarative sentence, "[O]n the faces of women and children I have seen the marks of wanton hunger," could be rewritten as an imperative: "Look at the marks of wanton hunger on the faces of the women and children."*

1. "I have seen your painted women under the gas lamps luring the farm boys."

_____

2. "I have seen the gunman kill and go free to kill again."

_____

3. " . . . here is a tall bold slugger set vivid against the little soft cities."

_____

4. "Pile the bodies high at Austerlitz and Waterloo."

_____

Name _____ Date _____

Support for Writing

To prepare to write your **essay** on Sandburg's use of repetition, enter material from the poems into the chart below.

Repetition in Sandburg's Poems

"Chicago": Examples of repetition	Effect of repetition on listener
"Grass": Examples of repetition	Effect of repetition on listener

On a separate page, write a draft of your essay. Summarize each poem briefly. Then, give examples of the repetitions used by the poet and the effects these have on the listener. When you revise, be sure your ideas are clear. Add more examples from the poems if you need to.

159

Name _____ Date _____

"Chicago" and "Grass" by Carl Sandburg
Support for Extend Your Learning

Listening and Speaking

Prepare for your **stand-up comedy routine** by doing research into Chicago's history. Find specific events you can turn into humorous anecdotes. Use these tips:

- Decide what your attitude will be—tough or sensitive.
- Find body language to fit your approach.
- Act as though you represent the city of Chicago.
- Think about how you can connect your experiences to those of your audience.

Research and Technology

To write a **report** on the population of Chicago over time, collect information from the Internet and enter it into the chart below.

Chicago's Population/Influences Over Time

Total Population in 1900	Number of Men in 1900	Number of Women in 1900	Number of Children in 1900	Total Population in 2000	Number of Men in 2000	Number of Women in 2000	Number of Children in 2000
Changes in Technology between 1900–2000:							
Changes in Society between 1900–2000:							
How Population Changes and History Connect:							

When you write your report, you may wish to include bar graphs, line graphs, or pie charts to help you explain the material you collected.

"Chicago" and **"Grass"** by Carl Sandburg
Enrichment: Career in Marketing

Carl Sandburg's poem "Chicago" acknowledges negative aspects of the city but argues that the city's positive aspects are more important. In the second section of the poem, Sandburg uses vivid images to cast the city in a positive light, comparing it to a hard worker and a fierce animal.

DIRECTIONS: *Assume the role of a marketing executive. Your job is to create vivid images about your community for a brochure that will be distributed to real estate companies. Think about what images would be appealing to someone thinking of living or starting a business in your community. Then answer the following questions.*

1. To what plant, animal, or force of nature can your community be compared?

   _____

2. What type of person provides the best example of your community?

   _____

   _____

3. What is your community's role in your state and in the country? (For example, is your community a center of trade, commerce, or industry? Is it a seat of government? What is the basis of your community's economy?)

   _____

   _____

   _____

   _____

   _____

4. Write a paragraph for a brochure advertising your community, using the images you created in response to questions 1, 2, and 3.

   _____

   _____

   _____

   _____

   _____

   _____

   _____

   _____

   _____

   _____

Name _____ Date _____

Selection Test A

Critical Reading *Identify the letter of the choice that best answers the question.*

_____ 1. In "Chicago," how do you know that Sandburg is addressing Chicago directly?
  A. He mentions railroads.
  B. He uses the word "And" to begin sentences.
  C. He uses "you" and "I."
  D. He respects the city's power.

_____ 2. How does Sandburg show that he thinks Chicago is strong in "Chicago"?
  A. He compares it to hunger.
  B. He compares it to a powerful young man.
  C. He compares it to hogs that are killed.
  D. He compares it to a tool factory.

_____ 3. What does Sandburg suggest in "Chicago" when he says that he has seen hunger "on the faces of women and children"?
  A. The city is filled with violence.
  B. The city is filled with families.
  C. The city is filled with poverty.
  D. The city is filled with people.

_____ 4. In "Chicago," to which of a reader's senses does the description of a city "singing so proud to be alive" appeal?
  A. sound
  B. smell
  C. sight
  D. touch

_____ 5. To whom is Sandburg referring when he describes "those who sneer at this my city" in "Chicago"?
  A. his relatives who live elsewhere
  B. people who dislike his poetry
  C. people who celebrate the city
  D. people who criticize the city

____ 6. Why do you think Sandburg chooses to address the city in "Chicago" as if it were a person?
   A. to suggest how hard it is to live there
   B. to show how much business the city does
   C. to suggest that the city is a living being
   D. to show how dangerous the city is

____ 7. Why does Sandburg directly address the city as "Hog Butcher for the World, / Tool Maker, Stacker of Wheat, / Player with Railroads and the Nation's Freight Handler; / Stormy, husky, brawling, / City of the Big Shoulders in "Chicago"?
   A. to show that it is full of families
   B. to show that rich people live there
   C. to show that it is big, loud, and busy
   D. to show that the weather is bad

____ 8. In "Chicago," to what sense does the poet appeal in describing the "pulse" that lies "under his [the city's] wrist"?
   A. smell
   B. touch
   C. taste
   D. sight

____ 9. What voice that covers "all" is speaking in the poem "Grass"?
   A. people who died
   B. a tourist
   C. the grass
   D. a train conductor

____ 10. What response might a reader have after reading "Grass"?
   A. War heroes should be honored.
   B. War is tragic and should be ended.
   C. People should leave grass alone.
   D. Battlefields should have labels.

____ 11. As the grass covers over what war has left behind, what does "Grass" suggest about the impact of nature on human events?
   A. The results of war are soon covered over.
   B. Friends and enemies can both be found easily.
   C. Cemeteries are popular spots for tourist trips.
   D. The sites of great battles should be respected.

Vocabulary and Grammar

___ 12. Which word best replaces *brutal* in this sentence: "The *brutal rain*storm caused mudslides"?
   A. light
   B. violent
   C. faraway
   D. evening

___ 13. Which sentence is **correctly** punctuated?
   A. I am grass?
   B. Pile the bodies high!
   C. Where are we now?
   D. Shovel them under,

Essay

14. In "Chicago," Sandburg compares Chicago to other cities by saying, "here is a tall bold slugger set vivid against the little soft cities." What do you think he means to suggest by this comparison? Write a brief essay to give your ideas.

15. What is your response to the poem "Grass"? What kind of speaker is the character of "Grass"? Do you think the character cares about the deaths of soldiers in war-time, or not? Write a brief essay to describe what you think of the character of grass in the poem.

Name _____ Date _____

Critical Reading *Identify the letter of the choice that best completes the statement or answers the question.*

____ 1. What is the theme of "Chicago"?
   A. People love their native cities no matter how brutal and poverty stricken they are.
   B. In its early days, Chicago had more variety and activity than any other American city.
   C. When cities get too big, they dwarf the lives of the people who live in them.
   D. Like people, cities grow up with their own personalities and have both good and bad traits.

____ 2. Which of the following lines from "Chicago" is an example of Sandburg's use of apostrophe?
   A. "I have seen the gunman kill and go free to kill again."
   B. "And they tell me you are crooked and I answer: Yes, it is true"
   C. "I turn once more to those who sneer at this my city"
   D. "Under the smoke, dust all over his mouth, laughing with white teeth"

____ 3. The passage below is the beginning of the poem "Chicago." What is the function of the passage?

   Hog Butcher for the World
   Tool Maker, Stacker of Wheat,
   Player with Railroads and the Nation's Freight Handler;
   Stormy, husky, brawling,
   City of the Big Shoulders:

   A. The narrator is addressing Chicago by its various nicknames.
   B. The narrator is describing Chicago to its critics.
   C. The narrator is complimenting Chicago on its accomplishments.
   D. The narrator is criticizing Chicago for its bad deeds.

____ 4. To which of these lines from "Chicago" would a reader respond with the sense of hearing?
   A. "I have seen your painted women under the gas lamps"
   B. "Flinging magnetic curses amid the toil of piling job on job"
   C. "here is a tall bold slugger set vivid against the little soft cities"
   D. "under his wrist is the pulse, and under his ribs the heart of the people"

____ 5. To which of these lines from "Chicago" would a reader respond with the sense of touch?
   A. "I have seen your painted women under the gas lamps"
   B. "Flinging magnetic curses amid the toil of piling job on job".
   C. "here is a tall bold slugger set vivid against the little soft cities"
   D. "under his wrist is the pulse, and under his ribs the heart of the people"

____ 6. The speaker in "Chicago" portrays the city as a
   A. brash, swaggering, and ignorant yet essentially good young man.
   B. cold and aloof yet cunning boy.
   C. excitable, enthusiastic, naive little child.
   D. somber, serious, determined adult.

_____ 7. In "Grass," the speaker makes the point that
A. nature can undo the damage that is wrought by war.
B. we should remember those who died in wars long ago.
C. battlefields become instant burial grounds for those who are killed.
D. the carnage of the war may not be remembered years later.

_____ 8. What is the theme of "Grass"?
A. Nature heals the damage that war wreaks on society.
B. People depend on time to help them forget the damage done by the war.
C. The tragedies of humanity are insignificant in comparison to the relentless forces of nature.
D. Nature is superior to humanity because it doesn't destroy itself.

_____ 9. To respond to the italicized words in these lines, which of the following would you use?
And pile them high at *Gettysburg*
And pile them high at *Ypres* and *Verdun*.

A. background knowledge
B. senses
C. emotions
D. knowledge about Sandburg

_____ 10. To respond to the entire poem "Grass," which of the following would you use?
I. background knowledge
II. senses
III. emotions
IV. knowledge about Sandburg
A. I and IV
B. II and III
C. I and III
D. I, II, and III

_____ 11. Why do you think that the grass says, "Let me work"?
A. Someone is trying to stop the grass from working.
B. The grass is in favor of war and likes to cover bodies.
C. The grass is ready to grow because that is what grass does.
D. The grass wants to hide the atrocities of war.

_____ 12. Who or what is the speaker in "Grass"?
A. the grass
B. a gravedigger
C. train passengers
D. a train conductor

_____ 13. Sandburg wrote his poem from the point of view of the grass in order to
A. emphasize the power of nature.
B. create a clearer image of the grass.
C. illustrate the forgetful nature of humanity.
D. inject a cynical element into the poem.

Vocabulary and Grammar

___ 14. What type of sentence is this?

I am the grass; I cover all.

A. interrogative
B. declarative
C. imperative
D. exclamatory

___ 15. Which of the following is closest in meaning to *brutal* and *wanton* as used here?

And they tell me you are brutal and my reply is: On the faces of women and children I have seen the marks of wanton hunger.

A. sad
B. desperate
C. careless
D. cruel

___ 16. In the next passage, what does *cunning* indicate about the city of Chicago?

Come and show me another city with lifted head singing so proud to be alive and coarse and strong and cunning.

A. The city has a loud voice.
B. The city survives partly because it struggles hard.
C. The city thrives in part because of its sharp wits.
D. The city tries to deceive other cities.

___ 17. What type of sentence is this one from "Grass"?

Shovel them under and let me work.

A. interrogative
B. declarative
C. exclamatory
D. imperative

Essay

18. In "Chicago," the speaker of the poem acts as a judge, arbitrating a dispute between the city and its critics. Write an essay discussing the charges of the critics against Chicago, and the speaker's verdict. Why does the speaker reach this verdict and not another one? Use details from the poem to support your answer.

19. "Chicago" describes the city by using images of violence, brutality, and suffering. In an essay, describe another image that you could use to portray this city. Explain your choice.

20. "Grass" could be understood as a reflection on the statement "Time heals all wounds." However, it could also be understood as a reflection on the pointlessness of fighting a war that may barely be remembered by future generations. In an essay, explain which inter pretation you think is more appropriate. Why do you think so? Use details from the poem to support your answer.

Vocabulary Warm-up Word Lists

Study these words from the selection. Then, complete the activities.

Word List A

circulation [ser kyoo LAY shun] *n.* the movement of blood through the body
   The extra weight of pregnancy can make a woman's circulation poor.

exchanged [eks CHAYNJED] *v.* gave in return for something else
   The sweater didn't fit, so Alison exchanged it for a larger size.

fumbled [FUM buhld] *v.* touched or handled nervously or awkwardly
   During his first date with Eloise, Ken fumbled with his necktie.

huddled [HUD uhld] *v.* crowded close together
   During the snowstorm, our entire family huddled around the fireside.

jilted [JILT uhd] *v.* rejected or cast off
   I felt jilted when my boyfriend didn't call or show up to visit.

marvel [MAR vuhl] *n.* someone or something that deserves admiration
   Hannah is so helpful and generous that she is truly a marvel.

rummaging [RUM uhj ing] *v.* searching thoroughly
   In his effort to find the tennis rackets, John was rummaging through the garage.

tactful [TAKT fuhl] *adj.* considerate; polite; discreet
   Diane is a tactful person, always thinking before she speaks.

Word List B

amethyst [AM uh thist] *n.* purple or violet semiprecious gemstone
   The birthstone for the month of February is amethyst.

everlasting [ev er LAST ing] *adj.* eternal
   Jessica thought that her love for Scott was everlasting, but now they've broken up.

flimsy [FLIM zee] *adj.* fragile; easily broken or damaged
   Those curtain rods are so flimsy that they will fall down if you even look at them.

hypodermic [hyp oh DER mik] *n.* injection; needle used to deliver an injection
   Liz is allergic to bees, and she must get a hypodermic if she is stung.

piety [PY uh tee] *n.* devotion to religious duties
   Nuns are known for their underline{piety}.

plague [PLAYG] *v.* to pester or annoy
   That dripping faucet will underline{plague} me until I get it fixed.

scandal [SKAN duhl] *n.* something that causes disgrace or outrage
   The last thing any politician needs is a televised underline{scandal}.

urgently [ER juhnt lee] *adv.* in a way that calls for haste or immediate action
   After the earthquake, food and medical supplies were underline{urgently} needed in that region.

Name _____ Date _____

"The Jilting of Granny Weatherall" by Katherine Anne Porter
Vocabulary Warm-up Exercises

Exercise A *Fill in the blanks, using each word from Word List A only once.*

Worried about the [1] _____ in his fingers and toes, Hank went to his doctor for a thorough checkup. Dr. Reese and Hank were old friends. As they [2] _____ jokes in the office, Dr. Reese suddenly grew serious. He said that Hank's blood pressure was abnormally high. [3] _____ and diplomatic but firm, he recommended that Hank check into the hospital for a series of tests. As Hank [4] _____ awkwardly with his calendar, Dr. Reese told him he looked like a(n) [5] _____ for an 86-year-old man. Even so, hypertension was a silent but dangerous enemy. The doctor was verbally [6] _____ for an appropriate way to describe high blood pressure. "Even a person who's been [7] _____ can't have any idea of the suffering a stroke can give you," he told Hank. Later that day, Hank [8] _____ with his wife, his children, and his grandchildren. They all agreed that Hank should have the hospital tests.

Exercise B *Decide whether each statement below is true or false. Circle T or F, and explain your answer.*

1. An <u>amethyst</u> is a reddish-pink colored stone.
   T / F _____

2. An <u>everlasting</u> agreement is not expected to end.
   T / F _____

3. A <u>flimsy</u> piece of furniture is strong and durable.
   T / F _____

4. You can use a <u>hypodermic</u> to administer injections.
   T / F _____

5. <u>Piety</u> involves carelessness and disrespect.
   T / F _____

6. It is delightful to be around children that <u>plague</u> their parents and older relatives.
   T / F _____

7. If you run for public office, a <u>scandal</u> is good to have on your record.
   T / F _____

8. If you need medical attention <u>urgently</u>, you should go to the hospital emergency room.
   T / F _____

"The Jilting of Granny Weatherall" by Katherine Anne Porter
Reading Warm-up A

Read the following passage. Pay special attention to the underlined words. Then, read it again, and complete the activities. Use a separate sheet of paper for your written answers.

Whatever his or her specialty—heart, lungs, skin, or <u>circulation</u> of the blood—every doctor is familiar with the Hippocratic Oath. The "oath" is really an ethical code of principles for a doctor's professional and personal life. It is named for the ancient Greek physician Hippocrates, who is said to have lived in the fifth century B.C. Last week, I was <u>rummaging</u> through some encyclopedia articles to find out more about the oath. Billy and I <u>exchanged</u> e-mails to share what we had learned.

Although Hippocrates was considered a <u>marvel</u> and a model doctor in his time, little is known for sure about his life. Historians have <u>fumbled</u> to find a suitable name for the body of writing he is said to have composed, but they have not come up with a really satisfactory title.

The Hippocratic Oath consists of two major parts. The first part describes the obligations of medical teachers and students to each other. Teachers must have a genuine interest in the welfare of their students; likewise, pupils must maintain a <u>tactful</u> and respectful attitude toward their mentors. If teachers or students were to betray this trust, the resulting damage would be greater than if a woman were to be <u>jilted</u> and abandoned by a suitor.

The second part of the oath directs doctors to prescribe only helpful treatments for their patients. If physicians <u>huddle</u> together to decide on the best treatment for a patient, they must keep the patient's welfare uppermost in mind. Finally, doctors pledge to do no harm or hurt and to lead an upstanding personal and professional life.

1. Underline the words in this sentence that give a clue to the meaning of <u>circulation</u>. Use the word *circulation* in an original sentence, being careful to use it the way it is used here.

2. Circle the words in this sentence that give a clue to the meaning of <u>rummaging</u>. What is a synonym for *rummaging*?

3. Underline the words that give a clue to the meaning of <u>exchanged</u>. What is a synonym for *exchanged*?

4. Circle the words that offer a clue to the meaning of <u>marvel</u> here. What kind of feeling does a *marvel* evoke?

5. Circle the words in this sentence that offer clues to the meaning of <u>fumbled</u>. What is a synonym for *fumbled*?

6. Underline the words in this sentence that give a clue to the meaning of <u>tactful</u>. What are two antonyms for *tactful*?

7. Circle the words in this sentence that give a clue to the meaning of <u>jilted</u>. Use a word meaning the opposite of *jilted* in an original sentence.

8. What clue can you find in this sentence to the meaning of <u>huddle</u>? What is an antonym for *huddle*?

Read the following passage. Pay special attention to the underlined words. Then, read it again, and complete the activities. Use a separate sheet of paper for your written answers.

David brought the latest issue of *Gossip* magazine to his grandmother's bedside, hoping to cheer her up. She had been sick for more than a month now, and beneath the sheets her body looked as <u>flimsy</u> as a paper doll. On the bedside table, the doctor had left an assortment of medications and a <u>hypodermic</u> needle, which David sometimes used to inject his grandmother's arm with pain medicine.

"I brought you the latest news," David said smiling, <u>urgently</u> trying to lighten the mood.

Before cancer had started to <u>plague</u> his grandmother's body, making her so weak, she had been full of mischief. Even now, she loved *Gossip* magazine, which each week brought another story of some celebrity caught in an embarrassing situation. Today, a famous actress had been caught shoplifting, a <u>scandal</u> that might ruin her career. David read the article to his grandmother in an exaggerated, serious voice, as if the news was of major importance.

His grandmother smiled, too weak to really laugh. She put her hand on his wrist and squeezed it. "Poor David," she said, "what are we going to do with our senses of humor?"

Her eyes were still a bright bluish-purple, the color of an <u>amethyst</u> stone. Old women were supposed to be serious and proper, figures of <u>piety</u>, but David's grandmother had never been like that.

He read her the rest of the magazine and eventually she fell asleep. Soon his mother would come home and he would go off to his job at the restaurant, and for awhile he would forget about his grandmother lying in her sickbed. He knew she would probably never recover, but he also knew that in his mind her bright spirit would continue, <u>everlasting</u>.

1. Underline the words that give a clue to the meaning of <u>flimsy</u>. Write a sentence using a word that means the opposite of *flimsy*.

2. Circle the words in this sentence that give a clue to the meaning of the word <u>hypodermic</u>.

3. Circle the words in this sentence that hint at the meaning of <u>urgently</u>. If you did something *urgently*, would you likely feel tense or relaxed?

4. Underline the words in this sentence that give clues to the meaning of <u>plague</u>. What are two synonyms for *plague*?

5. Underline the words in this sentence that hint at the meaning of <u>scandal</u>. What does a *scandal* often lead to?

6. Underline the words in this sentence that give a clue to the meaning of <u>amethyst</u>.

7. Circle the words in this sentence that hint at the meaning of <u>piety</u>. What is a synonym for *piety*?

8. Circle the words in this sentence that hint at the meaning of the word <u>everlasting</u>. What is an antonym for *everlasting*?

Name _____ Date _____

"The Jilting of Granny Weatherall" by Katherine Anne Porter
Literary Analysis: Stream of Consciousness

The **stream-of-consciousness** technique in literature is based on real-life thinking processes. You probably realize that your thoughts often jump around. An ordinary sight, a certain sound, or a flash of memory can serve as a trigger, causing your thoughts to drift to the past or evoking a series of images that are yours alone.

A. DIRECTIONS: *In Porter's story, the following triggers cause Granny's thoughts to drift. For each one, write one or two sentences that discuss the thoughts, feelings, and images that come to Granny's mind.*

1. the sight of Doctor Harry

   _____

   _____

2. jobs to do tomorrow

   _____

   _____

3. the distance of her daughter Lydia

   _____

   _____

4. the feel of the pillow

   _____

   _____

5. the arrival of Father Connolly

   _____

   _____

B. DIRECTIONS: *From the list above, choose the trigger you find most interesting. Using the stream-of-consciousness technique, write a paragraph from the perspective of another character, either a character in the story or a character of your own choosing. Show how the trigger evokes thoughts, feelings, and images in the character's mind.*

   _____

   _____

   _____

   _____

   _____

   _____

   _____

"The Jilting of Granny Weatherall" by Katherine Anne Porter
Reading Strategy: Clarify Sequence of Events

Granny Weatherall recalls that her father was interviewed by a newspaper reporter when he was 102 years old. Imagine that a reporter comes to interview Mrs. Weatherall just before she lapses into her final illness. The reporter wants to tell in sequence the major events of this woman's life and poses the sequential questions below. The reporter hopes to get Granny Weatherall's feelings, as well as facts.

Reply to each of the reporter's questions as if you were Granny Weatherall. Be sure to use the first person *I* in your answers.

1. What did you look like when you were twenty years old?

   _____

   _____

   _____

2. What kind of relationship did you have with your husband?

   _____

   _____

   _____

3. As a young widow, what tasks did you take on alone?

   _____

   _____

   _____

4. How would you describe your relationship with your children when they were young? How has that relationship changed?

   _____

   _____

   _____

5. You seem to be very unconcerned about death. Could you please explain your reasons for this attitude?

   _____

   _____

   _____

6. During this interview, you've frequently muttered the name "George." Please explain who George is and tell us why he is so important.

   _____

   _____

   _____

Name _____ Date _____

"The Jilting of Granny Weatherall" by Katherine Anne Porter
Vocabulary Builder

Using the Prefix *dys-*

A. DIRECTIONS: *The word* dyspepsia *combines the prefix* dys-, *meaning "difficult" or "bad," and the word root* pepsis, *meaning "digestion". The word* dyspepsia, *therefore, means "indigestion." The prefix* dys- *is often used in medical terminology. Using the information following each word and what you know about the prefix* dys-, *write the letter of the definition on the line next to the word it defines.*

____ 1. *dyscrasia* (*krasis* = a mixing)
____ 2. *dysgraphia* (*graphia* = writing)
____ 3. *dyskinesia* (*kin[e]sis* = motion)
____ 4. *dyslexia* (*lexis* = speech)
____ 5. *dysphagia* (*phag[ein]* = to eat)
____ 6. *dysphonia* (*ph[o]n[e]* = voice)
____ 7. *dyspnea* (*pnein* = breathing)

A. impairment of the ability to read
B. difficulty in swallowing
C. impairment of the ability to write
D. an abnormal imbalance in some part of the body, especially in the blood
E. shortness of breath
F. impairment of the ability to produce speech sounds
G. impairment of body movement

Using the Word List

| piety   frippery   dyspepsia |

B. DIRECTIONS: *Choose the word that best completes the meaning of each sentence and write it in the blank.*

1. Their frippery was evident in their _____ furnishings.
   A. gaudy
   B. functional
   C. old
   D. dark

2. His piety was demonstrated by his desire to _____
   A. spend
   B. sleep
   C. pray
   D. play

3. When her dyspepsia would act up, her _____ would hurt badly.
   A. back
   B. elbow
   C. head
   D. stomach

"The Jilting of Granny Weatherall" by Katherine Anne Porter
Grammar and Style: Imperative Sentences

An **imperative sentence** states a request or gives an order. The subject in an imperative sentence is not stated; rather, it is understood. In the following example from "The Jilting of Granny Weatherall," the word *You*, or a character's name, is implied in the italicized sentence.

> *Don't tell me what I'm going to be.* I'm on my feet now, morally speaking. It's Cornelia. I had to go to bed to get rid of her.

A. PRACTICE: *Read the following excerpts from the selection. Underline each imperative sentence or sentence fragment.*

1. "'Well, Missy, excuse me,' Doctor Harry patted her cheek. 'But I've got to warn you, haven't I?"

2. "Don't let good things rot for want of using. You waste life when you waste good food. Don't let things get lost. It's bitter to lose things."

3. "'There, wait a minute, here we are!' John, get the doctor now, Hapsy's time has come. But there was Hapsy standing by the bed in a white cap. 'Cornelia, tell Hapsy to take off her cap. I can't see her plain.'"

B. Writing Application: *Rewrite each example to make it an imperative sentence. If it is already an imperative sentence, write "Correct."*

1. "I'd have you respect your elders, young man."

   _____

2. "Get along and doctor your sick."

   _____

3. "Come in, children, don't stay out in the night air."

   _____

4. "I want you to pick all the fruit this year and see that nothing is wasted."

   _____

5. "I want you to find George."

   _____

6. "Give Father Connolly a chair."

   _____

7. "Now, Ellen, you must believe what I tell you. . . ."

   _____

8. "Cornelia, you're to have the amethyst set. . . ."

   _____

"The Jilting of Granny Weatherall" by Katherine Anne Porter
Support for Writing

To prepare to write your **monologue,** enter stream-of-consciousness writing in the chart below. You may write a monologue as yourself or as a character you create.

Words and Phrases That Relate to [character's name]

Actions _____ _____ _____ _____	Feelings _____ _____ _____ _____
Comments _____ _____ _____ _____	Attitudes _____ _____ _____ _____

On a separate page, write your monologue to focus on one or two major memories of your character. When you revise, be sure to show how the memories blend into one another without transitions.

"The Jilting of Granny Weatherall" by Katherine Anne Porter
Support for Extend Your Learning

With a partner, prepare to role-play a **conversation** between Granny and George. Suppose the two characters meet ten years after he has jilted her. What would they say to each other? Use these tips as guidelines:

- Note details about Ellen's life and how it has changed since the jilting.
- Create a story to explain George's behavior and his life since the jilting.
- What are each person's thoughts and feelings?

As you role play the conversation, try to use language similar to the time and place used in the story.

Research and Technology

To gather material for an **oral report** on hospice care today, use the Internet and library resources. Enter your findings into the organizer below.

Hospice Care

History of Hospice Care	How Hospice Care Works	Who Uses Hospice Care
1. What did Hospice care replace?	**1.** How does Hospice care work in patients' homes?	**1.** What groups of people need Hospice care?
2. How is it used today?	**2.** How does Hospice care work in institutions?	**2.** How does Hospice help patients' families?

Deliver your oral report to your classmates. Discuss how Granny might be cared for in a modern hospice setting.

Name _____   Date _____

"The Jilting of Granny Weatherall" by Katherine Anne Porter
Enrichment: Film Biography

In "The Jilting of Granny Weatherall," Porter writes "there was always a little margin over for peace: then a person could spread out the plan of life and tuck in the edges orderly." Granny's illness gives her the time to do just this through memory.

DIRECTIONS: *Plan a short film biography for a grandparent or other elderly person, using only three events in the person's life. Around which three events would you tell this person's story? You may decide to choose one event from the person's youth, one from middle age, and one from old age; or you may decide to choose three "turning point" events that occurred randomly in the person's life. Describe the three scenes. How and where would you film them?*

The Life of _____

Scene 1

Event: _____

Description of scene: _____

_____

_____

_____

_____

_____

Scene 2

Event: _____

Description of scene: _____

_____

_____

_____

_____

_____

Scene 3

Event: _____

Description of scene: _____

_____

_____

_____

_____

"The Jilting of Granny Weatherall" by Katherine Anne Porter
Selection Test A

Critical Reading *Identify the letter of the choice that best answers the question.*

_____ 1. In "The Jilting of Granny Weatherall," why is Granny upset at the doctor's presence?
   A. He does not treat her respectfully.
   B. She does not think she is ill.
   C. He has not been practicing long.
   D. It has taken him too long to come.

_____ 2. Which event happened earliest in "The Jilting of Granny Weatherall"?
   A. Granny married John.
   B. Granny moved in with Cornelia.
   C. Granny's husband John died.
   D. George jilted Granny at the altar.

_____ 3. In "The Jilting of Granny Weatherall," what is odd about Granny wanting to spank Cornelia?
   A. Cornelia ignores Granny.
   B. Cornelia is not a good daughter.
   C. Cornelia is good to her.
   D. Cornelia whispers about Granny.

_____ 4. In "The Jilting of Granny Weatherall," what does Granny's stream of consciousness reflect?
   A. the thoughts in her mind
   B. the feelings of her heart
   C. the words in her letters
   D. the speech in her mouth

_____ 5. In "The Jilting of Granny Weatherall," what memory still bothers Granny?
   A. Her husband John died.
   B. Cornelia treats her well.
   C. She was once very ill.
   D. George rejected her.

_____ 6. Who comes last to see Granny in "The Jilting of Granny Weatherall"?
   A. her children
   B. George
   C. her husband John
   D. the nurse

____ 7. In "The Jilting of Granny Weatherall," why doesn't Hapsy come to see her mother?
   A. She lives too far away.
   B. She is too ill to travel.
   C. She is angry at Granny.
   D. She has died.

____ 8. In "The Jilting of Granny Weatherall," how does stream of consciousness remind Granny of a sad event when Father Connelly appears?
   A. She remembers her children's births.
   B. She remembers her wasted wedding cake.
   C. She remembers when she needed a doctor.
   D. She remembers her husband John.

____ 9. Which of these is a message of "The Jilting of Granny Weatherall"?
   A. People in pain welcome death.
   B. Bad memories last until death.
   C. No one can outlive death.
   D. Old age welcomes death.

____ 10. In "The Jilting of Granny Weatherall," what first sorrow is Granny's greatest burden?
   A. the death of Hapsy
   B. the death of John
   C. the pain of her illness
   D. her jilting by George

____ 11. Which event happens last in "The Jilting of Granny Weatherall?"
   A. John dies.
   B. The nurse visits.
   C. Granny dies.
   D. George leaves.

Vocabulary and Grammar

____ 12. Which answer best replaces *piety* in this sentence: "The man showed his *piety* by going to church each week"?
   A. lack of feeling
   B. religious devotion
   C. kindness to others
   D. business ability

___ **13.** Which sentence is an imperative statement that gives an order?

  A. "There's nothing wrong with me."

  B. "Where were you forty years ago?"

  C. "Leave a well woman alone."

  D. "I want a lot of things."

Essay

14. Katherine Anne Porter names her character Granny Weatherall in "The Jilting of Granny Weatherall." What do you think Granny's last name might stand for? Think about what kind of character Granny is. Write a brief essay that discusses the meaning of her name.

15. At the end of "The Jilting of Granny Weatherall," Granny remembers that once again, there is "no bridegroom and the priest in the house." She then says that "there's nothing more cruel than this—I'll never forgive it." What does this final stream-of-consciousness tell readers about Granny's last thoughts? Write a brief essay to give your ideas.

"The Jilting of Granny Weatherall" by Katherine Anne Porter
Selection Test B

Critical Reading *Identify the letter of the choice that best completes the statement or answers the question.*

____ 1. At the beginning of the story, what disturbs Granny Weatherall most about Doctor Harry's presence?
   A. She feels that he treats her with insufficient respect.
   B. She refuses to acknowledge that she is not well.
   C. She remembers him from when he was a child.
   D. She thinks he is too young to practice medicine.

____ 2. John Weatherall would probably remember Ellen Weatherall as
   A. a dying, stubborn woman.
   B. feminine and fashionable.
   C. a fence builder.
   D. a grandmother.

____ 3. Which moment happens the latest in Granny Weatherall's life?
   A. Granny sends wine to Sister Borgia.
   B. Lydia asks Granny for advice about the grandchildren.
   C. Granny nurses the sick children.
   D. Granny wants to spank Cornelia for being dutiful.

____ 4. What do Granny's flashbacks reveal about her relationships with her children?
   A. Cornelia used to be her favorite child.
   B. She has always resented her children for restricting her life.
   C. She was a source of comfort to her children when they were young.
   D. She believes her children love their father more than they love her.

____ 5. What are the predominant character traits revealed by Granny's thoughts?
   A. strength and industriousness
   B. kindness and intelligence
   C. patience and indulgence
   D. confidence and compliance

____ 6. Granny Weatherall's thoughts about her old age are naturally linked to her thoughts about her children by her
   A. memories of her father's behavior.
   B. children's unwillingness to allow her to live her own life.
   C. thoughts about her work as a country nurse.
   D. children's treatment of her as if she were a child.

____ 7. Stream of consciousness is a narrative technique that presents thoughts as if they were coming directly from a character's _____.
   A. mouth
   B. heart
   C. mind
   D. diary

____ 8. Which of the following details do you learn through the use of flashbacks?
   A. Granny Weatherall lives with her daughter Cornelia.
   B. Cornelia has been a good and dutiful daughter.
   C. John Weatherall died when his wife was still a young woman.
   D. Granny Weatherall does not respect Doctor Harry.

____ 9. Which moment takes place in the story's present?
   A. Granny wants to give Cornelia the amethyst set.
   B. Granny faces the priest alone.
   C. Granny gathers the children around her as she lights the lamps.
   D. Granny dusts the bronze clock with the lion on top.

____ 10. Why was Father Connolly in the room?
   A. to have a cup of tea
   B. to give Granny the last rites
   C. to play cards with Cornelia and Hapsy
   D. to gossip with the family

____ 11. What is the story's theme?
   A. Death can be fought off with stubbornness and strength.
   B. Even the moment of death often provides no relief from one's memories of life's troubles.
   C. People who have suffered find relief as death approaches.
   D. Sorrows can be forgotten with the help of love and compassion.

____ 12. In what way does Granny Weatherall associate Father Connolly's presence with her jilting?
   A. Father Connolly reminds her of George, but with black eyes instead of blue.
   B. Her religious beliefs helped her recover from being jilted.
   C. She had always felt that being jilted was a sin she should have confessed.
   D. She had faced the priest alone when George didn't arrive for the wedding.

Vocabulary and Grammar

____ 13. Which of the following could be an example of *frippery*?
   A. saving love letters
   B. buying blue silk lampshades
   C. making sure no fruit is wasted
   D. digging post holes until a fence is finished

____ 14. Which of the following is an imperative sentence?
   A. "Leave a well woman alone."
   B. "She was never like this, never like this!"
   C. "What'd you say, Mother?"
   D. "I do."

____ 15. A person filled with *piety* would most likely
   A. pray a lot.
   B. enjoy raising children.
   C. be a good farmer.
   D. be jilted.

____ **16.** Someone with *dyspepsia* would most likely have
   A. a headache.
   B. an upset stomach.
   C. swollen legs.
   D. shortness of breath.

____ **17.** Which of the following is an imperative sentence?
   A. I should hope you would leave.
   B. I want you to leave right now.
   C. I hope to leave you.
   D. Leave now.

Essay

18. Katherine Anne Porter chose to call this story "The Jilting of Granny Weatherall." Write an essay stating why you think this title was chosen to represent this fictional work. What do you think this title signifies in the story? Use events from the story to back up your opinion.

19. Benjamin Disraeli, a British statesman, is credited with the statement, "Youth is a blunder; [adult]hood a struggle; old age a regret." Do you think Granny Weatherall would agree or disagree with this statement? State your position in an essay. Support your position with details from the selection.

20. Katherine Anne Porter uses the narrative technique of stream of consciousness to present Granny's thoughts and to indicate how close she is to death. Write a brief essay discussing Porter's use of this technique. How would you describe stream of consciousness? How well does it indicate how close Granny is to death? Include details from the selection that illustrate the technique.

Vocabulary Warm-up Word Lists

Study these words from the selections. Then, complete the activities.

Word List A

acclaim [uh KLAYM] *n.* enthusiastic applause or approval
   The prizewinning novelist enjoyed international <u>acclaim</u>.

agony [AG oh nee] *n.* extreme mental or physical pain
   We can tell that the dog is in <u>agony</u>, because he won't move and won't eat.

anguish [ANG wish] *n.* mental or physical pain
   Karen had to live for years with the <u>anguish</u> of a guilty conscience.

compassion [kahm PASH uhn] *n.* deep awareness of the suffering of others; pity
   People who work for the Animal Rescue League demonstrate <u>compassion</u> every day.

confidence [KAHN fi dens] *n.* trust in someone or something
   "I have great <u>confidence</u> in the students who work hard," said Ms. Rollins.

dense [DENS] *adj.* thick; hard to penetrate; closely compacted
   Many jungles are too <u>dense</u> to explore.

glade [GLAYD] *n.* open space surrounded by woods
   We stopped at a small clearing in the woods and enjoyed our picnic in the <u>glade</u>.

universal [yoo ni VERS uhl] *adj.* concerning or affecting all
   A <u>universal</u> truth is something that people all over the world will recognize.

Word List B

beeline [BEE lyn] *n.* direct, straight course
   When it started to rain, we made a <u>beeline</u> for the house to get indoors.

commensurate [kuh MEN suh ruht] *adj.* proportional with
   Many job ads include a notice that salary will be <u>commensurate</u> with experience.

dedication [ded i KAY shuhn] *n.* designation; purpose; devotion
   The <u>dedication</u> for that bequest in Ms. Wilcox's will was animal rights groups.

dodging [DOJ ing] *adj.* avoiding; moving by shifting or twisting
   The young boy was <u>dodging</u> through the crowd, and no one could catch him.

ephemeral [ee FEM uh ruhl] *adj.* short-lived; transitory
   Pam's resolution to lose weight was <u>ephemeral</u>, and she soon abandoned her diet.

pinnacle [PIN uh kuhl] *n.* summit; highest point; apex
   Clare reached the <u>pinnacle</u> of her career when she was elected president.

scrabbling [SKRAB ling] *v.* scrambling
   Angela saw a spider <u>scrabbling</u> up the wall.

thicket [THIK uht] *n.* dense group of shrubs; heavy undergrowth
   The dog pursued the rabbit and disappeared into a <u>thicket</u>.

Name _____ Date _____

Selections by William Faulkner
Vocabulary Warm-up Exercises

Exercise A *Fill in the blanks, using each word from Word List A only once.*

Over her long career as a novelist, Estelle had achieved international renown and

critical [1] _____. Her books had [2] _____ appeal, and had

been translated into many foreign languages. Packed and [3] _____ with

meaning, these works championed [4] _____ for the human condition.

When Estelle was young, she had not approached a writing career with much

[5] _____. Instead, she had suffered [6] _____ from the fear

of rejection. Setbacks, though, had sometimes proved to be blessings in disguise. The painful

[7] _____ of a bout with cancer had planted the seeds for a successful book.

Now a seasoned writer, Estelle thought of old age as a peaceful [8] _____ in

the woods, a clearing where she could rest from and reflect on the twists and turns of her life.

Exercise B *Revise each sentence so that the underlined vocabulary word is logical. Be sure to keep the vocabulary word in your revision.*

Example: Because the article was so <u>complex</u>, we read through it quickly.
Because the article was so <u>complex</u>, we read it slowly and carefully.

1. We made a <u>beeline</u> for the music store, visiting several shops along the way.

   _____

2. A salary <u>commensurate</u> with experience has no relationship to a person's previous knowledge.

   _____

3. The <u>dedication</u> of a charitable donation is the motivation of the donor.

   _____

4. If you are <u>dodging</u> snowballs, you are throwing them vigorously.

   _____

5. An <u>ephemeral</u> feeling usually lasts for days at a time.

   _____

6. We slowly clambered down the hillside to reach the <u>pinnacle</u>.

   _____

7. The squirrel was <u>scrabbling</u> through the underbrush, moving slowly and majestically.

   _____

8. Because of a large <u>thicket</u> of tall trees, our visibility across the meadow was excellent.

   _____

Name _____ Date _____

Selections by William Faulkner
Reading Warm-up A

Read the following passage. Pay special attention to the underlined words. Then, read it again, and complete the activities. Use a separate sheet of paper for your written answers.

Point of view is the vantage point from which a story is told. In first-person point of view, the narrator is a character inside the story. Because of their position as insiders, first-person narrators can tell about events with <u>confidence</u>. In third-person point of view, the narrator is an imaginary character or voice outside the story.

Early in his career, William Faulkner won literary <u>acclaim</u>, with many critics praising his radical experiments with point of view. In his first major novel, *The Sound and the Fury* (1929), Faulkner used first-person monologues by three different characters. They told a story about the <u>agony</u> of suffering and resentment afflicting a Southern family, the Compsons. In a fourth section, Faulkner used third-person point of view. This part conveys the sympathy and <u>compassion</u> of Dilsey, the family's black servant.

A year later, in a second novel entitled *As I Lay Dying* (1930), Faulkner went even further in his experiments. In this tale—the story of a journey by a large family to bury their mother—Faulkner used more than a dozen different points of view and many brief but <u>dense</u> sections of narrative. Some sections are less than a page long. The novel strikingly mingles <u>anguish</u> with humor, as we learn the reactions of the different characters.

Faulkner's genius was to realize that any single event typically involves multiple perspectives. No one sees a story in exactly the same way as anybody else. Therefore, the reader may need many points of view to gain a truly comprehensive, <u>universal</u> perspective on an action. Reading Faulkner can sometimes be difficult. By the end of one of his stories, though, you feel as if you had arrived in a forest <u>glade</u> or clearing—able to see all the characters, events, and relationships with a new clarity.

1. Underline the words that give a clue to the meaning of <u>confidence</u>. Use the word *confidence* in a sentence of your own.

2. Circle the words in this sentence that give a clue to the meaning of the word <u>acclaim</u>. What are two synonyms for *acclaim*?

3. Underline the words in this sentence that give a clue to the meaning of <u>agony</u>. What are two antonyms for *agony*?

4. Underline the words in this sentence that hint at the meaning of <u>compassion</u>. Use the word *compassion* in a sentence of your own.

5. What is a synonym for <u>dense</u>? What is an antonym for the word *dense*?

6. Circle the words in this sentence that offer a clue to the meaning of <u>anguish</u>. What is an antonym for *anguish*?

7. Underline the words in this sentence that hint at the meaning of <u>universal</u>. Use a word meaning the opposite of *universal* in a sentence of your own.

8. What clues can you find in this sentence to the meaning of the word <u>glade</u>?

Selections by William Faulkner
Reading Warm-up B

Read the following passage. Pay special attention to the underlined words. Then, read it again, and complete the activities. Use a separate sheet of paper for your written answers.

To get to the most difficult slope at Avalanche Ski Basin, Pedro and his friends switched from the chairlift to a simple towrope that dragged them all the way up to the mountain's <u>pinnacle</u>. From there, they skied their way around to the back side, <u>scrabbling</u> hastily through low trees that closed in on either side of the trail. After that, Pedro's friend Juan turned his skis downhill and made a <u>beeline</u> directly for the steep chute that everyone knew ended in a twenty-foot drop-off that you had to jump.

It was called Suicide Cliff, the most dangerous place you could go on the mountain, but the one place everyone in Pedro's group had to go. The only thing <u>commensurate</u> with the fear of jumping off that cliff was the desire to say that you had done it.

While his friends went ahead, shouting like crazy to mask their fear, Pedro hesitated for a moment at the top of the slope. He didn't know if he had the necessary focus and <u>dedication</u> to keep going. If he turned back now, they would think he was a coward. But what mattered more, his safety or their opinion of him?

He turned his skis down the hill, heading for the narrow chute at full speed. To either side of him lay a <u>thicket</u> of trees, which meant a certain crash. He made tight, weaving turns to slow down, but the steep slope made it difficult, his <u>dodging</u> body barely in control. He realized he was going too fast, his skis slippery beneath him. This realization, though, was <u>ephemeral</u>, over in a split second. The cliff rose in front of him, and the next thing he knew he was thirty feet above the ground.

1. Underline the words in this sentence that hint at the meaning of <u>pinnacle</u>. What is a synonym for *pinnacle*?

2. Circle the words in this sentence that hint at the meaning of <u>scrabbling</u>. Use the word *scrabbling* in an original sentence.

3. Underline the words in this sentence that hint at the meaning of <u>beeline</u>.

4. Underline the words in this sentence that hint at the meaning of <u>commensurate</u>. What is a synonym for *commensurate*?

5. Circle the words in this sentence that hint at the meaning of <u>dedication</u>.

6. Circle the words in this sentence that give a good clue to the meaning of <u>thicket</u>.

7. Underline the words in this sentence that hint at the meaning of <u>dodging</u>. What is a synonym for *dodging*?

8. Underline the words in this sentence that hint at the meaning of <u>ephemeral</u>. Use a word meaning the opposite of *ephemeral* in a sentence of your own.

Name _____ Date _____

"A Rose for Emily" and "Nobel Prize Acceptance Speech"
by William Faulkner
Literary Analysis: Conflict and Resolution

Conflict is the struggle between forces or characters that oppose each other. An **internal conflict** is a struggle between thoughts or emotions inside a character. You face an internal conflict, for example, when you know you have important work to complete, but you also want to talk to a friend on the phone. An **external conflict** is a struggle between a character and an outside force. For instance, society makes certain demands of us, as it does for Emily Grierson in "A Rose for Emily." The **resolution** to a conflict occurs when the struggle draws to a close.

A. DIRECTIONS: *On the lines provided, answer the following questions about conflict and resolution in "A Rose for Emily."*

1. What is the nature of the opening conflict between Emily Grierson and the Board of Aldermen in the town of Jefferson?

   _____

   _____

2. How does Miss Emily deal with the demand that is placed on her by the conflict?

   _____

   _____

3. Explain the nature of the conflict that is brought to the attention of Judge Stevens, the mayor of Jefferson.

   _____

   _____

4. Find at least one example that suggests that the narrator has an internal conflict about how he views Miss Emily.

   _____

   _____

5. How does finding the body of Homer Baron in the upstairs bedroom provide a resolution to the conflicting opinions about Miss Emily's unusual behavior?

   _____

   _____

B. DIRECTIONS: *In his "Nobel Prize Acceptance Speech," Faulkner describes the writer's responsibility to inspire others to face life with courage. Give an example of an internal or external conflict that people face that might lead them to seek courage through reading.*

_____

_____

_____

_____

Name _____ Date _____

Reading Strategy: Clarify Ambiguities

Ambiguity occurs when some part of a story can be interpreted in at least two different ways. When Miss Emily buys arsenic in "A Rose for Emily" and won't tell the druggist its purpose, the reader wonders if she intends to kill rats or if she has something else in mind. **Clarifying ambiguity** in a literary work requires that you look for clues or details that can help you make a reasonable interpretation. Sometimes it's helpful to re-examine description, action, or characterization.

A. DIRECTIONS: *Examine the following ambiguous statements from "A Rose for Emily" and choose the best interpretation provided. Include details or clues from the story to support your choice.*

1. "She vanquished them, horse and foot, just as she had vanquished them their fathers thirty years before about the smell." Where does the smell come from?
   A. Miss Emily's unclean house
   B. the decaying body of Homer Baron
   C. a rat or snake that was killed in Miss Emily's yard

   Supporting details: _____

   _____

2. "She told them that her father was not dead." Why does Miss Emily tell the visiting ladies this information?
   A. She has a good imagination.
   B. Her father is not really dead.
   C. She is too proud to accept their pity.

   Supporting details: _____

   _____

3. "'Do you suppose it's really so?' they said to one another. 'Of course it is. What else could. . .'" What fact does this open-ended sentence refer to?
   A. Miss Emily's possible relationship with a laborer
   B. the fact that Miss Emily has no family in Jefferson
   C. her father's legal troubles over the estate of old lady Wyatt

   Supporting details: _____

   _____

B. DIRECTIONS: *In his "Nobel Prize Acceptance Speech," Faulkner insists that humans will never die because they have voices. What details might you add to this statement to clarify its ambiguity?*

   _____

   _____

"A Rose for Emily" and **"Nobel Prize Acceptance Speech"**
by William Faulkner
Vocabulary Builder

Using the Prefix *in-*

The prefix *in-* typically means "not," as in *indecisive, inedible,* and *injustice.* However, the same prefix may also suggest a "location or direction," as in *infield, ingrown,* and *insert.*

A. DIRECTIONS: *Examine the following words and their meanings. Decide if the prefix suggests negativity or direction. Write an "N" or a "D" next to each word along with a brief sentence.*

1. inhumane ("unkind") _____

2. ingrain ("to plant inside") _____

3. inextricable ("unable to separate from") _____

Using the Word List

circumvent	divulge	encroached	imperviousness	thwarted
vanquished	vindicated	virulent	obliterated	

B. DIRECTIONS: *Briefly answer the following questions using words from the Word List.*

1. If you *divulge* too much personal information over the Internet, what might happen?

_____

2. If Midwest food crops are *obliterated,* how might that affect shoppers at the grocery store?

_____

3. If your efforts to get a job this summer are *thwarted,* what might you consider doing about it?

_____

4. If your father reacts with *imperviousness* to your requests for the car, how might you get to the mall?

_____

5. What often happens to people who *circumvent* the rules of a game?

_____

6. Why would it be surprising if a junior varsity team *vanquished* a varsity team?

_____

7. If a defendant is *vindicated* during a trial, what does this suggest about his or her guilt?

_____

8. If there were a *virulent* outbreak of chicken pox in town, what might doctors suggest?

_____

9. If your little brother *encroached* on a personal phone call, what might you ask him to do next time?

_____

Name _____ Date _____

"A Rose for Emily" and "Nobel Prize Acceptance Speech"
by William Faulkner
Grammar and Style: Semicolons

A **semicolon** is a punctuation mark used to join independent clauses instead of using a comma and a coordinating conjunction (*and, but, or*). It may also be used to correct a run-on sentence, which is caused by joining two independent clauses with only a comma.

Two independent clauses in two sentences:

Miss Emily felt superior. In this way, she was like the other Griersons.

Joined with a semicolon to make one sentence and emphasize an idea:

Miss Emily felt superior; in this way, she was like the other Griersons.

Run-on sentence:

Miss Emily did not often receive guests, she didn't care for the company.

Joined with a semicolon to correct the run-on sentence:

Miss Emily did not often receive guests; she didn't care for the company.

A. PRACTICE: *Use a semicolon to combine independent clauses into a compound sentence or to correct a run-on sentence.*

1. The men went to her father's funeral out of respectful affection, the women went out of curiosity. _____

_____

2. Miss Emily did not invite them inside to sit down. She stood in the doorway and listened.

_____

_____

3. After her father's funeral, a few ladies tried to visit Miss Emily to offer their condolences, they were not received. _____

_____

B. Writing Application: *Write about how Faulkner used his "Nobel Prize Acceptance Speech" as an opportunity to teach others about why writing is important. Use at least four independent clauses, and use coordinating conjunctions (*and, but, or*) or semicolons to link them.*

_____

_____

_____

_____

"A Rose for Emily" and **"Nobel Prize Acceptance Speech"**
by William Faulkner
Support for Writing

To prepare to write a **critical review** of a short story in terms of what Faulkner says is the duty of the writer, enter details into the graphic organizer below. Think about how the story you read helps people "endure [life] by lifting their hearts."

[Title of Short Story]

Characters: _____ _____ _____ _____	How do the characters act with courage and honor? _____ _____ _____ _____
Summary of Plot: _____ _____ _____ _____	How does the plot help the reader feel pride or compassion? _____ _____ _____ _____
Theme: _____ _____ _____ _____	In what ways does the theme inspire a sense of glory? _____ _____ _____ _____

On a separate page, write the draft of your critical review. Make an introductory statement to tell whether or not the story you have read fulfills Faulkner's guidelines. Then, give examples from the story to support your opinion. When you revise, be sure you have enough supporting material for your critical judgment.

"A Rose for Emily" and **"Nobel Acceptance Speech"**
by William Faulkner
Support for Extend Your Learning

Listening and Speaking

Work with a partner or small group to prepare for your **dramatic scene** from "A Rose for Emily."
Choose students to be the characters and use these tips for memorizing lines:

- Make a photocopy of the script. Highlight your lines and movements.
- Make sure you understand what each line means and why you are saying it.
- Record your cues—the words immediately before each of your lines.

Present your scene to your classmates and ask for critical feedback.

Research and Technology

Find critical articles about "A Rose for Emily" on the Internet. Find articles that approach the
story from different points of view. Enter information in the chart below.

Review #1—Title and Author: **Main ideas:**
Review #2—Title and Author: **Main ideas:**
Which review is closest to my point of view, and why?

Summarize the article you choose. Compare the author's opinion to yours as you present it
in an **oral report** to the class.

Name _____   Date _____

"A Rose for Emily" and "Nobel Prize Acceptance Speech"
by William Faulkner
Enrichment: Journalism

Consider for a moment the circumstances surrounding the discovery of the remains of Homer Baron and how that information would reach the public. How might a town the size of Jefferson, Mississippi, react to such shocking information about one of the community's most well-known citizens? Journalists look for information, even when the facts are as chilling as the ones in "A Rose for Emily." Suppose that you are the journalist responsible for breaking this story. What more would you like to find out? Whom would you talk to get additional details?

News stories have a very distinct formula. They begin with a brief but catchy headline and then answer the six most important journalistic questions: who, what, where, when, why, and how. Called an "inverted [upside-down] pyramid," newspaper articles begin with the most important details and end with the least important details. Write a news story about the discovery of Homer Baron's body. Make up what the short story doesn't tell you. For example, it would be a good idea to include a quotation or two from someone such as the chief of police, even though he does not appear in the short story.

DIRECTIONS: *Use the organizer below to write sentences that include the most important facts about the discovery of the body in Emily Grierson's house. Then, on a separate page, write a news story about the event.*

Headline: _____

Who? _____

_____

What? _____

_____

Where? _____

_____

When? _____

_____

Why? _____

_____

How? _____

_____

"A Rose for Emily" and **"Nobel Prize Acceptance Speech"** by William Faulkner

Selection Test A

Critical Reading *Identify the letter of the choice that best answers the question.*

____ 1. In the beginning of "A Rose for Emily," what conflict exists between the mayor and Emily?
  A. the condition of her house
  B. the payment of her taxes
  C. a marriage to Homer Baron
  D. giving lessons in china painting

____ 2. In "A Rose for Emily," what event clarifies information about the smell that comes from Emily's house?
  A. Her father has died.
  B. The taxes are set aside.
  C. Homer Barron disappears.
  D. She dies and is buried.

____ 3. In "A Rose for Emily," what does Emily do after the death of her father?
  A. She denies that he has died.
  B. She welcomes people into her home.
  C. She sprinkles lime around the house.
  D. She begins to teach china painting.

____ 4. Which word describes the attitude of the town toward Emily in "A Rose for Emily"?
  A. amused
  B. forgetful
  C. uncaring
  D. pitying

____ 5. In "A Rose for Emily," what is unclear to the reader when Emily buys rat poison from the druggist?
  A. the amount of rat poison she buys
  B. the reason that she buys the poison
  C. the amount she pays for the poison
  D. the kind of poison she wants to buy

____ **6.** Why do the townsfolk think it is a disgrace for Emily to consider marrying Homer Barron in "A Rose for Emily"?

    A. He is much older than she is.

    B. He is much poorer than she is.

    C. He is much younger than she it.

    D. He is of a different class than she is.

____ **7.** What is an important internal conflict in the story "A Rose for Emily"?

    A. Emily struggles with herself about what to do about Homer Barron.

    B. Emily struggles with herself about what to do about the taxes.

    C. The townspeople struggle about what to do about the smell.

    D. The mayor struggles with Emily about what to do about the taxes.

____ **8.** In "A Rose for Emily," what is unclear to the reader after Homer Barron returns to town?

    A. where the wedding is held

    B. what becomes of Homer

    C. where Homer has been

    D. what Homer brings Emily

____ **9.** In Faulkner's "Nobel Prize Acceptance Speech," why does he say young writers do not write about problems of the human heart?

    A. They are too young to know about such problems.

    B. They are worried about other things, such as dying in a nuclear war.

    C. They do not have the talent to write about such things.

    D. They are too busy earning a living at other jobs to write novels.

____ **10.** What is the main idea in Faulkner's "Nobel Prize Acceptance Speech"?

    A. Writers must give people hope.

    B. Writers must write romantic novels.

    C. Humankind must accept its end.

    D. Writers must work for peace.

____ **11.** According to Faulkner's "Nobel Prize Acceptance Speech," what is the tragedy of the modern world?

    A. People live in fear.

    B. People are too busy.

    C. People have too much time.

    D. People cannot live together.

Vocabulary and Grammar

___ **12.** Which word best replaces *thwarted* in this sentence: "She *thwarted* her play-mate's attempts to find her by hiding in a closet"?

A. pitied

B. frustrated

C. drove

D. disappeared

___ **13.** Which sentence contains the **correct** use of a semicolon?

A. When she died; our whole town went to her funeral.

B. She went out very little; people hardly saw her at all.

C. When her father died; the house was all that was left to her.

D. Just as they were about to enter; she let them come in.

Essay

14. In "A Rose for Emily," what did you think had happened to Homer Barron before you read the end of the story? What other possibilities are there, apart from what you learn at the end? Write a brief essay about how the author keeps the ending of the story a mystery.

15. In his "Nobel Prize Acceptance Speech," Faulkner says that the fear of nuclear war creates other problems. How does this fear affect writers? How do the fears of writers affect others? Write a brief essay to discuss these questions.

"A Rose for Emily" and **"Nobel Prize Acceptance Speech"** by William Faulkner
Selection Test B

Critical Reading *Identify the letter of the choice that best completes the statement or answers the question.*

____ 1. In "A Rose for Emily," what kind of conflict is the aldermen's attempt to get Miss Emily to pay taxes?
   A. an internal conflict within herself
   B. an external conflict with an outside source
   C. an ambiguity that is unclear
   D. a resolution that solves a problem

____ 2. How does Faulkner create ambiguity in "A Rose for Emily"?
   A. He provides a narrator that can't be trusted.
   B. He limits information about the true order of events.
   C. He leaves out the most important facts in the story.
   D. He uses no dialogue to tell the story of Miss Emily.

____ 3. In "A Rose for Emily," why is Miss Emily being watched more carefully than in the past?
   A. A new generation of leaders is changing things.
   B. Northerners are arriving in the South in greater numbers.
   C. People who were once rich cannot expect to be treated the same way.
   D. It is suddenly fashionable to gossip about those in power.

____ 4. In "A Rose for Emily," why were the people glad when it was learned that after Miss Emily's father died, all that was left to her was the house?
   A. They had always envied her good fortune.
   B. She had suddenly become more like them.
   C. The people of Jefferson were gossips.
   D. The house was worth a lot of money.

____ 5. In "A Rose for Emily," when Miss Emily tells the ladies who have come to offer their condolences that her father is not dead, how does this action establish ambiguity?
   A. It shows that she has friends who visit.
   B. It shows that she needs to feel superior.
   C. It shows her strange state of mind.
   D. It shows her sheltered way of life.

____ 6. In "A Rose for Emily," why does the appearance of Homer Barron in Miss Emily's life cause concern for the "older people" of Jefferson?
   A. They knew that Mr. Grierson didn't want Emily to marry anyone at all.
   B. He is big and loud, and he is frequently seen laughing in public.
   C. They think Emily is lonely and should have family around.
   D. They believed she should not be with a Yankee day laborer.

_____ 7. When Miss Emily purchases poison in "A Rose for Emily," what does Faulkner avoid revealing in order to create more ambiguity?
   A. the amount she purchases
   B. the type she purchases
   C. the reason she purchases it
   D. the price of the purchase

_____ 8. In "A Rose for Emily," what type of conflict is shown by Homer Barron's not being "a marrying man"?
   A. internal conflict in Miss Emily's mind
   B. external conflict between Homer and Miss Emily
   C. ambiguity about what Homer may have felt
   D. resolution to the problem their marriage might pose

_____ 9. In "A Rose for Emily," why did the ladies of Jefferson force the minister to call on Emily?
   A. Emily was in need of counseling during her loss.
   B. Emily had sinned and they wanted her to pray.
   C. Emily was in need of charity but wouldn't admit it.
   D. Emily was becoming a disgrace and setting a bad example.

_____ 10. How might the result of the minister's visit in "A Rose for Emily" be considered ambiguous?
   A. The reader knows he refused to go back but can only guess what may have happened.
   B. The reader sees how Emily treats visitors, and his experience was similar.
   C. The reader knows that Emily is not easily influenced, so the minister gave up.
   D. The reader can assume the minister was successful.

_____ 11. In "A Rose for Emily," what does the discovery of the body provide in terms of the story's unanswered questions and conflicts?
   A. a surprise ending
   B. a theme
   C. a resolution
   D. another conflict

_____ 12. In his "Nobel Prize Acceptance Speech," Faulkner wants writers to act responsibly by writing about "the heart." What does he want them to do?
   A. write about light romance
   B. write about medical topics
   C. write fiction instead of nonfiction
   D. write about subjects that really matter

_____ 13. What is Faulkner's main point about a writer's duty in his "Nobel Prize Acceptance Speech"?
   A. The writer must learn not to be afraid of living in the modern world.
   B. The writer's duty is to help human beings face life with courage.
   C. Writers are unworthy of receiving special prizes.
   D. Writers should use prize money for some worthy cause.

Vocabulary and Grammar

___ **14.** Which word best replaces *divulge* in this sentence: "The author's aim was to *divulge* just enough information to keep the story interesting"?
- **A.** hide
- **B.** read
- **C.** reveal
- **D.** question

___ **15.** Which word best replaces *thwarted* in this sentence: "The lawyer was *thwarted* in his attempt to change the judge's mind"?
- **A.** welcomed
- **B.** frustrated
- **C.** hugged
- **D.** confused

___ **16.** In which of the following sentences is the semicolon used **correctly**?
- **A.** Early in her life; she didn't display such unusual behavior.
- **B.** She was a proud young lady; from a good family.
- **C.** She did what her father asked; she never complained.
- **D.** However; people began to notice a change as she grew older.

___ **17.** In which of the following sentences should a semicolon be used to **correctly** join two independent clauses?
- **A.** Faulkner did not feel he earned the prize as a person, but he accepted it for his work.
- **B.** He used his speech to remind writers not to forget the problems of the human heart.
- **C.** He says the writer must learn everything again, he must write with pity and compassion.
- **D.** Even if everything is destroyed, there will still be a voice.

Essay

18. What does the narrator mean in "A Rose for Emily" when he says, "Alive, Miss Emily had been a tradition, a duty, and a care"? In an essay, explain Miss Emily's relationship to the people of Jefferson through one of these three characteristics—tradition, duty, or care. Provide examples to support your response.

19. In "A Rose for Emily," When Miss Emily's father dies, she does not want to let go of him. When Homer Barron's body is discovered, it too appears that Miss Emily could not let go. In an essay, explain why Faulkner's main character is caught in the past. In your opinion, is Faulkner trying to show the reader that we are all like, or unlike, Miss Emily?

20. In his "Nobel Prize Acceptance Speech," Faulkner says that writing about "the human heart in conflict with itself" is what makes writing worthwhile. Write an essay in which you explain how Faulkner investigated internal conflict in either the narrator or Miss Emily in "A Rose for Emily."

Vocabulary Warm-up Word Lists

Study these words from the selections. Then, complete the activities.

Word List A

boulders [BOHL duhrz] *n.* large rocks
Being careful not to slip, we clambered over the wet boulders in the stream.

limp [LIMP] *adj.* drooping; lacking firmness or energy
After a hard day's work, my entire body felt limp with fatigue.

mischief [MIS chif] *n.* harm or damage; playful trick or prank; misbehavior
Tom Sawyer's aunt often suspected that he had been up to some mischief or other.

offense [uh FENS] *n.* wrong; occasion for disrespect
Tina's tactless remark did not mean to give any offense.

poise [POYZ] *n.* balance; confident, dignified bearing
Many of Kate's classmates admired her poise as a classical ballet dancer.

proclaimed [proh KLAYMD] *v.* formally announced
Memorial Day was proclaimed as a national holiday at end of the Civil War.

shed [SHED] *v.* to cast off
In our area, birches are some of the first trees to shed their leaves in early autumn.

subdued [suhb DOOD] *v.* conquered; vanished
In 1870, the Germans subdued the French in the Franco-Prussian War.

Word List B

abreast [uh BREST] *adv.* side by side
That road is wide enough for two vehicles to pass abreast.

artless [ART les] *adj.* naïve; straightforward
Darrell is so artless that the idea of lying would never occur to him.

downy [DOW nee] *adj.* soft
The downy snowflakes left a beautiful pattern of white on the streets.

forthwith [forth WITH] *adv.* immediately
Celebrations of the nation's victory should begin forthwith.

outright [OUT ryt] *adj.* unconditional
Lottie's will provided for outright bequests of $10,000 to each child.

rueful [ROO fuhl] *adj.* sorrowful; regretful
Sebastian was rueful when he admitted that he had not studied for the exam.

snarled [SNARLD] *v.* made a harsh, disagreeable noise
The chain saw snarled all afternoon as we worked to cut down the huge dead tree.

willfully [WIL fuhl ee] *adv.* stubbornly; irresponsibly
Chuck willfully made the dangerous trip rather than staying home.

Name _____ Date _____

Poems by Robert Frost
Vocabulary Warm-up Exercises

Exercise A *Fill in the blanks, using each word from Word List A only once.*

In his dream, Tom was up to [1] _____ again, playing hooky from

school. He officially [2] _____ to Ralph, his best friend, that the weather

was too nice to spend the day indoors studying reading and math. When Ralph objected

that they would be punished, Tom [3] _____ all his buddy's doubts by

pointing out that they could use their trip to the swimming hole as a field trip, collecting

rock samples for science class. The boys spent all morning jumping over the large

[4] _____ in the river. Before they [5] _____ their

clothes to go swimming, Tom insisted that they carry out their field trip mission. With

considerable [6] _____, he identified several types of mineral deposits in

the rocks. Ralph discovered a dead fish, lying [7] _____ at the bottom of

a shallow pool. "I wonder what it died of," he said. Tom suggested it might have been poi-

soned. Both boys knew it was a serious [8] _____ to let polluted run-off

get into the river, so they decided to report their finding at school the next day.

Exercise B *Decide whether each statement below is true or false. Circle T or F, and explain
your answer.*

1. If two vehicles can move <u>abreast</u> on a road, there is room for them side by side.
   T / F _____

2. An <u>artless</u> person is usually candid and honest.
   T / F _____

3. If something is <u>downy</u> to the touch, it is sharp or hard.
   T / F _____

4. An action that is ordered <u>forthwith</u> begins immediately.
   T / F _____

5. An <u>outright</u> gift is unconditional.
   T / F _____

6. Regret and sorrow are sometimes expressed by a <u>rueful</u> look on a person's face.
   T / F _____

7. An animal that has <u>snarled</u> at you should be avoided, because it is possibly dangerous.
   T / F _____

8. If your neighbors have acted <u>willfully</u>, you usually feel like praising them.
   T / F _____

Poems by Robert Frost
Reading Warm-up A

Read the following passage. Pay special attention to the underlined words. Then, read it again, and complete the activities. Use a separate sheet of paper for your written answers.

Another person might have felt sorry for Wayne, but Uncle Bob loudly <u>proclaimed</u> that only a fool would break his ankle on a raft trip. As soon as Wayne could walk in his cast, Uncle Bob sent him out to the cow barn to carry on with his chores.

Wayne knew that his uncle had a point. If it hadn't been for his own <u>mischief</u>, standing up and dancing around the raft like a clown, he would never have fallen in the river. He had committed the <u>offense</u> of stupidity, and the result was his broken ankle. As soon as he fell in the water, he found himself in a stretch of rapids. The water churned swiftly over rocks and <u>boulders</u> the size of wheelbarrows. He watched his body flop and twirl without <u>poise</u>, like a stuffed toy. Then his foot got caught on a rock and the pain made him lose his breath. He heard the snap of his ankle and then he lost track of where he was until he had washed up onshore.

Now he made his way toward the cow barn with a milk pail in his hand. The ankle cast made him <u>limp</u>, each step clumsy and painful. He wanted to throw the pail to the ground and curse, but he knew that his Uncle Bob would never stand for a temper tantrum, so he <u>subdued</u> himself, remaining calm.

To make matters worse, it was 90 degrees outside and he was already sweating. He <u>shed</u> his jeans jacket and kept moving toward the barn. He understood that he had made a stupid mistake, but wasn't it punishment enough to suffer through the broken ankle? In his Uncle Bob's world, being young was not an excuse.

1. Underline the words in this sentence that give a clue to the meaning of <u>proclaimed</u>. Use the word **proclaimed** in an original sentence.

2. Circle the words in this sentence that give a clue to the meaning of <u>mischief</u>. Use a word or phrase meaning the opposite of **mischief** in a sentence of your own.

3. Underline the words in this and the previous sentence that give a clue to the meaning of <u>offense</u>. What is a synonym for **offense**?

4. Circle the words that offer a clue to the meaning of <u>boulders</u> here. Are **boulders** usually large or small?

5. Circle the words in this sentence that offer a clue to the meaning of <u>poise</u>. What is a synonym for **poise**?

6. Underline the words in this sentence that give a clue to the meaning of <u>limp</u>. What are two antonyms for **limp**?

7. What is a synonym for <u>subdued</u>? Which words in this sentence hint at the meaning of **subdued**?

8. Underline the words in this and the previous sentence that hint at the meaning of <u>shed</u>. What is a synonym for the word **shed**?

Poems by Robert Frost
Reading Warm-up B

Read the following passage. Pay special attention to the underlined words. Then, read it again, and complete the activities. Use a separate sheet of paper for your written answers.

Writers use repetition for a variety of purposes. Repetition often serves to emphasize a point, for example, and within a short poem it can be especially meaningful. Robert Frost uses the device with special skill in some of his poems. For example, in "Mending Wall," he has the speaker repeat the first line, "Something there is that doesn't love a wall," at line 35. The speaker seems a bit sad, or even <u>rueful</u>, about the yearly ritual of repairing the wall. Another repetition balances this one, when the neighbor, perhaps a little stubbornly or <u>willfully</u>, insists that "good fences make good neighbors" (lines 27 and 45). The two sets of lines are like wagons traveling <u>abreast</u> on a road, parallel yet different.

In "Out, Out—", Frost uses the phrase "snarled and rattled" three times in the poem's opening lines. The verb <u>snarled</u> suggests that the buzz saw has come to life as an enemy, determined to injure the innocent, <u>artless</u> boy who handles it.

Finally, in "Stopping by Woods on a Snowy Evening," Frost closes the poem with two identical lines: "And miles to go before I sleep." The soft, <u>downy</u> flakes of snow and the dark beauty of the woods have lulled the speaker into a temporary sense of security and relaxation. He realizes, though, that he cannot make an <u>outright</u> surrender to the temptations of standing still or giving up. He must continue on <u>forthwith</u>, with an immediate resolution to keep life's promises and do his duty. The repetition underlines the speaker's renewed sense of commitment.

1. Underline the words that give a clue to the meaning of <u>rueful</u>. Write a sentence of your own using the word *rueful*.

2. Circle the words in this sentence that give a clue to the meaning of <u>willfully</u>. Use a word meaning the opposite of *willfully* in a sentence of your own.

3. What is a definition of the word <u>abreast</u>?

4. Underline the words in this sentence that give a clue to the meaning of <u>snarled</u>. Are the connotations of this word positive or negative?

5. What are two synonyms for the word <u>artless</u>? What are two antonyms for the word *artless*?

6. What is a synonym for <u>downy</u>? What is an antonym for the word *downy*?

7. Underline the words in this sentence that hint at the meaning of <u>outright</u>. Use the word *outright* in an original sentence.

8. Circle the word in this sentence that hints at the meaning of the word <u>forthwith</u>. What is an antonym for *forthwith*?

Name _____ Date _____

Robert Frost's Poetry
Literary Analysis: Blank Verse

Robert Frost was a versatile poet equally skilled at writing in rhymed and unrhymed formats. In his poem "Stopping by Woods on a Snowy Evening," for example, he uses the technique of rhyming first, second, and fourth lines until the final stanza which has end rhymes on all four lines:

> The woods are lovely, dark and deep,
> But I have promises to keep,
> And miles to go before I sleep,
> And miles to go before I sleep.

Despite this formal rhyme scheme, the poem has an unforced musical quality that reveals both the speaker's joy at the beauty of nature and his wistfulness at the many obligations he must fulfill before his day is done.

However, in "The Gift Outright," "Birches," and "'Out, Out—'," Frost writes in quite a different style. These poems are written in **blank verse,** which is composed of unrhymed lines of **iambic pentameter.** The basic unit of this type of meter is the iamb, which is made up of one unstressed syllable immediately followed by a stressed syllable. In iambic pentameter there are five iambs per poetic line. This meter recreates the flow of human speech patterns. Poems written in iambic pentameter, therefore, lend themselves especially to being read aloud.

DIRECTIONS: *Read the following excerpt from Robert Frost's poem "Birches." Underline each stressed syllable. Then read the excerpt aloud to observe especially the poem's rhythm.*

> And so I dream of going back to be.
> It's when I'm weary of considerations,
> And life is too much like a pathless wood
> Where your face burns and tickles with the cobwebs
> Broken across it, and one eye is weeping
> From a twig's having lashed across it open.

Robert Frost's Poetry
Reading Strategy: Read Blank Verse

Many of Robert Frost's poems are written in blank verse. With this type of poetry, it is a good idea to read the words aloud and track each sentence from beginning to end, rather than to pause at the end of each poetic line. By reading the poem as a group of sentences, readers can help themselves interpret and enjoy the rich meanings and the more subtle nuances of the words.

A. DIRECTIONS: *Reread the following passage from Robert Frost's poem "Acquainted with the Night." Then answer the questions below.*

I have stood still and stopped the sound of feet
When far away an interrupted cry
Came over houses from another street,

But not to call me back or say good-by;
And further still at an unearthly height
One luminary clock against the sky

Proclaimed the time was neither wrong nor right.

1. How many lines are there in the passage? _____
2. How many sentences are there in the passage? _____

B. DIRECTIONS: *As you read the six Frost poems, use this chart to note first the number of sentences in each one. Then remember to read the poems by pausing only at the ends of the sentences.*

Poem	Number of Sentences
"Birches"	
"Mending Wall"	
"'Out, Out—'"	
"Stopping by Woods on a Snowy Evening"	
"Acquainted with the Night"	
"The Gift Outright"	

Unit 5 Resources: Disillusion, Defiance, and Discontent
207

Robert Frost's Poetry
Vocabulary Builder

Using the Root *-lum-*

A. DIRECTIONS: *The following words contain the root -lum-, meaning "light." Look carefully at each word and its definition; then write a sentence in which you use the word. Pay close attention to the part of speech of each word.*

1. *luminary, n,* a person of prominence or brilliant achievement

    _____

    _____

2. *luminary, adj,* giving off light

    _____

    _____

3. *luminous, adj,* emitting or reflecting steady, suffused, or glowing light

    _____

    _____

4. *luminosity, n,* the quality or state of being luminous

    _____

    _____

5. *illuminate, vt,* 1: to enlighten spiritually or intellectually 2: to supply or brighten with light

    _____

    _____

Using the Word List

poise	rueful	luminary

B. DIRECTIONS: *Fill in each blank with the vocabulary word that best completes the sentence.*

1. The moon cast its _____ glow against the night sky.

2. In the poem "'Out, Out—,'" the young boy's first expression of shock about his accident is a _____ laugh.

3. The neighbor in the poem "Mending Wall" shows his _____ with the repeated comment "Good fences make good neighbors."

Name _____ Date _____

Robert Frost's Poetry
Grammar and Style: Uses of Infinitives

An **infinitive** is a common verb form that consists of the base verb preceded by the word *to*. Infinitives can function in a sentence as nouns, adjectives, or adverbs. The following line from Robert Frost's "Birches" contains an example of an infinitive used as a noun. The underlined infinitive is the direct object of the verb *prefer*.

I should prefer <u>to have</u> some boy bend them. . . .

The following line from "Stopping by Woods on a Snowy Evening" contains an infinitive used as an adverb, modifying *gives*.

He <u>gives</u> his harness bells a shake/<u>To ask</u> if there is some mistake.

An **infinitive phrase** consists of an infinitive plus its complements or modifiers.

A. PRACTICE: *Read the following sentences and underline the infinitive or infinitive phrase. Then in the blank, identify how it is used in the sentence: as a noun (N), an adjective (ADJ), or an adverb (ADV).*

_____ 1. "I'd like to get away from earth a while/And then come back to it and begin over."

_____ 2. "As he swung toward them holding up the hand,/Half in appeal, but half as if to keep/ The life from spilling. . . ."

_____ 3. "No more to build on there."

B. Writing Application: *Rewrite each of these sentences, replacing the underlined verb with an infinitive. Add or change other words in the sentence as necessary. The first one has been done for you.*

1. Robert Frost <u>gave</u> many speeches during his lifetime.
   Robert Frost was asked to give many speeches during his lifetime.
   _____

2. He often <u>wrote</u> about New Englanders and the rural landscape of the eastern part of the United States.
   _____

3. "Mending Wall" is about two neighbors <u>putting</u> up a fence between their property.
   _____

4. "Stopping by Woods on a Snowy Evening" is about a man pausing <u>and reflecting</u> on the beauty of nature.
   _____

Robert Frost's Poetry
Support for Writing

Prepare to write an introduction of a collection of Robert Frost's poetry. You may focus on the poems in this selection. Enter information about the poems in the graphic organizer below.

Poem	Style	Theme	Details that support theme
"Birches"			
"Stopping by Woods on a Snowy Evening"			
"Mending Wall"			
"Out, Out—"			
"The Gift Outright"			
"Acquainted With the Night"			

On a separate page, write a draft of your introduction to this collection of poetry. Tell why you have chosen these poems and develop your introduction paragraph by paragraph. When you revise, be sure your ideas are linked by clear transitions.

Robert Frost's Poetry
Support for Extend Your Learning

Listening and Speaking

Prepare to deliver a **eulogy** for the boy who dies in the poem "Out, Out—". Use these tips to help develop your ideas:

- Use clues in the poem to create a sense of the boy's personality.
- Pay tribute to the boy "who did a man's work."
- Address the boy's family politely, with sympathy.

Deliver your eulogy as part of a "memorial service" held in your classroom. Listen to the eulogies of your classmates and share your reactions.

Research and Technology

Find recordings of Frost reading his own poetry. Prepare an **interpretive presentation** using two of his poems. Take notes on the lines below to help you with your presentation.

Why I chose this poem:

_____

_____

_____

How Frost's reading of the poem affects me:

_____

_____

_____

What I notice most about this poem:

_____

_____

_____

After your presentation, ask listeners for feedback. Discuss their opinions about Frost's delivery.

Name _____ Date _____

Robert Frost's Poetry
Enrichment: Photography

Robert Frost was a great observer of nature and of the people who inhabited the New England countryside near where he spent much of his life. His astute observations of people and landscapes endow his poems with a unique and distinctly American sensibility. Note, for example, "Mending Wall," Frost's poetic depiction of two neighbors mending a wall between their properties. The poem begins with an assertion that nature rebels against fences and walls, as evidenced by the fact that over time the walls naturally fall down. The speaker of the poem, perhaps Frost himself, then argues that there is also something within human beings that rebels against walling apart the landscape. However, his neighbor's response is to repeat, in typical New England fashion, that "Good fences make good neighbors." The argument, friendly in tone but serious in intent, speaks volumes about the two men and their very different attitudes toward land and neighbors. Robert Frost's ability to create memorable poetry out of seemingly common scenes and situations secured him a reputation as one of America's finest and best-loved poets.

A. DIRECTIONS: *Look at the photographs that accompany "Birches," "Mending Walls," "Out, Out," and "Stopping by Woods on a Snowy Evening."*

1. Do you think these photographs make good illustrations for Frost's poems? Why or why not?

   _____

   _____

   _____

   Write a few sentences about each photograph. Tell what each photograph makes you think of and what emotions it brings to your mind.

2. Birch trees

   _____

   _____

3. Stone wall in a New England field

   _____

   _____

4. Barn building

   _____

   _____

5. Snow-covered New England landscape

   _____

   _____

B. DIRECTIONS: *Now choose one of the photographs—or another one of a landscape, building, or situation from your own experience—and create a poem about it on a separate piece of paper. You can use blank verse or a rhyme scheme. The important thing is to write something that re-creates the way you feel about your subject.*

Robert Frost's Poetry
Selection Test A

Critical Reading *Identify the letter of the choice that best answers the question.*

____ 1. In poetry, what is a characteristic of blank verse?
   A. It rhymes at the end of each line.
   B. It does not rhyme.
   C. It rhymes at the end of every other line.
   D. It is set to music.

____ 2. What is the main conflict in the speaker's mind in "Birches"?
   A. between friends and neighbors
   B. between fun and duty
   C. between childhood and adulthood
   D. between farming and logging

____ 3. What is the appropriate way to read poetry that is written in blank verse?
   A. Follow the punctuation.
   B. Read each line separately.
   C. Focus only on the images.
   D. Emphasize the rhymes.

____ 4. Which of these shows the correct emphasis if "Stopping By Woods on a Snowy Evening" were read aloud?
   A. WHOSE woods these are I think I know,
   B. His house is in the village THOUGH
   C. HE WILL NOT SEE me stopping here
   D. To WATCH his WOODS fill UP with SNOW

____ 5. In "Stopping By Woods on a Snowy Evening," why can't the poet stay in the woods?
   A. His horse is getting cold.
   B. The snow is getting heavier.
   C. He has other responsibilities.
   D. The owner would not approve.

____ 6. In "Mending Wall," what is it that doesn't love a wall that often grows around it or under it?
   A. elves
   B. cows
   C. nature
   D. neighbors

___ 7. Where does the accident with the saw take place in the poem "Out, Out—"?
   A. a farm
   B. a doctor's office
   C. a kitchen
   D. a city

___ 8. How does the family react to the boy's death in "Out, Out—"?
   A. They are grief-stricken.
   B. They accept it quietly.
   C. They blame the doctor.
   D. They plan his funeral.

___ 9. According to "The Gift Outright," to what place did most colonists feel loyal, even though they had come to a new land?
   A. the west
   B. Virginia
   C. Massachusetts
   D. England

___ 10. How do the rhyming lines in "Acquainted With the Night" tell you it is not blank verse?
   A. The lines are very short.
   B. It is a short poem.
   C. Blank verse has no rhyme.
   D. The poet uses the word "I."

___ 11. How many feet—each with one stressed and one unstressed syllable—are in this line from "Acquainted With the Night"?
   I have passed by the watchman on his beat
   A. five
   B. eight
   C. ten
   D. none

Vocabulary and Grammar

___ 12. Which word best replaces *poise* in this sentence: "She danced with grace and *poise*"?
   A. balance
   B. fear
   C. sadness
   D. loyalty

____ **13.** Which answer contains an infinitive phrase that contains the base form of a
verb?
  A. I brought the bird to its nest.
  B. He dragged the branch on the ground.
  C. He climbed to the top of the tree.
  D. I want to work with wood.

Essay

14. In the poem "Out, Out—" a boy in a farming family is cut by a buzz saw and dies.
The final two lines read: "And they, since they / Were not the one dead, turned to
their affairs." What do you think these lines mean about the boy's family? Are they
heartless? Or is his death something that they cannot control? Write a brief essay to
give your ideas.

15. In "Mending Wall," the speaker says, "Before I built a wall I'd ask to know / What I
was walling in or walling out." What does the speaker think of walls, based on these
lines? Write a brief essay to address these questions.

Robert Frost's Poetry
Selection Test B

Critical Reading *Identify the letter of the choice that best completes the statement or answers the question.*

____ 1. For the speaker in "Birches," what does swinging on birch trees most clearly symbolize?
A. a novel way to control and manipulate nature
B. a temporary return to a youthful, carefree state
C. a creative way to achieve and exercise virtue
D. a permanent escape from the physical, material world

____ 2. For the speaker of "Mending Wall," what does the wall itself most clearly symbolize?
A. suspicion, mistrust, and bias
B. safety, security, and strength
C. family, history, and custom
D. order, harmony, and discipline

____ 3. The neighbor in "Mending Wall" tells the speaker of the poem that good fences make good neighbors. What does he mean by this?
A. He doesn't want the speaker on his property.
B. He doesn't want to get to know the speaker any better.
C. He has had problems with other landowners in the past.
D. All the other neighbors have fences on their property.

____ 4. The buzz saw in "'Out, Out—'" most likely symbolizes
A. uncontrollable technology.
B. nature in its unspoiled state.
C. the inevitability of death.
D. order, discipline, and hard work.

____ 5. A central idea of "Stopping by Woods on a Snowy Evening" is the conflict between the attractions of
A. virtue and temptation.
B. solitude and society.
C. town and country.
D. duty and rest.

____ 6. For the speaker of "Acquainted With the Night," what does night itself most likely symbolize?
A. adventure and mystery
B. danger and peril
C. loneliness and doubt
D. protection and comfort

____ 7. What is an iamb?
A. five lines of poetry
B. unrhymed verse
C. one unstressed syllable followed by a stressed syllable
D. one line of blank verse

___ 8. What is the form of blank verse?
  A. unrhymed lines of iambic pentameter
  B. rhymed lines of iambic pentameter
  C. one unstressed syllable followed by a stressed syllable
  D. the flow of human speech

___ 9. Reading blank verse as a group of sentences rather than a group of poetic lines allows the reader to hear
  A. how the verse captures the poet's dense imagery.
  B. each individual iamb.
  C. how the verse captures the rhythm of human speech.
  D. the unstressed beats in the poem.

___ 10. For what reason does Robert Frost sometimes deviate from the blank-verse structure he has set up?
  A. to force the reader to hear the poem's stressed and unstressed syllables
  B. to emphasize an image, event, or idea
  C. to achieve metrical variety
  D. to make the poem easier to understand

___ 11. One of the best ways to understand a poem written in blank verse is to
  A. pick out key words in each line.
  B. figure out its rhyme scheme.
  C. mark the stressed and unstressed syllables.
  D. read it out loud as a group of sentences.

Vocabulary and Grammar

___ 12. A person who shows great *poise* is probably _____.
  A. confident
  B. happy
  C. nervous
  D. interesting

___ 13. If a person's facial expression is *rueful,* that person is probably experiencing _____.
  A. confusion
  B. joy
  C. regret
  D. pity

___ 14. Which of the following lines from "Birches" contains an infinitive?
  A. "When I see birches bend to left and right"
  B. "He always kept his poise / To the top branches, climbing carefully"
  C. "So was I once myself a swinger of birches."
  D. "And they seem not to break"

____ **15.** Which of the following lines from "Stopping by Woods on a Snowy Evening" does *not* use an infinitive as an adjective?
   A. "He will not see me stopping here / To watch his woods fill up with snow."
   B. "My little horse must think it queer / To stop without a farmhouse near."
   C. "He gives his harness bells a shake / To ask if there is some mistake."
   D. "The woods are lovely, dark, and deep, / But I have promises to keep"

____ **16.** If you describe the moon as *luminary*, you mean that it
   A. gives off heat.
   B. gives off light.
   C. is surrounded by bright stars.
   D. can be seen only at night.

____ **17.** What is an infinitive?
   A. a verb form
   B. a subject compound
   C. a subject complement
   D. a word root

Essay

18. As you read Frost's poems, you probably noted that they are often tinged with a feeling of regret. Many of Frost's poems contain a sense of rueful longing for lost childhood or for a bygone way of life. In an essay, discuss specific examples from the poems concerning this loss of innocence, the death of childhood, the end of life, the longing for a simpler way of life, and so on. Use quotations from the poems to illustrate your points. Why do you think such themes hold such mass appeal?

19. Robert Frost is famous for having written poems that seem simple but actually operate on a number of different emotional and intellectual levels. For example, in "Mending Wall," Frost depicts two neighbors with very different attitudes toward the fence line that divides their property. One, the speaker, proclaims that "Something there is that doesn't love a wall, that wants it down." The other, the speaker's neighbor, insists that "Good fences make good neighbors." Consider the two statements, and write an essay about the merits of each point of view. In what situations might the speaker's attitude about the unimportance of boundaries and walls backfire? How might the neighbor's unyielding stance about the necessity of defined boundaries cause problems? Discuss how these statements might be said to illustrate two common American points of view.

20. Most poets are known for more than one or two poems. Robert Frost wrote perhaps the greatest number of poems that are familiar to American readers. Of them, Frost called "Stopping by Woods on a Snowy Evening" his "best bid for remembrance." The poem excels in the three parts that Frost regarded as essential: the point or idea; the details that develop it; and the technique with which it is crafted. Write an essay in which you analyze Frost's "Stopping by Woods on a Snowy Evening," exploring each of these three parts. Be as specific as possible.

Study these words from the selections. Then, complete the activities.

Word List A

aspiration [as pi RAY shuhn] *n.* hope or goal for the future; strong ambition
It is Thelma's <u>aspiration</u> to become a research chemist.

ceased [SEESD] *v.* stopped
When the movie began, people in the audience <u>ceased</u> talking.

commendably [kuh MEN duh blee] *adv.* in a praiseworthy fashion
Janice, who skates <u>commendably</u>, won first prize in the competition.

compelled [kuhm PELD] *v.* forced; drove
A sense of duty <u>compelled</u> the hospital nurses to work overtime.

intervene [in ter VEEN] *v.* to come between
I must <u>intervene</u> to make peace between my brothers again.

perpetual [per PECH yoo uhl] *adj.* lasting for a long time; eternal
Tom has been on a <u>perpetual</u> diet and is finally losing weight.

retreat [ree TREET] *v.* to draw back; to withdraw or retire
Seeing that the position was hopeless, the general ordered his troops to <u>retreat</u>.

vigorous [VIG uhr uhs] *adj.* energetic
Will gave <u>vigorous</u> kicks as he swam the length of the pool.

Word List B

claustrophobia [klaw struh PHOH bee uh] *n.* fear of enclosed spaces
Aaron's <u>claustrophobia</u> prevents him from riding in elevators.

confines [KAHN fynz] *n.* inside space
You cannot smoke cigarettes within the <u>confines</u> of any public building.

implausible [im PLAW zuh buhl] *adj.* not believable
Don't give your teacher an <u>implausible</u> excuse for not doing your homework.

incomparable [in KAHM puh ruh buhl] *adj.* matchless
The restaurant served <u>incomparable</u> meals and soon became extremely popular.

insoluble [in SAHL yoo buhl] *adj.* not capable of being solved
<u>Insoluble</u> riddles keep everyone guessing for hours.

intuitively [in TOO uh tiv lee] *adv.* instinctively
Mark <u>intuitively</u> sensed his daughter's fear and put his arm around her.

transient [TRAN zhuhnt] *n.* person who moves from place to place
Bill has been a <u>transient</u> his entire adult life and has lived in 20 different states.

vagrant [VAY gruhnt] *n.* person who drifts around or lives on the street
That homeless man has been a <u>vagrant</u> for as long as I can remember.

Selections by James Thurber and E. B. White
Vocabulary Warm-up Exercises

Exercise A *Fill in the blanks, using each word from Word List A only once.*

Bill's teachers thought that, for an adolescent, he was [1] _____ focused on the future. Bill's goal or [2] _____ was for a career in politics and public service. He was a talented athlete, and his interest in a career in sports had not completely [3] _____. A realistic view, however, [4] _____ him to recognize that very few athletes are good enough to make it into the professional ranks. In addition, aging, injuries, and other factors often force pro athletes to [5] _____ to the sidelines. As a public servant in his community, Bill thought he could offer a(n) [6] _____ and creative program to improve civic life. College and graduate school, of course, would [7] _____ before he would run for public office. Although the years of further schooling stretched ahead like a(n) [8] _____ treadmill, Bill knew that if he worked hard, he could achieve his dream.

Exercise B *Revise each sentence so that the underlined vocabulary word is logical. Be sure to keep the vocabulary word in your revision.*

Example: Because the diagram was so intricate, we understood it at once.
Because the diagram was so intricate, we studied it carefully.

1. Because of her claustrophobia, she would not climb to the top of the hill.
   _____

2. The confines of a building are defined by the space around it.
   _____

3. Because the theory was so implausible, we put absolute trust in it.
   _____

4. She felt she gave an incomparable performance, and practiced hard to improve it.
   _____

5. When we realized the problem was insoluble, we continued to work on it.
   _____

6. A person who works intuitively depends heavily on his or her analytical ability.
   _____

7. Because he was a transient by nature, he decided to settle down in one place for a year.
   _____

8. He is known throughout the neighborhood as a vagrant, living in style in a mansion.
   _____

Selections by James Thurber and E. B. White
Reading Warm-up A

Read the following passage. Pay special attention to the underlined words. Then, read it again, and complete the activities. Use a separate sheet of paper for your written answers.

People were always telling Jimmy to quiet down or even to shut up, especially his teachers. In the classroom, Jimmy could not stop clowning, a <u>perpetual</u> stream of wisecracks issuing from his mouth. If someone made a mistake, Jimmy was the first to notice and point it out. If someone performed <u>commendably</u>, getting an answer right, Jimmy would make fun of the student for trying too hard. The joking and insults never <u>ceased</u>. Finally, his math teacher, Miss McCue, was <u>compelled</u> to send Jimmy to the principal's office for his behavior. When that didn't work, he was given two weeks' detention. Jimmy's father threatened to send him to a military academy if he didn't clean up his act, but nothing could make Jimmy <u>retreat</u> from his outrageous behavior.

What no one knew was that Jimmy's actions were part of a plan. He thought he was practicing for a future career as a stand-up comedian, an <u>aspiration</u> he'd had for a long time. He had seen them on TV, wild men who would say anything for a laugh, who never backed down or shied away from embarrassing the audience. In fact, the more controversial the subject, the more <u>vigorous</u> the comedian would be in his efforts to make people squirm. For Jimmy, the best jokes were the ones that made people so uncomfortable that all they could do was laugh.

But back in school, of course, he continued to have problems and was on the verge of being expelled. His teachers and fellow students did not appreciate being the targets of his humor, especially when he got too personal. Who would <u>intervene</u> and make him stop? There was a rumor going around now that the football team had a plan.

1. Underline the words in this sentence that give a clue to the meaning of <u>perpetual</u>. Use this word in a sentence of your own.

2. Circle the words in this sentence that give a clue to the meaning of <u>commendably</u>. What is a synonym for the word *commendably*?

3. What is a synonym for <u>ceased</u>? What is an antonym for the word *ceased*?

4. What is a synonym for <u>compelled</u>? Why was Miss McCue *compelled* to send Jimmy to the principal's office?

5. Circle the words in this sentence that offer a clue to the meaning of <u>retreat</u>. Use a word meaning the opposite of *retreat* in a sentence of your own.

6. Circle the words in this sentence that hint at the meaning of <u>aspiration</u>. What is a synonym for *aspiration*?

7. What is a synonym for <u>vigorous</u>? Use the word *vigorous* in an original sentence.

8. Underline the words in this sentence that give a clue to the meaning of <u>intervene</u>. What is an antonym for *intervene*?

Selections by James Thurber and E. B. White
Reading Warm-up B

Read the following passage. Pay special attention to the underlined words. Then, read it again, and complete the activities. Use a separate sheet of paper for your written answers.

What makes a good informal essay? James Thurber and E. B. White are among the masters of this literary form, and many critics consider that these writers produced underline{incomparable} or matchless essays. It may be true that certain writers excel <u>intuitively</u> at the essay: their instincts lead them unconsciously in the right direction. For the rest of us who profit by learning rules, however, there are a few helpful hints to keep in mind in writing an essay.

First, choose a subject that can be covered reasonably within the limited <u>confines</u> of a short piece. To discuss the true meaning of life within 500 words of so is an <u>implausible</u> task, and you sacrifice the reader's sense of interest and belief if you bite off more than you can chew. Huge questions are simply <u>insoluble</u> within the limits of an essay, so narrow your topic to ensure it is focused.

Second, give your writing a sense of movement. Some definitions of an essay speak of it as a search for self-discovery or as an effort to answer a question. Pace your writing so readers have a sense that you are moving toward a target. You don't want to seem like a <u>transient</u>, hopping around from topic to topic; however, you shouldn't seem like a <u>vagrant</u> either, wandering aimlessly in and around the topic's twists and turns.

Finally, put your personality into your writing. Essays are a good remedy for <u>claustrophobia</u>, since they are a means of escaping enclosed spaces. Reach out to your readers, giving them a sense that they are meeting you in person through your writing. Make your essay *personal* as vividly as you can.

1. Underline the words in this sentence that hint at the meaning of <u>incomparable</u>. What does the prefix *in-* mean in this word?

2. Circle the words in this sentence that hint at the meaning of <u>intuitively</u>. What is a synonym for *intuitively*?

3. Underline the words in this sentence that hint at the meaning of <u>confines</u>. Use *confines* in an original sentence.

4. Underline the word in this sentence that hint at the meaning of <u>implausible</u>. Use a word meaning the opposite of *implausible* in an original sentence.

5. Circle the words in this sentence that hint at the meaning of <u>insoluble</u>. What is an antonym for the word *insoluble*?

6. Circle the words in this sentence that give a good clue to the meaning of <u>transient</u>.

7. Underline the words in this sentence that hint at the meaning of <u>vagrant</u>. What is a synonym for *vagrant*?

8. Underline the words in this sentence that hint at the meaning of <u>claustrophobia</u>.

"The Night the Ghost Got In" by James Thurber
from **Here Is New York** by E. B. White

Literary Analysis: Informal Essay

You would probably agree that informal essays are fun to read because of their casual style, everyday language, and informal organization. Their subjects are usually clearly defined and down-to-earth. In **informal essays,** authors chat, digress as the spirit moves them, express their opinions, and reveal their personalities.

DIRECTIONS: *Read the following passages from "The Night the Ghost Got In" and "Here Is New York." Briefly describe what makes each passage characteristic of an informal essay. Use extra paper if you need to.*

1. "Glass tinkled into the bedroom occupied by a retired engraver named Bodwell and his wife. Bodwell had been for some years in rather a bad way and was subject to mild 'attacks.' Most everybody we know or lived near had *some* kind of attacks."

   _____

   _____

   _____

   _____

2. "One of them found an old zither that Roy had won in a pool tournament. 'Looky here, Joe,' he said, strumming it with a big paw. The cop named Joe took it and turned it over. 'What is it?' he asked me. 'It's an old zither our guinea pig used to sleep on,' I said. It was true that a pet guinea pig we once had would never sleep anywhere except on the zither, but I should never have said so. Joe and the other cop looked at me a long time. They put the zither back on a shelf."

   _____

   _____

   _____

   _____

3. "Every time the residents brush their teeth, millions of gallons of water must be drawn from the Catskills and the hills of Westchester. When a young man in Manhattan writes a letter to his girl in Brooklyn, the love message gets blown to her through a pneumatic tube—pfft—just like that."

   _____

   _____

   _____

   _____

Name _____ Date _____

Reading Strategy: Recognize Hyperbole

Hyperbole is a deliberate exaggeration or overstatement, often used for comic effect. By enlarging on details or stretching the reader's credence, the writer can create amusing characters and situations. Often, these lively exaggerations are juxtaposed with a mild, understated commentary that serves to highlight the ridiculous parts of the story.

On the lines following each of the passages from "The Night the Ghost Got In," write what is exaggerated in the passage and how the exaggeration adds to the humor of the story.

1. "'Awp,' he said, in the low, hopeless tone of a despondent beagle—"

   _____

   _____

   _____

   _____

2. "'Nothing,' he said, gruffly, but he was, in color, a light green."

   _____

   _____

   _____

   _____

3. "Bodwell was at the window in a minute, shouting, frothing a little, shaking his fist. 'We'll sell the house and go back to Peoria,' we could hear Mrs. Bodwell saying."

   _____

   _____

   _____

   _____

4. "'There were two or three of them,' mother said, 'whooping and carrying on and slamming doors.'"

   _____

   _____

   _____

   _____

5. "He bounded out of bed wearing a long flannel nightgown over long woolen underwear, a nightcap, and a leather jacket around his chest."

   _____

   _____

   _____

   _____

"The Night the Ghost Got In" by James Thurber
from **Here Is New York** by E. B. White
Vocabulary Builder

Using the Root *-terr-*

The root *-terr-* comes from the Latin word *terra*, meaning "earth." Many English words are formed from *-terr-* with a variety of suffixes and prefixes.

A. DIRECTIONS: *Fill each blank in the sentences below with one of the listed words. Then explain how the meaning is related to that of -terr-. Use a dictionary if necessary.*

terrace	terrestrial	terrier	territorial

1. Kelp is not a _____ plant because it grows in the ocean.

   _____

2. The wolf is a _____ animal because it defends the area where it lives.

   _____

3. The hunter waited as his _____ dug into the underground burrow.

   _____

4. Sliding doors opened onto a _____ at the back of the house.

   _____

Using the Word List

intuitively	blaspheming	aspiration
subterranean	claustrophobia	cosmopolitan

B. DIRECTIONS: *Select the Word List word that is related best to each situation or thing and write it in the blank.*

1. a series of caves located under the base of a mountain _____

2. someone trapped in a broken-down elevator _____

3. a homeowner accidentally hitting his thumb with a hammer _____

4. a student practicing hours every day to become a pianist _____

5. a restaurant serving foods of many nations _____

6. a detective following a hunch to question a minor suspect _____

"The Night the Ghost Got In" by James Thurber
from **Here Is New York** by E. B. White
Grammar and Style: Commas in Series

Writers sometimes string together details in a *series*—three or more parallel items linked together by commas. A conjunction such as *and* or *or* often comes before the final item. Some writers leave out the comma before that conjunction. However, to make your writing clear, you should always include a comma before the conjunction. Study these examples from the selections:

Thurber: Instantly the steps began again, circled the dining-room table like a man running, **and** started up the stairs toward us. . . .

White: . . . the great walls and towers rising, the smoke rising, the heat not yet rising, the hopes and ferments of so many awakening millions rising. . . .

A. PRACTICE: *Read the sentences below. Write* correct *on the line after each passage in which commas are correctly used. In the others, insert commas in the appropriate places.*

1. ". . . [D]oors were yanked open drawers were yanked open windows were shot up and pulled down furniture fell with dull thumps." _____

2. "They began to ransack the floor: pulled beds away from walls tore clothes off hooks in the closets pulled suitcases and boxes off shelves." _____

3. "[T]hey sit in stalled subways without claustrophobia they extricate themselves from panic situations by some lucky wisecrack they meet confusion and congestion with patience and grit. . . ." _____

B. Writing Application: *Read each group of sentences. Then combine them to form a single sentence made up of a series of items. Insert commas in the correct places.*

1. As I left for the airport, I turned on my alarm system. Then I danced out the door and slammed it joyfully behind me. I suddenly realized I had left all my keys on the kitchen counter.

_____

_____

2. A stuffed woodchuck in a lifelike pose dominated the shelf. The shelf also held a ceramic mug bearing the image of a long-forgotten politician. There was an assortment of dusty quartz crystals. Six or seven tiny plastic dolls were scattered like casualties on a battlefield. Last but not least, there was a grimy ball of aluminum foil the size of a human head.

_____

_____

Name _____ Date _____

"The Night the Ghost Got In" by James Thurber
from Here Is New York by E. B. White
Support for Writing

To prepare to write an **essay** to support E. B. White's statement that "The most widely appreciated humorists are those who create characters and tall tales," enter information from either piece of writing in the graphic organizer below.

Character or person:	Character or person:	Character or person:
_____	_____	_____
Why is he or she humorous?	Why is he or she humorous?	Why is he or she humorous?
_____	_____	_____
_____	_____	_____
_____	_____	_____
_____	_____	_____

What about this tale or essay is humorous? _____

_____

_____

_____

On a separate page, write your draft. Begin by responding with your opinion of White's statement. Then, add information about the characters or people in the Thurber story or essay. When you revise, add direct quotations to support your opinions.

"The Night the Ghost Got In" by James Thurber
from **Here Is New York** by E. B. White
Support for Extend Your Learning

Listening and Speaking

With a partner, create a **role play** of Thurber and White discussing their essays. Have them constructively criticize each other's work and talk about the writing of humor. Follow these tips:

- What makes the essays funny?
- In what ways are they similar?
- In what ways do they differ?
- What would you add or change?
- What is each person's "philosophy" about humor?

Present your role play to the class and ask for helpful feedback.

Research and Technology

Find information on the Internet about "The Algonquin Roundtable," a group of humorists who wrote for the *New Yorker.* Collect information about some of the writers who belonged to this group.

"The Algonquin Roundtable"

Writer Who Was a Member	Best Known For

Use a separate page to deliver your findings as a **written report** to your classmates.

Name _____ Date _____

"The Night the Ghost Got In" by James Thurber
from Here Is New York by E. B. White
Enrichment: The Police

The mother in "The Night the Ghost Got In" has to use her wits to summon the police when the suspicion of burglars keeps her from venturing downstairs to make a phone call. Today, extension and portable phones would have made her innovative solution unnecessary. The dangers Thurber's police faced in confronting an unstable family member, although humorously presented, are serious and at least as real now as they were in the 1930s.

DIRECTIONS: *Think about the people who are responsible for protecting law and order in today's communities. Use the incidents involving the police in "The Night the Ghost Got In" as a framework for an essay discussing police and their work today. Do research and use your own personal experience (not what you've seen on TV or in films) to jot down some answers to the following questions. Then use these answers to help you write your essay.*

1. What methods and technical devices do people have to summon the police to their homes or to report a crime today?

   _____

   _____

   _____

2. What are other answers to crime protection used in your own neighborhood or community?

   _____

   _____

   _____

3. What do you think police would do today if they were summoned to a home where a burglary was possibly in progress? Would they use the same methods as Thurber's cops? How might they interact with the people living in the home?

   _____

   _____

   _____

4. How could today's police officers handle upset or agitated people more effectively than Thurber's cops handled the grandfather?

   _____

   _____

   _____

5. These days, how the do police officers protect themselves against dangerous encounters like the one with the grandfather?

   _____

   _____

   _____

Name _____ Date _____

"**The Night the Ghost Got In**" by James Thurber
from **Here Is New York** by E. B. White
Selection Test A

Critical Reading *Identify the letter of the choice that best answers the question.*

____ 1. What is the subject of the informal essay titled "The Night the Ghost Got In"?
   A. the author's neighbors
   B. the author's strange family
   C. the behavior of the police
   D. the behavior of friends

____ 2. What is the likely meaning of the hyperbole in "The Night the Ghost Got In" that stretches the truth by saying that most of the family's neighbors had "*some kind of attacks*"?
   A. The family lived near a hospital.
   B. The family knew lots of sick people.
   C. The family members were often sick.
   D. The family made others nervous.

____ 3. In "The Night the Ghost Got In," why does the author's mother try to throw a second shoe at the neighbors' window?
   A. She was thrilled by throwing the first one.
   B. She is scared by the "burglars."
   C. She doesn't like the neighbors.
   D. She hopes to hit one of the "burglars."

____ 4. In "The Night the Ghost Got In," who first hears the steps in the dining room as he is upstairs stepping out of the bathtub?
   A. the author's brother Herman
   B. the author's mother
   C. the author
   D. the author's grandfather

____ 5. What conclusion can you draw about the grandfather in "The Night the Ghost Got In," based on his grabbing a gun to attack the police?
   A. He has served in the Army.
   B. He thinks there is a ghost.
   C. He can sleep through anything.
   D. He wants to catch the burglars.

6. In "The Night the Ghost Got In," what does the author's casual style tell readers about him?
   A. He is embarrassed by his family.
   B. He is often angry at his family.
   C. He overreacts to the slightest event.
   D. He is used to his family's strangeness.

7. According to *Here is New York*, what is the author's view of New York City?
   A. It is a city that people only want to visit.
   B. It is a city like no other city in the world.
   C. It is a city he tries to avoid at all costs.
   D. It is a city with far too many people.

8. What is a main idea in *Here is New York*?
   A. New York has many tall buildings.
   B. New York is a city of smaller cities.
   C. New York is full of non New Yorkers.
   D. New York is like Paris and London.

9. Which of these ideas from *Here Is New York* is meant to be hyperbole, in which the reader knows the author is stretching the truth?
   A. Every facility in New York is overcrowded.
   B. Other cities are unlike New York.
   C. New York has skyscrapers.
   D. There are many barbershops in New York.

10. What is the author's view of New Yorkers in *Here Is New York*?
   A. They spend their summers elsewhere.
   B. They can handle any challenge.
   C. They would prefer a smaller city.
   D. They become upset very easily.

11. What does the author of *Here is New York* say makes up for New York's hazards?
   A. its size
   B. its streets
   C. its uniqueness
   D. its restaurants

Vocabulary and Grammar

____ 12. Which word best replaces *subterranean* in this sentence: "The trains travel a *subterranean* route under the city's streets"?

    A. underground

    B. loud

    C. upward

    D. frightening

____ 13. Which sentence contains an example of commas used to separate a series?

    A. When I got to the attic, people were confused.

    B. New Yorkers are usually quite calm, even when things go wrong.

    C. There's no place left to build, if you're looking at the ground.

    D. He wore pajamas, a cap, and socks to sleep in.

Essay

14. In "The Night the Ghost Got In," do you think the behavior of the police is believable? Would they behave this way in real life? Why or why not? Write a brief essay to give your opinions, using examples from the story.

15. What does E. B. White think of New Yorkers, according to *Here is New York*? What examples can you give to show his attitude toward people who live in New York? Write a brief essay to give your ideas.

Name _____ Date _____

"The Night the Ghost Got In" by James Thurber
from **Here Is New York** by E. B. White
Selection Test B

Critical Reading *Identify the letter of the choice that best completes the statement or answers the question.*

_____ 1. Writers often create humor by depicting serious events in a comic light. Which aspect of "The Night the Ghost Got In" would not be amusing without Thurber's embellishment?
    A. the unidentified sound in the house
    B. the mother breaking the neighbor's window
    C. the grandfather bounding out of bed in his nightshirt and leather jacket
    D. the behavior of the police

_____ 2. Thurber notes that his "grandfather was in the attic, in the old walnut bed which, as you will remember, once fell on my father." How does this detail contribute to the essay's humor?
    A. It helps the reader identify with the experience Thurber describes.
    B. Thurber displays his conversational style in this detail.
    C. Thurber exaggerates the importance of the bed.
    D. It emphasizes the family's tendency toward mishaps.

_____ 3. Which aspect of the interaction between Thurber's mother and Mr. Bodwell is an example of hyperbole?
    A. the narrator's mother shouting "Burglars!"
    B. Mr. Bodwell "shouting, frothing a little, shaking his fist"
    C. Mr. Bodwell being confused about where the burglars were
    D. the narrator's mother wanting to throw another shoe

_____ 4. What does the cop mean to say when he tells his colleagues that the mother seems "historical"?
    A. horticultural
    B. hospitable
    C. hysterical
    D. hypocritical

_____ 5. Which of the following statements best summarizes the theme of "The Night the Ghost Got In"?
    A. A small misunderstanding can have extreme implications.
    B. The police are not as dependable as they are expected to be.
    C. People who seem to be out of touch with reality are often quite sane.
    D. Jumping too quickly to conclusions usually leads to trouble.

_____ 6. What is the most significant contribution of Thurber's shower to the subsequent events in the essay?
    A. The shower prevents him from hearing the footsteps clearly.
    B. His lack of clothes makes the police suspicious of him.
    C. His naked state keeps his mother from letting in the police.
    D. The towel around his waist makes his grandfather think he is a deserter.

_____ 7. Thurber uses hyperbole in presenting the actions of the police when he
   A. creates the impression that they destroy the house in their search for the burglar.
   B. relates their disappointment at finding no clues.
   C. tells how they lock the grandfather in the attic.
   D. describes their quick reaction to the creaking in the attic.

_____ 8. In "The Night the Ghost Got In," which detail is a digression that has little purpose other than comic effect
   A. the footsteps
   B. the narrator's towel
   C. the shoe
   D. the zither

_____ 9. What is E. B. White's meaning in this sentence about New York?
   Each area is a city within a city within a city.

   A. New York has many governmental bodies.
   B. New York has a variety of ethnic and cultural groups.
   C. New York has small neighborhoods, each of which is almost self-sufficient.
   D. New York has huge apartment buildings that residents hardly ever leave.

_____ 10. Which of the following excerpts from White's essay is an example of hyperbole?
   A. "The oft-quoted thumbnail sketch of New York is, of course: 'It's a wonderful place, but I'd hate to live there.'"
   B. "Let him walk two blocks from his corner and he is in a strange land and will feel uneasy till he gets back."
   C. "Manhattan has been compelled to expand skyward because of the absence of any other direction in which to grow."
   D. "To an outlander a stay in New York can be and often is a series of small embarrassments and discomforts and disappointments."

_____ 11. What informal essay characteristic does this *Here Is New York* excerpt exemplify?
   I have an idea that people from villages and small towns, people accustomed to the convenience and the friendliness of neighborhood over-the-fence living, are unaware that life in New York follows the neighborhood pattern.

   A. loose organization
   B. expression of the author's opinion
   C. tendency to digress
   D. clear purpose to entertain

_____ 12. Which sentence best states E. B. White's opinion about New York?
   A. It is a majestic city of which all Americans can be proud.
   B. It is one of the world's most sophisticated and charming cities.
   C. It is fascinating, complex, difficult—and there is no other city like it.
   D. It is hot, difficult, and too big, with nothing of interest to anyone except tourists.

____ 13. Which line most strongly suggests that the *Here Is New York* excerpt is an informal essay?
   A. "But the curious thing about New York is that each large geographical unit is composed of countless small neighborhoods."
   B. "This, more than any other thing, is responsible for its physical majesty."
   C. "The city is literally a composite of tens of thousands of tiny neighborhood units."
   D. "It is a miracle that New York works at all. The whole thing is implausible."

Vocabulary and Grammar

____ 14. When E. B. White describes the smoke-fog from New Jersey as "leaving the high offices suspended, men groping and depressed, and the sense of world's end," he is using
   A. a digression.
   B. informal language.
   C. commas in series.
   D. conversational style.

____ 15. Choose the pair that best expresses a relationship similar to that in the pair in capital letters.
      SUBTERRANEAN : SUBMARINE ::
   A. buried : sunken
   B. cold : damp
   C. terrestrial : floating
   D. dirty : clean

____ 16. Choose the pair that best expresses a relationship similar to that in the pair in capital letters.
      FEAR : CLAUSTROPHOBIA ::
   A. year : hour
   B. disease : measles
   C. anger : emotion
   D. food : diet

____ 17. The word that best describes how Mrs. Thurber approached the events retold in "The Night the Ghost Got In" is _____.
   A. claustrophobically
   B. blasphemously
   C. intuitively
   D. fearfully

Essay

18. Eccentric characters are one of the traditional features of humorous writing. Usually these characters act in ways that stretch the bounds of credibility without becoming completely preposterous. In Thurber's "The Night the Ghost Got In," the narrator's mother and grandfather fit this description. Write an essay in which you describe the personalities and actions of the narrator's mother and grandfather. Comment on their believability.

19. One critic said of E. B. White, "His interests are broad—nothing, it seems, that is human is alien to him. His eye and intelligence see what lies beneath the surface." In an essay, discuss how *Here Is New York* supports these points, citing specific examples from the text. What does "nothing . . . human is alien to him" imply?

Unit 5: Disillusion, Defiance, and Discontent
Benchmark Test 8

MULTIPLE CHOICE

Literary Analysis and Reading Skills

1. What do the first-person point of view and limited third-person point of view have in common?
   A. The narrator is part of the action and refers to himself with the pronoun *I*.
   B. The narrator is not part of the action and refers to characters as *he* or *she*.
   C. The narrator provides just one character's thoughts and impressions of story events.
   D. The narrator provides many characters' thoughts and impressions of story events.

2. What does stream-of-consciousness writing try to capture?
   A. the natural flow of characters' thoughts
   B. the natural rhythm of everyday speech
   C. the experiences and outlook of childhood
   D. the social concerns important to the author

3. What is the basic unit of meter in poetry called?
   A. a foot
   B. an iamb
   C. iambic pentameter
   D. blank verse

4. Which of these choices is most clearly an example of an internal conflict?
   A. the main character is a farmer who hides her family during a tornado
   B. the main character is a reformer who fights against unjust laws
   C. the main character is a student who comes to an important decision
   D. the main character is a police detective who tracks down a wanted criminal

5. Which of the following characteristics is typical of an informal essay?
   A. It addresses a broad subject.
   B. It rarely strays from the main point of the essay.
   C. It is tightly organized.
   D. It gives you a glimpse of the writer's personality.

6. Which of the following is an example of hyperbole?
   A. "Yes, it did sting a little," said the stuntman after leaping out of a speeding car.
   B. Take the child's toy, and you'll be treated to a torrent of tears rivaling Niagara Falls.
   C. He broke her vase and her heart.
   D. In this case, it is cruel to be kind: Just tell him the bad news.

Name _____ Date _____

Read this story. Then, answer the questions that follow.

"Hartsoles was started by my grandfather, and someone in the family has to be the main shareholder—it's tradition." Lucy Hart was furious. "I will not let that weasel, Joe Campion, buy up more stock."

For the next three months, Lucy worked hard to raise funds. She obtained loans from her local bank and two others. Three Hart cousins promised to sell their stock to her rather than to Joe Campion.

By June, Lucy was ready to tell Campion that she, not he, would be the main shareholder. She couldn't wait for the board meeting. Campion would be there—the slimy sneak. She would tell him off.

Entering the elegant wood-paneled room, Lucy was ready. She sat at the head of the table, waiting for Campion to appear. But surprisingly, Campion never showed up. Later, Lucy learned he had stopped trying to buy Hartsoles weeks ago.

7. From what point of view is the story told?
   A. first person, only from the point of view of Lucy Hart
   B. first person, from the point of view of Joe Campion
   C. third person, limited to the thoughts and impressions of Lucy Hart
   D. third person, providing the thoughts and impressions of several characters

8. What is the central conflict of the story?
   A. Lucy's external conflict with Joe Campion, whom she wants to keep from buying the family business
   B. Lucy's external conflict with a society that puts limits women's achievements in the corporate world
   C. Lucy's internal conflict to choose between devoting her time to her family business or her home life
   D. Lucy's internal conflict to recognize that she is fighting a losing battle in trying to keep family tradition alive

9. What makes the climax an anticlimax?
   A. Readers realize that Hartsoles is a worthless company.
   B. Readers realize that Campion has lost interest in Hartsoles.
   C. Readers realize that Lucy Hart is a very foolish person.
   D. Readers realize that the other shareholders have tricked Lucy.

10. Which of these experiences would best help a reader relate to the character of Lucy?
   A. buying a comfortable pair of shoes
   B. getting a loan from a bank
   C. sitting at the head of a large table
   D. being concerned about family tradition

Read this stanza from "To Helen" by Edgar Allan Poe. Then, answer the questions that follow.

> Helen, thy beauty is to me
>   Like those Nicean barks of yore,
> That gently, o'er a perfumed sea,
>   That weary, way-worn wanderer bore
>   To his own native shore.

Unit 5 Resources: Disillusion, Defiance, and Discontent

11. What example of apostrophe does the stanza contain?
    A. It addresses Helen as if she is really present and listening to the speaker.
    B. It addresses Helen's beauty as if her beauty is a person capable of hearing.
    C. It addresses the Nicean barks of yore as if they are people who can hear.
    D. It addresses the wanderer as if he is present and listening to the speaker.

12. What central comparison does the simile in this stanza make?
    A. It compares Helen to the Nicean barks of yore.
    B. It compares Helen's beauty to the Nicean barks of yore.
    C. It compares Helen to a weary, way-worn wanderer.
    D. It compares the perfumed sea to the shore reached by the wanderer.

13. Which statement best paraphrases the stanza?
    A. Helen, your beauty is like ancient Nicean boats on a sweet-smelling sea that gently carry a tired wanderer home.
    B. Helen's beauty, you are like ancient Nicean boats that carry a traveler across a sweet-smelling sea to land.
    C. Helen, you are like those old Nicean boats that transport perfume and weary wanderers to their home countries.
    D. Helen, you are like that Nicean breed of dog that brings perfume to weary travelers at sea longing to reach home.

Read this selection from a story. Then, answer the questions that follow.

Soon after they left Chicago, the land grew flat as a pancake. The suburbs faded away, and they passed cornfield after cornfield. "We could buy an old farm and move out here," Jonathan told her. "It would be a nice, peaceful place for you to write."

Deb stared at the passing landscape. She remembered the same flat land from her own childhood in Colorado. Her father had loved ranch life. She remembered how he used to sing as he worked in the fields.

Yes, this part of Illinois had the same look. Didn't Abe Lincoln grow up around here? Was it here that he had made his long walks to school? She remembered waiting for the school bus back in Colorado. The land was so flat you could see the bus for miles. She turned to Jonathan. "Of course we can live here, darling. It would be a lovely change."

14. Where in the selection does Deb's stream of consciousness start?
    A. the sentence beginning, "The suburbs faded away"
    B. the sentence, "Deb stared at the passing landscape"
    C. the sentence beginning, "She remembered the same flat land"
    D. the sentence beginning, "She remembered waiting for the school bus"

15. Which of these events in the selection came first?
    A. Deb and Jonathan leaving Chicago
    B. Deb's family settling in Colorado
    C. Deb's father singing while he worked
    D. Deb agreeing to live on the prairie

16. Which detail is ambiguous in this portion of the selection?
    A. why they might move
    B. what town they will move to
    C. whether Deb will agree to move
    D. who wants to move

17. From the details provided, which of these predictions do you think is the most likely to occur later in the selection?
    A. Deb and Jonathan will move to this part of Illinois.
    B. Deb and Jonathan will argue about moving.
    C. Deb will read a book about Abe Lincoln.
    D. Deb will become a famous writer.

Read these opening lines from "Thanatopsis" by William Cullen Bryant. Then, answer the questions that follow.

> To him who in the love of nature holds
> Communion with her visible forms, she speaks
> A various language; for his gayer hours
> She has a voice of gladness, and a smile
> And eloquence of beauty, and she glides
> Into his darker musing, with a mild
> And healing sympathy, that steals away
> Their sharpness, ere he is aware.

18. What verse form does the poem use?
    A. blank verse
    B. free verse
    C. rhymed couplets
    D. sonnet

19. In reading these lines of the poem, where should you make your first two pauses?
    A. after *holds* and *speaks*
    B. after *holds* and *forms*
    C. after *speaks* and *forms*
    D. after *forms* and *language*

20. How might you best respond to the message in these lines of the poem?
    A. by thinking about the way nature can reflect your moods
    B. by thinking about the harm that natural disasters can cause
    C. by thinking about the way ancient peoples worshipped nature
    D. by thinking about the effects of pollution on the environment

Vocabulary

21. Based on your understanding of the root -temp- and the context clues in this sentence, what do you do think *temporal* means?

    As a young man, he worried about *temporal*, everyday concerns.

    A. angry
    B. long lasting
    C. uncontrollable
    D. not permanent

22. From your knowledge of Latin prefixes, what do you think a *subbasement* is?
    A. a basement level below the main basement in a building
    B. a basement level above the main basement in a building
    C. a basement room behind the main basement level in a building
    D. a basement room in front of the main basement level in a building

23. Based on your understanding of the prefix *in-* and the root -val-, what is an *invalid* argument?
    A. one that goes on for a long time
    B. one that ends in friendship
    C. one that ends in bitter anger
    D. one that makes little or no sense

24. From your understanding of the prefix *in-* and the root -terr-, who is most likely to *inter* a human body?
    A. a doctor
    B. a sculptor
    C. a personal trainer
    D. an undertaker

25. Which of these is the most likely term for a unit used to measure the flow of light?
    A. satis
    B. dys
    C. lumen
    D. brute

Grammar

26. Which sentence contains a participial phrase?
    A. Walking five miles a day is healthy exercise.
    B. My dad is participating in a charity walk on Saturday.
    C. Marisa tired after she went just a few miles.
    D. Tired after a few miles, Marisa quit the walk.

Name _____ Date _____

27. Which sentence is punctuated correctly?
   A. Ernest Hemingway working as a war correspondent witnessed the Spanish Civil War.
   B. Ernest Hemingway William Faulkner and Pearl S. Buck all won the Nobel Prize.
   C. Thomas Wolfe grew up in North Carolina; he later moved away.
   D. "I have led a full life", said Granny Weatherall.

28. Which sentence is punctuated correctly?
   A. The two sisters joined the town pool; Alice is the one, wearing the purple swimsuit.
   B. I always bring a towel, sunscreen and a folding chair to the pool.
   C. "Did your cousin join the pool"? Anita asked.
   D. Lionel responded, "Alex joined last Thursday."

29. What is the subject complement in this sentence?

   Eudora Welty was a talented writer from the American South.

   A. talented
   B. writer
   C. American
   D. South

30. Which of these sentences is correctly labeled according to its type?
   A. Robert Frost recited a poem at President Kennedy's inauguration—interrogative
   B. Did you ever hear a recording of Frost reciting his own poetry?—exclamatory
   C. Read along as you listen to him recite the poem.—imperative
   D. What a wonderful poet he is!—declarative

31. Which of these sentences includes an infinitive phrase functioning as a noun?
   A. I love to read humorous essays.
   B. I have one essay to read as a school assignment.
   C. I brought the textbook to the park with me.
   D. One writer to savor for his humor is James Thurber.

ESSAY

32. Think of two works of literature that have common plots or subjects but are different in other ways. It might be something you read in your textbook or a work from the library or someplace else. On your paper or on a separate sheet, write a brief comparison-and-contrast essay that serves as a critical response or critical review of the two works.

33. On your paper or on a separate sheet, write a memorial speech that could have been delivered at the funeral of a favorite author. The person you choose can be an author in your textbook or another favorite from your outside reading.

34. Create a stream-of-consciousness passage that presents the thoughts, memories, and associations of a fictional character. The character could be someone that you create from your imagination, or it could be someone whom you have already read about.

Unit 5: Disillusion, Defiance, and Discontent
Diagnostic Test 9

MULTIPLE CHOICE

Read the selection. Then, answer the questions that follow.

Wild animals have fascinated people in every culture for thousands of years. In ancient Egypt, wild animals were regarded as treasures, and people often gave them as gifts to the pharoahs. In fact, Queen Hatshepsut received so many wild animals as gifts that she created a zoo in 1500 B.C. to safely house her collection.

In the centuries that followed, rulers in China, Northern Africa, Asia, India, Mexico, and Europe established private menageries to house the animals they had received. The size and scope of each menagerie indicated the extent of the ruler's power and wealth. Sadly, most rulers confined their animals in pens. Only a few created parklike environments to duplicate the actual living conditions the animals experienced in nature. One such leader was Wen Wang of China, who in 1000 B.C. built the vast Garden of Intelligence to afford his wild animals freedom of movement and natural habitats.

The ancient Romans captured wild animals to create spectacles. Legions of people crowded into public arenas to watch lions, tigers, elephants, leopards, and bears fight each other. In some events, men known as gladiators fought against wild animals. The Romans also punished prisoners by throwing them into dens filled with lions. Such "games" and other gory spectacles continued for more than 500 years. No one seemed concerned about such cruel treatment of animals, and the term *endangered species* did not yet exist.

1. Based on the selection, which is the most accurate definition of *pharoah*?
   A. a wild animal native to Egypt
   B. a parklike habitat for captive animals
   C. a ruler, such as a king or queen
   D. something precious, like a rare jewel

2. Based on the selection, what is the most probable reason that a ruler would want to have a menagerie that was larger than those of other rulers?
   A. to emphasize his or her greater power and wealth
   B. to give the captive animals large cages
   C. to show respect for other rulers
   D. to please his or her children

3. In what important way was Wen Wang's menagerie different from that of most rulers?
   A. Wen Wang's animals lived in large cages.
   B. Wen Wang's animals lived in natural habitats.
   C. It was a private menagerie rather than a public menagerie.
   D. It had far more elephants than the menageries of other rulers.

4. The word *spectacles* is a multiple-meaning word. What does it mean in the sentence *The ancient Romans captured wild animals to create spectacles*?
   A. activities that make a person look foolish or silly
   B. a pair of eyeglasses
   C. extravagant public shows, like circuses or fiestas
   D. unusual displays, as in an art museum

5. Based on the selection, which statement is accurate?
   A. The size of the crowds shows that Roman people did not approve of the animal fights.
   B. The Romans were generally not cruel toward wild animals.
   C. The Romans had a deep understanding of the term *endangered species*.
   D. Animal fights were considered great entertainment in ancient Rome.

6. Based on the selection, what is a gladiator?
   A. a soldier who defends his country
   B. a person who fights animals or other men
   C. a prisoner
   D. a person who captures wild animals

7. What is the most probable reason that the author of this selection used quotation marks in the phrase *Such "games" and other gory spectacles*?
   A. to quote the words of another person
   B. to set off the title of a work from the rest of the sentence
   C. to indicate the definition of a nearby word
   D. to stress that the Romans' games were far more deadly than modern games

Read the selection. Then, answer the questions that follow.

Unlike many ancient civilizations, which considered wild animals only as sources of entertainment, the ancient Greeks took great care to make sure their captured wild animals were treated humanely. They created large public zoos, and charged people admission in order to support the care and nourishment of the animals. Students were expected to make regular visits to these zoos, and to dedicate themselves to the study of plants and animals. In addition, great teachers, such as Aristotle, routinely held classes and lectures at the zoos, creating public awareness and scholarly attention to the needs and habits of wild creatures.

In the late fifteenth century, European explorers brought back exotic species of animals and birds from the New World. Most of these animals were bought by wealthy people and kept on their private estates. European zoos opened to the public in the 1800s. Sadly, they featured row upon row of small cages, where animals lived under harsh conditions.

In the twentieth century, the emotional and physical needs of captive animals were finally addressed when travel, television documentaries, and nature specials all helped to raise public awareness about animal welfare and endangered species. As a result, zoos stopped being cramped sideshows and developed instead into centers for conservation, preservation, and education.

8. According to the selection, in what important way were the Greeks different from many other ancient civilizations?
   A. They treated their captive wild animals humanely.
   B. They considered wild animals to be a major source of entertainment.
   C. They created laws to prohibit cruelty to animals.
   D. They kept wild animals as pets in their homes.

9. Based on the selection, who was Aristotle?
   A. a zookeeper in ancient Greece
   B. a ruler in ancient Greece
   C. a scientist in ancient Greece
   D. a great teacher in ancient Greece

10. According to the selection, which of the following statements is accurate?
   A. In Greece, zoos were built on private estates.
   B. The Greeks perceived of zoos as places to learn about animals.
   C. The Greeks imported many exotic creatures from India and other parts of the world.
   D. The Greeks did not really care about the welfare of animals.

11. In the sentence *European explorers brought back exotic species of animals and plants from the New World*, what is the meaning of *exotic*?
   A. colorful
   B. strange and fascinating
   C. wild and fierce
   D. weak or sick

12. What happened to most of the animals that the explorers brought back to Europe from the New World?
   A. Scholars studied them to learn more about their needs and habits.
   B. They became circus performers and toured throughout Europe.
   C. They lived in public park settings, in vast natural habitats.
   D. Wealthy people bought them and kept them as pets on their private estates.

13. According to the selection, in what important way were the zoos of Europe different from the zoos of ancient Greece?
   A. Many animals in the European zoos were poorly treated.
   B. Many animals in the European zoos were treated humanely.
   C. Thanks to the European zoos, public awareness about endangered species flourished.
   D. Visitors to the European zoos had to pay steep admission fees.

14. According to the selection, what effect have modern television documentaries had on animal welfare?
   A. Several zoos have closed due to the critical reports of television documentaries.
   B. Thanks to television documentaries, new laws now protect the natural habitats of wild animals.
   C. Thanks to television documentaries, the public is more aware of the need to preserve endangered species.
   D. Thanks to television documentaries, more people now keep wild animals as pets.

15. What contrast is suggested by the terms *cramped sideshows and centers of conservation, preservation, and education*?
   A. Zoos are generally larger today than they used to be.
   B. Most zoos are now places for study rather than poorly run centers for entertainment.
   C. Most zoos used to be owned by entertainers, but now they are owned by teachers.
   D. Most zoos used to have small, crowded cages, but modern zoos have bigger cages.

Vocabulary Warm-up Word Lists

Study these words from the selection. Then, complete the activities.

Word List A

angelic [an JEL ik] *adj.* very well behaved; resembling an angel
  Aidan was an angelic baby, almost never waking her parents at night.

avarice [AV uh ris] *n.* greed
  Long ago, the miser succumbed to avarice and hoarded his money obsessively.

consciousness [KAHN shuhs nes] *n.* awareness
  Ted's consciousness of danger increased sharply when the bear growled at him.

duration [doo RAY shuhn] *n.* length or span of time in which something happens
  A cold drizzle fell for the entire duration of the football game.

experimentally [eks per i MEN tuhl ee] *adv.* in a fashion marked by trial and error
  Scientists often perform their work experimentally, testing various alternatives.

monarch [MAHN ark] *n.* ruler
  One noteworthy English monarch was Queen Elizabeth I.

realm [RELM] *n.* kingdom
  Queen Elizabeth I was universally respected and often loved throughout her realm.

tingled [TING uhld] *v.* set on edge with excitement
  The movie was so suspenseful that we tingled with excitement.

Word List B

brazenness [BRAY zuhn nes] *n.* shameful or shocking boldness; audacity
  Mario's brazenness in boasting about his cooking skills took us by surprise.

caper [KAY puhr] *n.* amusing or mischievous prank
  Nan wondered if her parents would punish her for her caper of skipping school yesterday.

chums [CHUMZ] *n.* close friends
  Yesterday, Glen and his chums took off from work to go fishing.

foreknowledge [for NAHL uj] *n.* knowledge in advance
  Without my foreknowledge, the club decided to adopt new bylaws.

indifferent [in DIF uh ruhnt] *adj.* uncaring; uninvolved
  Gloria wanted badly to become Rita's friend, but Rita was indifferent.

plucked [PLUKD] *v.* picked, as from a vine or stem
  Carlos plucked several ripe oranges from a tree in the orchard.

sported [SPORT uhd] *v.* wore in a dashing or stylish way
  Mr. Aconley sported a Sherlock Holmes-like cap every day to work.

tread [TRED] *n.* footfall
  The measured pace of the horses' tread gave the state funeral a solemn air.

245

Name _____ Date _____

from Dust Tracks on a Road by Zora Neale Hurston
Vocabulary Warm-up Exercises

Exercise A *Fill in the blanks, using each word from Word List A only once.*

The day her family moved to the first house they had ever owned, Alicia

[1] _____ with excitement. Although she was normally quiet, even

[2] _____, in her behavior, she couldn't stop talking about the move. In

her inner mind, she had a deep [3] _____ that this change was marking

a milestone in the family's life. Alicia's parents spent the [4] _____ of

their first day in the new home mostly indoors. They moved around all the rooms,

[5] _____ placing the furniture unloaded from the moving van to see

how it would fit in various spaces. Alicia, though, spent most of the day outdoors

in the backyard. She felt like a(n) [6] _____ exploring her new

[7] _____. She had never had a back yard before, and she looked on it

with [8] _____, treasuring up the experience so she could savor it later.

Exercise B *Decide whether each statement below is true or false. Circle T or F, and explain your answer.*

1. A shy person can be expected to act with a certain amount of <u>brazenness</u>.
   T / F _____

2. If you participate in a <u>caper</u>, you're usually involved in a mischievous prank.
   T / F _____

3. <u>Chums</u> are usually people you dislike.
   T / F _____

4. You are better prepared for a situation if you possess some <u>foreknowledge</u> about it.
   T / F _____

5. If you are <u>indifferent</u> to a book or movie, you really like it.
   T / F _____

6. If people <u>plucked</u> the fruit, they probably thought it was ripe enough to eat.
   T / F _____

7. A person who <u>sported</u> a new hat was probably proud and pleased with it.
   T / F _____

8. People's <u>tread</u> is the sound they make when they sneeze.
   T / F _____

Name _____ Date _____

from Dust Tracks on a Road by Zora Neale Hurston
Reading Warm-up A

Read the following passage. Pay special attention to the underlined words. Then, read it again, and complete the activities. Use a separate sheet of paper for your written answers.

Zora Neale Hurston is famous for her pioneering contributions in collecting and documenting African American folk tales. How should a folk tale be defined? In most folk tales, there are at least four important features.

First, most folk tales spring from the mindset or consciousness of an entire people. These tales are usually anonymous, with no known author, and they have roots in oral tradition, being passed down by word of mouth from one generation to the next. The duration or time span of a single tale's popularity may be centuries long. At various points, retellings of the tale may experimentally alter some of the details, so many folk tales exist in hundreds of different versions.

Second, the characters and places in a folk tale often lack names. A king or queen in a folk tale is simply a character type, rather any particular historical monarch. In many tales, no specific realm or region serves as the setting: the tale simply unfolds in a vaguely defined landscape.

Thirdly, folk tales often feature animal characters. How many listeners have tingled with excitement when they've heard about the big bad wolf in "Little Red Riding Hood"? How many audiences have chuckled with excitement as they have savored the ingenuity of Br'er Fox or Br'er Rabbit?

Finally, folk tales often contain a moral or message about prudent behavior and good sense. A tale about a miser, for example, might point out the dangers of avarice. A tale about three sisters—one of them angelic and the other two envious and wicked—might underline the virtue of good and the nastiness of evil. Folk tales usually do not preach a sermon, but they often suggest a lesson.

1. Underline the words in this and the previous sentence that give a clue to the meaning of the word consciousness. What is a synonym for the word *consciousness*?

2. Circle the words in this sentence that give a clue to the meaning of duration. How many days are contained in a week's *duration*?

3. Underline the words that give a clue to the meaning of experimentally. Whose work might be described as performed *experimentally*?

4. Circle the words that offer a clue to the meaning of monarch here. What is a synonym for *monarch*?

5. Circle the words in this sentence that offer clues to the meaning of the word realm. What is a synonym for *realm*?

6. Underline the words in this sentence that give a clue to the meaning of tingled. What is a synonym for *tingled*?

7. Circle the words in this sentence that give a clue to the meaning of avarice. Use a word meaning the opposite of *avarice* in an original sentence.

8. Underline the words in this sentence that hint at the meaning of angelic. What is a synonym for *angelic*?

Name _____   Date _____

from **Dust Tracks on a Road** by Zora Neale Hurston
Reading Warm-up B

Read the following passage. Pay special attention to the underlined words. Then, read it again, *and complete the activities. Use a separate sheet of paper for your written answers.*

Tyrone's band was known all over the school for their <u>brazenness</u>. "Bold and beautiful" was their motto, and it was true that they were musical trailblazers, audaciously blending styles in brand-new ways. This afternoon, before Tyrone met with his <u>chums</u> for a friendly jam session, his head was buzzing with ideas for next week's concert. The concert would be an improvisation, the way they always were, but the group had to go into the performance with a certain amount of <u>foreknowledge</u>—some advance ideas about what direction the music would take. Tyrone thought they would need a stunning new <u>caper</u>: something that would really make a mark on the audience. After all, he reflected, you're only as good as your last time onstage, and if you don't outdo yourself the next time, your fans become <u>indifferent</u> and jaded, unwilling to pay you respect.

Tyrone absentmindedly <u>plucked</u> the strings of his guitar as he waited for the others to arrive. Then he heard the heavy <u>tread</u> of some of the band members as they plodded up the stairs. When Randolph and Darrell appeared, Tyrone noticed that Darrell <u>sported</u> a bright orange cap, tilted to the side at a rakish angle. The cap was the color of autumn leaves, and it reminded Tyrone of an album cover he'd once seen in a record store—something about a classical piece called *The Four Seasons*. Tyrone felt the stirrings of an idea: for their new improvisation, the band would go classical-rap, combining two styles again in a new way. They'd prepare by brainstorming for lyrics and tunes that suggested autumn, winter, spring, and summer. Tyrone knew he was onto something, but, he wondered, how would he explain it to the band?

1. Underline the words in this and the next sentence that give a clue to the meaning of <u>brazenness</u>. Use a word meaning the opposite of *brazenness* in a sentence of your own.

2. Circle the word in this sentence that gives a clue to the meaning of <u>chums</u>. What is a synonym for *chums*?

3. When would you use <u>foreknowledge</u>: before or after something happened?

4. Underline the words in this sentence that give a clue to the meaning of <u>caper</u>.

5. Circle the words in this sentence that give a clue to the meaning of <u>indifferent</u>. Use a word meaning the opposite of *indifferent* in a sentence of your own.

6. Underline the words in this sentence that hint at the meaning of <u>plucked</u>. What other things might you *pluck*?

7. Circle the words in this sentence that hint at the meaning of <u>tread</u>.

8. Circle the words in this sentence that hint at the meaning of the word <u>sported</u>. Are the connotations of *sported* positive or negative?

Name _____   Date _____

from **Dust Tracks on a Road** by Zora Neale Hurston
Literary Analysis: Social Context in Autobiography

Zora Neale Hurston's autobiography, *Dust Tracks on a Road,* is clearly written from the point of view of an adult reflecting on her childhood in the segregated South. Although she remembers these early events in great detail, she makes it clear that her interpretation happened long after the incidents occurred. She is able to fit her own story into the social context of the time period in which she grew up. For example, in the second paragraph Hurston comments on the white travelers' allowing her to accompany them a short way: "I know now that I must have caused a great deal of amusement among them, but my self-assurance must have carried the point, for I was always invited to come along." As a child she was not aware of why asking to walk along with white people was frowned upon by her family, but as an adult, she places her behavior in a social context and sees how her actions were very unusual among African Americans at that time.

By combining narration and reflection on the social situation, autobiographers not only reveal something about themselves and their social context, they also lead us to contemplate our own social context and its influence upon us.

DIRECTIONS: *For each of the following quotations, discuss what Zora Neale Hurston reveals about the social context of her writing. Then briefly explain how each quotation might relate to something in your current social context.*

1. "Git down offa dat gate-post! You li'l sow, you! Git down! Setting up dere looking dem white folks right in de face! They's gowine to lynch you, yet. And don't stand in dat doorway gazing out at 'em neither. Youse too brazen to live long."

   _____

   _____

   _____

2. The village seemed dull to me most of the time. If the village was singing a chorus, I must have missed the tune.

   _____

   _____

   _____

3. The whites that came down from the North were often brought by their friends to visit the village school. A Negro school was something strange to them, and while they were always sympathetic and kind, curiosity must have been present.

   _____

   _____

   _____

Name _____ Date _____

from Dust Tracks on a Road by Zora Neale Hurston
Reading Strategy: Analyze How a Writer Achieves Purpose

Writers usually have one or more **purposes** in mind when they write. The words, characters, events, and details of their works are chosen to achieve their purposes or goals. In her autobiography, Zora Neale Hurston wrote to describe her own personal experiences, her own character, and the vital African American community in which she grew up.

DIRECTIONS: *The first column of the chart below lists summaries of scenes, events, and comments from Zora Neale Hurston's autobiography. Read the summaries and, in the second column, record your analysis of the author's purpose in choosing each scene. Then choose two more scenes, events, or comments, summarize them in the first column, and analyze their purpose in the second. If necessary, use extra paper.*

Scene, Event, or Comment of Writer	Analysis of Writer's Purpose
1. Zora marvels at the fingers of the white women with their pink tips.	
2. The white ladies ask Zora to read from a magazine when she visits them in their hotel.	
3. Zora finds Hercules a moving hero because he chooses duty over pleasure. She likes David because he is a strong, active character.	
4.	
5.	

Name _____ Date _____

Vocabulary Builder

Using the Root -graph-

The root *-graph-* comes from a Greek word meaning "write." In English, this root appears in a variety of words.

A. DIRECTIONS: *Write each word listed below in the blank following the situation to which it is most closely related.*

lithograph (*litho* = stone)	graphology
calligraphy (*calli* = beautiful)	graphic

1. the study of handwriting to analyze personalities _____
2. a reporter describing a crime in clear and vivid detail _____
3. a picture created from an image drawn on a stone plate _____
4. an invitation written in a decorative script _____

Using the Word List

foreknowledge	brazenness	caper
exalted	geography	avarice

B. DIRECTIONS: *Match each word in the left column with its definition in the right column.*

___ 1. foreknowledge

___ 2. brazenness

___ 3. caper

___ 4. exalted

___ 5. avarice

___ 6. geography

A. filled with joy or pride; elated

B. an extreme desire for wealth; greed

C. awareness of something before it happens

D. study of the earth

E. prank

F. shamelessness; boldness

from **Dust Tracks on a Road** by Zora Neale Hurston

Grammar and Style: Parallelism in Coordinate Elements

Parallel grammatical elements in a sentence may be linked by coordinating conjunctions—*and, but, or,* and *nor.* Parallel elements are of the same type—nouns, verbs, adjectives, adverbs, clauses, or phrases. They are also the same in structure.

You will find something *significant* and *enjoyable* in most mythological stories.

In the example, *significant* and *enjoyable* are equivalent elements—they are both adjectives with the same structure.

Jerry preferred *walking* and *to run* over riding.

Walking and *to run* are not parallel: one is the gerund form of a verb and one is the infinitive form of a verb.

Jerry preferred *walking* and *running* over *riding.*

A. PRACTICE: *Read the sentences below. Circle the coordinating conjunction(s) and underline the parallel coordinate elements.*

1. "I was fifth or sixth down the line."

2. "Last thing, I was given a handkerchief to carry, warned again about my behavior, and sent off. . . ."

3. "I seemed to remember seeing Thor swing his mighty short-handled hammer as he sped across the sky in rumbling thunder, lightning flashing from the tread of his steeds and the wheels of his chariot."

B. Writing Application: *Read each group of sentences. Then combine them to form a single sentence with a coordinating conjunction to link parallel elements.*

1. The two white ladies who visited her school had fingers that were long. Their fingers were also white. However, they were pink near the tips.

   _____

2. Zora liked to read mythological stories. She also enjoyed studying geography. She liked game playing.

   _____

3. Zora didn't know whether she would get a reward. She didn't know whether she would be whipped.

   _____

Name _____ Date _____

from **Dust Tracks on a Road** by Zora Neale Hurston
Support for Writing

Prepare to write a **personal narrative** about an event in your life that changed you in some important way by inspiring you. Think about some of your hobbies or interests and how you first gained an interest in them. Enter information in the graphic organizer below.

How This Event Changed My Life

How old I was and what the event was:
What I thought and felt while the event was happening:
What I did that was new after the event happened:
How the event has changed the way I think or feel today:

On a separate page, begin your essay by stating how the event changed your life. Then, analyze how the cause created certain effects in your life. When you revise, be sure the connection between the event and your life today is clear.

from **Dust Tracks on a Road** by Zora Neale Hurston
Support for Extend Your Learning

Listening and Speaking

Prepare a **campaign speech** in which young Zora persuades her classmates to vote for her for class president. How will the speech show Zora's self-confidence and character? Use these tips:

- Review the selection to identify Zora's qualities.
- Outline her accomplishments.
- Discuss goals that will benefit the class.
- Plan to speak with expression and emphasis.

Practice the speech with a classmate before delivering it to the whole class.

Research and Technology

Work with a group to create a **folk tale collection** using three selections from Hurston's *Mules and Men* or from another anthology of American folk tales. Write an introduction to your collection and include illustrations of your own or from the Internet. Enter information into the graphic organizer below.

Title 1:_____
What is moving, inspiring, or amusing about this tale?

Title 2:_____
What is moving, inspiring, or amusing about this tale?

Title 3:_____
What is moving, inspiring, or amusing about this tale?

Choices for Illustrations:

Present your collection to the class and then place your anthology in the classroom library.

Name _____ Date _____

from **Dust Tracks on a Road** by Zora Neale Hurston
Enrichment: Community and Personal Identity

Living in Eatonville, a "fully incorporated African American township," contributed to Zora Neale Hurston's identity in positive ways, bolstering her self-esteem and supporting her achievements. She must have been used to seeing African Americans in positions of responsibility, running the village, its institutions, and businesses. Perhaps in Eatonville, African Americans could realize more of their ambitions and live freer of racial tensions and stereotyping than elsewhere.

DIRECTIONS: *Consider your own personal identity—who you are, your interests and character. Then think about the community in which you spent most of your life: How has this community contributed to the person that you are? Answer the questions below to help you explore your identity and the contributions of your community. Using these questions as a guide, write a letter to a new pen pal describing who you are and the contributions your community—its people, values, and institutions—have made to your identity.*

1. What are the first things you'd say to introduce yourself to your new pen pal?

_____

_____

_____

2. What are your main interests and ambitions?

_____

_____

3. What character traits distinguish you?

_____

_____

_____

4. How would you describe your community to your new pen pal?

_____

_____

_____

5. What values have you learned from your community?

_____

_____

_____

_____

6. How does your community support and foster your interests and ambitions?

_____

_____

_____

from **Dust Tracks on a Road** by Zora Neale Hurston
Selection Test A

Critical Reading *Identify the letter of the choice that best answers the question.*

_____ 1. In *Dust Tracks on a Road*, why did the author travel with whites outside her town?
  A. to make her grandmother angry
  B. to see how far she could walk
  C. to conquer her fear of whites
  D. to get away from her dull village

_____ 2. In *Dust Tracks on a Road*, why did the author's grandmother worry about her attitude toward whites?
  A. She feared that whites would not have any respect for the author.
  B. She feared that whites would hurt the author for being bold.
  C. She feared that whites would keep the author from going to school.
  D. She feared that whites would not understand the author.

_____ 3. What is the author's attitude toward whites at the beginning of *Dust Tracks on a Road*?
  A. She is afraid of them.
  B. She is curious about them.
  C. She is bored with them.
  D. She is angry with them.

_____ 4. In *Dust Tracks on a Road*, why were the white women so impressed with Hurston?
  A. She was a good reader.
  B. She had on a new dress.
  C. She was very polite to them.
  D. She had clean fingernails.

_____ 5. In *Dust Tracks on a Road*, what kind of literature did the young Hurston like best that made her think of heroic deeds?
  A. stories that were sad
  B. stories of math geniuses
  C. stories that were great myths
  D. stories about young women

Name _____ Date _____

_____ 6. Hurston says in *Dust Tracks on a Road:* "I hated things I couldn't do anything about." What does this statement tell you about her character?

A. She didn't like any of her teachers.

B. She didn't like not having power.

C. She didn't like sitting in school.

D. She didn't like making decisions.

_____ 7. Why were the teachers in *Dust Tracks on a Road* so nervous when white visitors appeared?

A. They wanted to impress the visitors.

B. Bad teachers would be dismissed.

C. The students often misbehaved.

D. The whites supported the school.

_____ 8. In *Dust Tracks on a Road*, what can you infer based on the author's fascination with the white women's fingers?

A. The author had never seen fingers with rings on them.

B. The author was used to seeing people with gloves on.

C. The author was easily distracted from her reading aloud.

D. The author had rarely seen white people up close.

_____ 9. What is the main reason the author loved the roll of shiny new pennies in *Dust Tracks on a Road*?

A. The pennies were something she could play with.

B. The pennies were shiny and beautiful.

C. The pennies would buy a new book.

D. The pennies showed her importance.

_____ 10. Why did the white women give Hurston gifts in *Dust Tracks on a Road*?

A. They felt sorry for her.

B. They were impressed by her intelligence.

C. They thought she was too bold.

D. They didn't like her manners.

_____ 11. For what purpose might the author have written this section of *Dust Tracks on a Road*?

A. to show that she often did things that frightened her grandmother

B. to show that she was willing to take advice from whites

C. to show that she was going to be her own person in life

D. to show that her grandmother influenced her greatly

Vocabulary and Grammar

____ 12. Which word best replaces *capers* in this sentence: "The students were told to avoid doing any *capers* when visitors came to the class"?

A. reading

B. boredom

C. tricks

D. standing

____ 13. Which sentence contains parallel coordinate elements linked by a conjunction such as *and* or *but*?

A. "I was observing our visitors, who had a book between them"

B. "There was no music written there, just the words."

C. "Not only was I barefooted, but my feet and legs were dusty."

D. "They were long and thin, and very white, except up near the tips."

Essay

14. In *Dust Tracks on a Road*, you learn that Zora Neale Hurston was not afraid of white people but that her grandmother was. What was the difference in the life experiences of the two women that might account for their different views of whites? Write a brief essay to address this question.

15. Some readers might say that the white women who visited the school in *Dust Tracks on a Road* expected the black children and teacher to perform for them, which is an insulting thing to ask. Why might Hurston be willing to go along with this "performance"? Write a brief essay to discuss what Hurston's reasons for being so cooperative.

Name _____ Date _____

from **Dust Tracks on a Road** by Zora Neale Hurston
Selection Test B

Critical Reading *Identify the letter of the choice that best completes the statement or answers the question.*

_____ 1. This excerpt from *Dust Tracks on a Road* is mostly an account of a writer's
A. early experiences with the outside world.
B. escape from her humble origins.
C. struggle against racism.
D. literary tastes.

_____ 2. What can you infer about Hurston's attitude toward whites at the beginning of the selection?
A. She was afraid of them.
B. She saw whites as a way to expand her experience.
C. She regarded them as something curious.
D. She felt that they looked down on her.

_____ 3. Why did Hurston's grandmother find her brazenness "unthinkable"?
A. She thought Zora's actions reflected badly on her.
B. She thought Zora's activities were illegal.
C. She knew Negroes who had been lynched for minor offenses.
D. She knew that she was not as creative as her granddaughter.

_____ 4. What do the dust tracks in the title symbolize?
A. poverty in a backwater southern community
B. the path to a new way of life
C. finding the way home after getting lost
D. returning to one's roots

_____ 5. Why was a Negro school a curiosity to visitors?
A. There was little contact between races at the time the writer describes.
B. The educational practices differed from those in schools for whites.
C. The children were better educated than in the schools the visitors knew.
D. The visitors had never met Negro children before.

_____ 6. Why were the schoolchildren threatened when visitors came to observe them?
A. The teachers would get in trouble if the children misbehaved.
B. The visitors rewarded the teachers if the children were well-behaved.
C. The teachers were concerned about making a good impression.
D. The visitors wanted to observe the teachers' disciplinary techniques.

_____ 7. Hurston carefully describes her reading likes and dislikes for the purpose of
A. persuading others that reading is important.
B. revealing her character and personality.
C. helping children choose appropriate books.
D. showing that she liked the same things white people did.

____ 8. Which might best explain Hurston's purpose in presenting her critical feelings about school?

A. to confess that she was a liar

B. to show that being educated is not dependent on loving school

C. to reveal how inferior her school was

D. to show how little she values education

____ 9. Which of the following was probably *not* one of Zora Neale Hurston's purposes in writing her autobiography?

A. to portray the African American culture of her community

B. to share the experiences of her life

C. to show how she struggled against racism and prejudice

D. to inspire others to get an education

____ 10. What do you think the author's purpose was for writing this sentence?

If white people liked trashy singing like that, there must be something funny about them that I had not noticed before.

A. to show how much contempt she had for white people

B. to reveal a moment of doubt in her positive view of white people

C. to explain why she disliked white people's way of worshiping

D. to emphasize her belief that white people had bad taste in music

____ 11. Which excerpt best shows that Zora Neale Hurston wanted to present herself as an unusual child who did not fit stereotypes?

A. "I slipped one hand behind me and switched my dress tail at them, indicating scorn."

B. "I liked geography and reading, and I liked to play at recess time. Whoever it was invented writing and arithmetic got no thanks from me."

C. "I had never been too keen on dressing up. It called for hard scrubbings with Octagon soap suds getting in my eyes, and none too gentle fingers scrubbing my neck and gouging in my ears."

D. "I came to start reading the Bible through my mother. She gave me a licking one afternoon for repeating something I had overheard. . . . She locked me in her room . . . and the Bible was the only thing in there for me to read."

____ 12. Which is a possible reason Hurston might have had for emphasizing the mythology she read and loved as a child?

A. to show the origins of her later career as a folklorist

B. to make clear how much she liked white culture

C. to make a case for reading stories to children

D. to emphasize the importance of reading for education

Vocabulary and Grammar

____ 13. Which event is the best example of a *caper?*
   A. Zora's friends snickering so she could hear them when she is called to Mr. Calhoun's desk
   B. the white ladies telling Zora not to open her cylinder-shaped present until she got home
   C. Zora reading the myth of Pluto and Persephone to the visitors
   D. Zora hailing white travelers from her gatepost

____ 14. It was not _____ that made Zora take such delight in the gift of pennies, but rather their beauty.
   A. brazenness
   B. foreknowledge
   C. poverty
   D. avarice

____ 15. Usually, Zora's school had some _____ when people were going to visit, but not when the two white ladies from Minnesota came.
   A. avarice
   B. preparations
   C. foreknowledge
   D. fears

____ 16. Which excerpt contains an example of parallelism in coordinate elements?
   A. "But I knew better than to bring that up right there, so I said yes, I *loved* school."
   B. "Perhaps a year before the old man died, I came to know two other white people for myself."
   C. "But the books gave me more pleasure than the clothes."
   D. "He put his hand on my shoulder and gave me little pats."

____ 17. Which sentence contains an error in parallelism?
   A. The author's purpose was to tell about her childhood, describe her community, and give insight into her character.
   B. Zora went off to see the ladies scrubbed, clad in a gingham dress, and her hair tied by a red ribbon.
   C. Zora didn't know whether Hennie, Stell, or someone else had laughed loudest.
   D. The white visitors were kind and sympathetic, but curious.

Essay

18. The episodes writers choose to include in an autobiography reflect their perceptions about experiences that helped mold their character. In an essay, explain what the information in this selection reveals to you about Zora Neale Hurston's character. Include details from the selection to support your conclusion.

19. Zora's encounters with white people not only show us things about her but also reveal some attitudes and feelings of these people toward African Americans. In an essay, discuss these attitudes and feelings as they are revealed in this narrative. Are they all directly stated, or must some be inferred from events? Why do you think the white women provide Zora with books and clothing? Use specific examples to make your points.

Study these words from the selections. Then, complete the activities.

Word List A

dawns [DAWNZ] *n.* periods just before sunrise; beginnings
Many sunny <u>dawns</u> passed before it finally rained.

fit [FIT] *adj.* suitable for
The food at that restaurant was so bad that it was not <u>fit</u> to be served to customers.

liberty [LIB er tee] *n.* freedom
The United States won its <u>liberty</u> as a nation in the Revolutionary War.

longing [LAWNG ing] *n.* yearning
Jane felt nostalgia for the happy summers she had spent at camp.

lulled [LULD] *v.* soothed
After the drone of the crickets <u>lulled</u> him to sleep, Patrick napped for two hours.

pale [PAYL] *adj.* whitish or colorless; pallid; wan
Yesterday, Burt looked very <u>pale</u>, as if he might be coming down with the flu.

slim [SLIM] *adj.* thin; slender
To remain <u>slim</u>, you must eat healthfully and exercise regularly.

whirl [WERL] *v.* to turn rapidly in a circle; to twirl
We admired the ballet dancers' ability to <u>whirl</u> gracefully across the stage.

Word List B

benediction [ben uh DIK shuhn] *n.* blessing
Many pictures of saints show them with one hand raised in <u>benediction</u>.

bosom [BOOZ uhm] *n.* the inside or midst
Beth didn't want to leave the <u>bosom</u> of her family to go away to school.

dewy [DOO wee] *adj.* wet or damp with dew
In the early mornings, the lawn is always <u>dewy</u>.

dusky [DUS kee] *adj.* dark; shadowy
It was difficult to see far ahead when we were in the <u>dusky</u> tunnel.

gaze [GAYZ] *v.* to look intently and steadily; to stare
From her back porch, Mrs. Hawkins likes to <u>gaze</u> at the sunset.

laden [LAYD uhn] *adj.* weighed down; loaded; burdened
In early April, the cherry trees in the park were <u>laden</u> with beautiful blossoms.

mystical [MIST ik uhl] *adj.* spiritually significant; unfathomable
Cooper's attachment to the game of golf was almost <u>mystical</u> in its intensity.

parish [PAR ish] *n.* civil or administrative division corresponding to a county
A <u>parish</u> in Louisiana corresponds to a county in other states.

Name _____ Date _____

Exercise A *Fill in each blank below using the appropriate word from Word List A.*

Rachel's memories of her first trip to the ocean stayed with her for years. A(n)

[1] _____ for the sea had consumed much of her childhood. She dreamed of

the day when the salt air and the sound of the surf would gently [2] _____

her to sleep. She imagined the sun rising, [3] _____ and whitish-gold, over a

vast expanse of dark blue water. Such [4] _____ would be magnificent, she

thought, altogether suitable and [5] _____ for an oil painting or a watercolor.

For Rachel, the ocean was a symbol of [6] _____, freedom for her mind,

soul, and spirit. When she finally fulfilled her dream, she was not disappointed. The first

afternoon of her visit, she glimpsed a flight of graceful, [7] _____ pelicans

skimming over the water. Dreamily, she watched eddies of water from breaking waves

[8] _____ back from the shore.

Exercise B *Revise each sentence so that the underlined vocabulary word is logical. Be sure
to keep the vocabulary word in your revision.*

Example: Because Lou was so <u>studious</u>, he was poorly prepared for the exam.
Because Lou was so <u>studious</u>, he was well prepared for the exam.

1. One expects judges to give their <u>benediction</u> to violations of the law.
   _____

2. She wanted to stay far from home, safe in the <u>bosom</u> of her family.
   _____

3. The flower's petals were <u>dewy</u>, dry and shriveled from the extended drought.
   _____

4. In the <u>dusky</u> light at high noon, it is easy to see the line of hills on the horizon.
   _____

5. He wanted badly to <u>gaze</u> at the temple ruins, but his ears were blocked.
   _____

6. <u>Laden</u> with blossoms, the cherry trees were almost bare.
   _____

7. For Paul, the concert was a <u>mystical</u> experience that he found dull and insignificant.
   _____

8. The entire <u>parish</u> consisted of one medium-sized village.
   _____

Name _____ Date _____

Poems by Langston Hughes and Claude McKay
Reading Warm-up A

Read the following passage. Pay special attention to the underlined words. Then, read it again, and complete the activities. Use a separate sheet of paper for your written answers.

During the Harlem Renaissance, jazz and the blues had a huge influence on artists and writers. The artist Romare Bearden, for example, sometimes portrays jazz bands. Because of his unique style, the musicians with their <u>slim</u>, slender saxophones seem almost to move within the pictures. He also paints dancers who <u>whirl</u> and twirl to the music at Harlem nightclubs. In his poem "The Weary Blues," Langston Hughes powerfully expresses the yearning or <u>longing</u> that the sound of blues music inspires in the soul.

Blues music has soothed and <u>lulled</u> the pain of generations of African Americans since the time when they longed for true <u>liberty</u> after the Civil War. Even though formerly enslaved blacks had gained their freedom legally, they had few chances during Reconstruction for social justice or equality of opportunity. The <u>dawns</u> of musical styles are exceptionally hard to trace. However, historians date the origins of the blues to this period in the south. There seem to have been many influences on the development of the blues. The work songs and field hollers sung by farm workers were <u>fit</u> for combining with other genres, suitable for ragtime, minstrel show music, church music, folk music, and popular music of other groups.

Blues soon became greater than the sum of its parts. By the 1920s and 1930s, blues had become a major musical style in cities such as Memphis, St. Louis, Chicago, and New York. Blues recordings started to be made. A generation later, blues music had an important influence on early rock singers, such as Elvis Presley. It is clear that the early blues musicians were hardly muted stylists. They certainly do not <u>pale</u> in comparison to the many artists and musicians they have influenced over the years.

1. Circle the word that means nearly the same as <u>slim</u>. What other musical instruments, or parts of instruments, could be described as *slim*?

2. Circle the word that gives a clue to the meaning of <u>whirl</u>. Give an example of something that can *whirl*.

3. Circle the word in this sentence that means nearly the same as <u>longing</u>. Write a sentence about an event or situation that might fill you with *longing*.

4. Underline the word in this sentence that means nearly the same as <u>lulled</u>. What is the opposite of *lulled*?

5. Underline the phrases in this sentence that give clues to the meaning of <u>liberty</u>. What is a synonym for *liberty*?

6. Underline the word in the next sentence that gives a clue to the meaning of <u>dawns</u>. Is *dawns* used literally or figuratively here?

7. Circle the word in this sentence that gives means nearly the same as <u>fit</u>. What are two antonyms for *fit*?

8. Underline the word in the previous sentence that gives a clue to the meaning of <u>pale</u>. Why might sparrows *pale* in comparison to parrots?

Poems by Langston Hughes and Claude McKay
Reading Warm-up B

Read the following passage. Pay special attention to the underlined words. Then, read it again, and complete the activities. Use a separate sheet of paper for your written answers.

Claude McKay's native island of Jamaica is located in the <u>bosom</u> of the Caribbean Sea, in the midst of pleasant waters approximately 100 miles west of Haiti and 90 miles south of Cuba. The first European to <u>gaze</u> at Jamaica was Christopher Columbus, who sighted the island in 1494. Columbus's favorable and graceful words about Jamaica sound like a <u>benediction</u>; he called it "the fairest isle that eyes have beheld."

Much of Jamaica's colonial history under the Spanish and the English was dominated by the sugar plantations, and most of the island's people are descendants of slaves brought in by the European colonists. Jamaica has been an independent country since 1962.

Today, Jamaica's major industry is tourism. Especially during the winter months, visitors wander the length and breadth of this large island, admiring the unfathomable, almost <u>mystical</u> beauty of a tropical paradise. At resorts in the westernmost <u>parish</u>, as counties are called in Jamaica, tourists gather at resorts to admire the spectacular sunsets before eating dinner by candlelight on <u>dusky</u> terraces. Furthermore, there is no shortage of outdoor activities: water skiing, hang gliding, and parasailing are all popular recreational sports on this jewel of the Caribbean islands. Many people simply like to soak in the island's natural beauty, though, because if you take a walk in the early morning, you can see dozens of varieties of brightly colored, tropical flowers, their petals <u>dewy</u> with moisture. Fruit trees <u>laden</u> heavily with many guavas, mangoes, or bananas rustle in a warm breeze. No wonder Claude McKay felt homesick for the beautiful island of his birth!

1. Underline the words in this sentence that give a clue to the meaning of <u>bosom</u>. From the way *bosom* is used here, where might you expect to find Jamaica on a map of the Caribbean region?

2. Circle the word in this sentence that gives a clue to the meaning of <u>gaze</u>. What are two synonyms for *gaze*?

3. Underline the words in this sentence that give a clue to the meaning of <u>benediction</u>. Use *benediction* in a sentence.

4. Underline the word in this sentence that means nearly the same as <u>mystical</u>. What is an antonym of *mystical*?

5. Circle the words in this sentence that give a clue to the meaning of <u>parish</u>. What might a *parish* be called in an American state?

6. Underline the phrases in this sentence that give clues to the meaning of <u>dusky</u>. Write a sentence of your own using *dusky*.

7. Circle the word in this sentence that gives a clue to the meaning of <u>dewy</u>. When would you most likely find *dewy* grass?

8. Underline the words in this sentence that give a clue to the meaning of <u>laden</u>. What are two synonyms for *laden*?

"The Negro Speaks of Rivers," "I, Too," "Dream Variations,"
and **"Refugee in America"**
by Langston Hughes
"The Tropics in New York" by Claude McKay

Literary Analysis: Speaker

The **speaker** is the voice of a poem. There are several possibilities as to who the speaker may be: the author, another person, an imaginary person, a group of people, an animal, or an object. Often, clues from the poem can help the reader figure out who the speaker is.

DIRECTIONS: *Reread each poem in the selection. Decide who the speaker is for each poem. Then tell what clues helped you figure out who the speaker is.*

"Refugee in America" by Langston Hughes

Who is the speaker of the poem? _____

How do you know?

_____

"I, Too" by Langston Hughes

Who is the speaker of the poem? _____

How do you know?

_____

"The Negro Speaks of Rivers" by Langston Hughes

Who is the speaker of the poem? _____

How do you know?

_____

"Dream Variations" by Langston Hughes

Who is the speaker of the poem? _____

How do you know?

_____

"The Tropics in New York" by Claude McKay

Who is the speaker of the poem? _____

How do you know?

_____

Name _____ Date _____

"The Negro Speaks of Rivers," "I, Too," "Dream Variations,"
and **"Refugee in America"**
by Langston Hughes
"The Tropics in New York" by Claude McKay

Reading Strategy: Draw Inferences About the Speaker

Often, a poem's speaker isn't stated directly. Rather, the reader must **draw inferences,** or draw conclusions, about the speaker's identity, attitudes, feelings, and experiences. To make these inferences, the reader must pay close attention to the words, ideas, and details in the poem.

DIRECTIONS: *Reread the following poems. Use the graphic organizer below to help you determine the attitudes, feelings, and experiences of the speaker for each poem. Write down words, ideas, and details from each poem that help you make inferences about the speaker. Then tell what inferences the clues helped you to make.*

Poem	Words, Ideas, or Details	Inferences About the Speaker
"Refugee in America"		
"The Negro Speaks of Rivers"		
"The Tropics in New York"		

"The Negro Speaks of Rivers," "I, Too," "Dream Variations,"
and **"Refugee in America"**
by Langston Hughes
"The Tropics in New York" by Claude McKay
Vocabulary Builder

Using the Root *-lib-*

A. DIRECTIONS: *The word root -lib- derives from* liber, *the Latin word for "free."*

Complete each of the sentences below with one of the words or phrases in the box. To help figure out which word or phrase to use, determine which part of speech—noun, verb, adverb—is missing in the sentence.

liberalize	liberal arts	liberally	libertarian

1. Since basketball games often did not end until about 11:00 P.M., Anthony began a campaign to _____ the curfew laws.
2. Literature, philosophy, and history are considered to be part of the _____ because studying them helps students to develop their general ability to think and reason.
3. Scowling at the steamed broccoli, Maura poured cheese sauce over it _____.
4. A person who believes that liberty should be absolute and unrestricted is a _____.

Using the Word List

lulled	dusky	liberty

B. DIRECTIONS: *In each blank, write the letter of the one best answer.*

____ 1. A baby would most likely be lulled to sleep by
    A. a deep bellow.   C. a loud yell.
    B. a sharp screech.   D. a soft song.

____ 2. It is *dusky* outside when
    A. it is completely dark.   C. the sun is high in the sky.
    B. it is almost dark.   D. the sun is behind clouds.

____ 3. A prisoner who is told that he is at *liberty* to go may safely assume that
    A. he may leave and go wherever he wants to.
    B. he may leave if he keeps in touch with authorities.
    C. he is only free to go home and go to work.
    D. he must stay in prison.

Name _____ Date _____

"The Negro Speaks of Rivers," "I, Too," "Dream Variations,"
and **"Refugee in America"**
by Langston Hughes
"The Tropics in New York" by Claude McKay

Grammar and Style: Verb Tenses—Past and Present Perfect

The **past tense** shows an action or condition that began or ended at a given time in the past. No helping verb is used when forming the past tense. The **present perfect tense** shows an action or condition that occurred at an indefinite time in the past or that began in the past but continues in the present. The helping verb *has* or *have* is placed before the past participle of the main verb when forming the present perfect tense.

A. PRACTICE: *For each item, underline the words used to express the tense. Then circle the verb tense used in the sentence.*

1. "I've known rivers ancient as the world. . . ."   PAST or PRESENT PERFECT
2. "I built my hut near the Congo. . . ."   PAST or PRESENT PERFECT
3. "and it lulled me to sleep."   PAST or PRESENT PERFECT
4. "I heard the singing of the Mississippi. . . ."   PAST or PRESENT PERFECT
5. "I've seen its muddy bosom. . . ."   PAST or PRESENT PERFECT
6. "My soul has grown deep like the rivers."   PAST or PRESENT PERFECT

B. Writing Application: *Write two short sentences—one in the past tense and one in the present tense—using each of the words below.*

1. rivers

    (past) _____

    (present perfect) _____

2. home

    (past) _____

    (present perfect) _____

3. history

    (past) _____

    (present perfect) _____

4. pride

    (past) _____

    (present perfect) _____

"The Negro Speaks of Rivers," "I, Too," "Dream Variations,"
and **"Refugee in America"**
by Langston Hughes
"The Tropics in New York" by Claude McKay
Support for Writing

Prepare to write an essay about the poems of Langston Hughes, including "I, Too," by entering material into the graphic organizer below. Think about the issues of racial identity, pride, and perseverance as you think about his work.

"The Negro Speaks of Rivers"	Theme: _____ _____	Images used: _____ _____
"Dream Variations"	Theme: _____ _____	Images used: _____ _____
"Refugee in America"	Theme: _____ _____	Images used: _____ _____
"I, Too"	Theme: _____ _____	Images used: _____ _____

On a separate page, draft your essay and begin by identifying the common themes in the poems. Then, choose two poems to compare and contrast. When you revise your essay, be sure to include quotations from the poems.

"The Negro Speaks of Rivers," "I, Too," "Dream Variations"
and "Refugee in America"
by Langston Hughes
"The Tropics in New York" by Claude McKay
Support for Extend Your Learning

Speaking and Listening

Collect photos, books, and historic records of life in Jamaica. List the characteristics you find most intriguing. Follow these tips as you research:

- What are the unique aspects of Jamaican culture?
- Compare Jamaican ideas, beliefs, or customs with those of American culture.
- What is alike and different about the two cultures?
- What do you most appreciate in Jamaican culture?

Give a **presentation** to your classmates to compare the cultures of Jamaica and the United States.

Research and Technology

Prepare to create **posters** that reflect African American artists' contributions in the 1920s. Do research on the Internet and enter information in the chart below.

African Americans in the 1920s	What were their names, and what work did they contribute?
Writers	
Visual Artists	
Musicians	
Playwrights	

Display your posters for the class. Then, add them to a poster collection in the classroom.

"The Negro Speaks of Rivers," "I, Too," "Dream Variations,"
and **"Refugee in America"**
by Langston Hughes
"The Tropics in New York" by Claude McKay

Enrichment: Science

Langston Hughes wrote "The Negro Speaks of Rivers" in his teen years. The poem won him national recognition in a writing contest and launched his career. A lot of literature has been written about rivers or about the effect rivers have on people's lives. People are often drawn inexplicably to rivers. For example, although people living on the banks of rivers suffer when rivers flood, they usually return to their homes afterward.

A. DIRECTIONS: *Research how rivers and water ecology can affect the people who live near or depend on rivers. Use the following questions to guide your research.*

1. How do natural disasters affect rivers and the people who live near them?

   _____

   _____

   _____

2. How does human habitation affect rivers?

   _____

   _____

   _____

3. What are people doing to protect rivers?

   _____

   _____

   _____

B. DIRECTIONS: *Review how Hughes used rivers in his poem. Then use your research to write your own poem to a particular river or to rivers in general. How do rivers affect your life or the lives of people living near one?*

_____

_____

_____

_____

_____

_____

_____

_____

"The Negro Speaks of Rivers," "I, Too," "Dream Variations," and "Refugee in America"
by Langston Hughes
"The Tropics in New York" by Claude McKay
Selection Test A

Critical Reading *Identify the letter of the choice that best answers the question.*

_____ 1. Who is the speaker in "The Negro Speaks of Rivers"?
   A. a fisherman
   B. the black community
   C. a slave
   D. an African sailor

_____ 2. In "The Negro Speaks of Rivers," the poet says rivers are like years and years of events in the lives of Africans and African Americans. What does he compare the rivers to?
   A. black history
   B. African slavery
   C. Egypt's pyramids
   D. beautiful sunsets

_____ 3. How has the speaker's soul become like the rivers in "The Negro Speaks of Rivers"?
   A. Both have grown deep.
   B. Both have long histories.
   C. Both are part of Africa.
   D. Both are ancient as the world.

_____ 4. Read the following lines from "I, Too".
   I'll be at the table / When company comes.

   What do you think these lines mean?
   A. He will no longer eat in the kitchen.
   B. He will become powerful.
   C. His family will no longer be ashamed of him.
   D. Eventually, there will be equality.

_____ 5. Who is the speaker in "I, Too"?
   A. America
   B. Walt Whitman
   C. Langston Hughes
   D. A student

___ 6. In "Dream Variations," how does the African American poet say he is like the night?

    A. The night is full of dancing.

    B. The night is dark and black.

    C. The night is cool and pale.

    D. The night is a time of rest.

___ 7. What kind of person is the speaker, who wants to "fling [his] arms wide" have in "Dream Variations"?

    A. serious

    B. angry

    C. lively

    D. sad

___ 8. In "Refugee in America," who would be likely to be moved by hearing the word *Freedom*?

    A. someone who does not understand it

    B. someone who takes it from others

    C. someone who had never had it

    D. someone who has it all the time

___ 9. Who can the reader assume to be the speaker who calls freedom "sweet and wonderful" in "Refugee in America"?

    A. a longtime citizen of America

    B. a recent immigrant to America

    C. a person leaving America

    D. a visitor to America

___ 10. Who is the speaker in "The Tropics in New York" who remembers mangoes from his past?

    A. someone from the tropics now living in New York

    B. someone living in New York who runs a fruit market

    C. someone who delivers tropical fruit to New York

    D. someone who has moved from New York to the tropics

___ 11. In "The Tropics of New York," what memories does the speaker have of his tropical home that he longs to experience again?

    A. stores and crowds

    B. city streets

    C. fruit and landscapes

    D. cars and trucks

Vocabulary and Grammar

____ 12. Which word best replaces *lulled* in the sentence: "The children were *lulled* to sleep by the sounds of the river"?
  A. danced
  B. soothed
  C. cheered
  D. sailed

____ 13. Which line contains a verb in the present perfect tense that shows an action that started in the past and continues into the present?
  A. "There are words like *Freedom*."
  B. "My eyes grew dim."
  C. "I turned aside and bowed my head."
  D. "My soul has grown deep like the rivers."

Essay

14. The title of the poem "Refugee in America" suggests that the speaker in the poem is a new immigrant to America. Is there someone else the speaker could be? Keeping in mind that the poem is written by an African American, write a brief essay to suggest another identity for the speaker of this poem, who speaks of what wonderful words "freedom" and "liberty" are.

15. In "The Negro Speaks of Rivers," Hughes describes rivers in various lines as *ancient*, *dusky*, *deep*, and *muddy*. How might these words also be used to describe African Americans or their history? Write a brief essay to give your ideas.

"The Negro Speaks of Rivers," "I, Too," "Dream Variations," and **"Refugee in America"**
by Langston Hughes
"The Tropics in New York" by Claude McKay

Selection Test B

Critical Reading *Identify the letter of the choice that best completes the statement or answers the question.*

_____ 1. Which line from "Refugee in America" gives you a clue about who the speaker is?
A. "On my heart-strings freedom sings"
B. "All day everyday."
C. "There are words like *Liberty*"
D. "You would know why."

_____ 2. In "I, Too," what does the word "too" in the first and last lines emphasize in the poem?
A. The speaker is part of the American experience.
B. The speaker is a well-known American musician.
C. The speaker is anticipating a radical change.
D. The speaker is American.

_____ 3. What can you infer about the speaker's attitude from "I, Too"?
A. The speaker is angry.
B. The speaker is resigned.
C. The speaker is optimistic.
D. The speaker is content.

_____ 4. The theme of the "The Negro Speaks of Rivers" concerns the
A. long history of the black race.
B. human qualities of rivers.
C. religious beliefs of blacks.
D. travels of black explorers.

_____ 5. In "The Negro Speaks of Rivers," which word best describes the speaker's attitude?
A. arrogant
B. humble
C. proud
D. self-deprecating

_____ 6. In "Dream Variations," the speaker sees day as a time to _____.
A. eat
B. rest
C. dance
D. write

_____ 7. In "Dream Variations," which phrase best describes the "dream"?
A. to have joyous days and restful nights
B. to feel the warmth of the tropical sun
C. to be dark like the night
D. to have pleasant dreams while sleeping

8. Which line from "Dream Variations" gives you a clue about what the speaker looks like?
   A. "To fling my arms wide"
   B. "Dark like me—"
   C. "That is my dream!"
   D. "A tall, slim tree . . ."

9. With which statement would the speaker of "Dream Variations" be most likely to agree?
   A. Night is a time for dreaming.
   B. Night is a time for celebration.
   C. Night is a time for revitalization.
   D. Night is a time for variations.

10. In "The Tropics in New York," the speaker remembers the homeland's skies as being
    A. blocked by skyscrapers.
    B. forever cloudy.
    C. dusky gray.
    D. mystical blue.

11. Which line from "The Tropics in New York" tells you the speaker is not in the tropics when the poem is written?
    A. "Bananas ripe and green, and ginger-root"
    B. "Set in the window, bringing memories"
    C. "In benediction over nun-like hills."
    D. "I turned aside and bowed my head and wept."

Vocabulary and Grammar

12. In "The Negro Speaks of Rivers," Hughes describes rivers as "dusky" to call attention to their _____.
    A. darkness
    B. age
    C. mystery
    D. sadness

13. In "The Negro Speaks of Rivers," the Congo probably "lulled" the speaker to sleep with
    A. rampaging rapids.
    B. a gentle murmur.
    C. a magnificent waterfall.
    D. stillness and quiet.

14. Which line from "The Negro Speaks of Rivers" is written in the present perfect tense?
    A. "My soul has grown deep like the rivers."
    B. "I bathed in the Euphrates when dawns were young."
    C. "I built my hut near the Congo and it lulled me to sleep."
    D. "I heard the singing of the Mississippi. . . ."

____ **15.** Which line from "The Tropics in New York" is written in the past tense?
  A. "Cocoa in pods and alligator pears"
  B. "In benediction over nun-like hills."
  C. "And, hungry for the old, familiar ways"
  D. "I turned aside and bowed my head and wept."

Essay

16. Langston Hughes's "The Negro Speaks of Rivers," created a powerful impression when it was published in 1921. Black readers recognized it immediately as a great poem about their heritage. The poem celebrates the black experience more movingly than any prior poem, and contributes to black awareness and black pride. Write an essay in which you analyze how the poem achieves its effectiveness.

17. Although the pronoun *I* is used for the speakers, or voices, of the poems, in "Refugee in America," "The Negro Speaks of Rivers," and "The Tropics in New York" the speakers are not all the same. Write an essay comparing and contrasting the speakers in these three poems. Whom does the *I* represent in each poem? In each poem, what effect does the use of *I* have on the reader?

Study these words from the selections. Then, complete the activities.

Word List A

beguile [bee GYL] *v.* to charm or delight; to deceive
Each evening, the concert violinist would <u>beguile</u> her audiences with charming melodies.

crumple [KRUM puhl] *v.* to crush together into creases or wrinkles; to cause to collapse
The force of the collision was sufficient to <u>crumple</u> the right fender of my car.

eternally [ee TER nuhl ee] *adv.* everlastingly
Ross was <u>eternally</u> curious about American history and read all he could on the subject.

lean [LEEN] *adj.* deficient; lacking in richness or profit
Last winter, snow was so plentiful that the birds had a <u>lean</u> time, finding little food.

mellow [MEL oh] *adj.* full, rich, and soft
The <u>mellow</u> flute music put me in a relaxed mood.

piteous [PIT ee uhs] *adj.* arousing or deserving pity or compassion
Hannah was in a <u>piteous</u> state, having suffered for weeks from illness and insomnia.

stark [STAHRK] *adj.* harsh; severe
Central Australia presents the visitor with a <u>stark</u>, even forbidding, landscape.

subtle [SUT uhl] *adj.* clever; crafty; not obvious
Pia was <u>subtle</u>, seldom revealing her motivations or intentions to anyone.

Word List B

abject [AB jekt] *adj.* of the lowest degree; miserable; wretched; degraded
The people in the makeshift shanties by the roadside lived in <u>abject</u> poverty.

brute [BROOT] *n.* wild, fierce, or cruel animal or person
The grizzly bear was a ferocious <u>brute</u>, weighing more than a thousand pounds.

glean [GLEEN] *v.* to collect
If you read that book carefully, you will <u>glean</u> much knowledge about the Civil War.

gorgeously [GOHR juhs lee] *adv.* splendidly
The party tent was <u>gorgeously</u> decorated with flowers and colored lanterns.

increment [IN kruh muhnt] *n.* measured portion
Stan regularly deposited an <u>increment</u> of his salary in a savings account.

sable [SAY buhl] *adj.* dark brown or black
The horse's rich, <u>sable</u> coat looked glossy and sleek.

stalk [STAWK] *n.* main stem of a plant
The fresh <u>stalk</u> of celery was very crisp and tasted delicious.

yields [YEELDZ] *v.* provides; offers; gives upon harvesting
That recipe for banana cream pie <u>yields</u> six good-sized portions.

Poems by Countee Cullen, Arna Bontemps, and Jean Toomer
Vocabulary Warm-up Exercises

Exercise A *Fill in each blank below using the appropriate word from Word List A.*

Warren was the best trumpet player in our high school band. In his hands, the trumpet became a magical instrument, able to [1] _____ any listeners that heard it. Some of the pieces Warren liked to play were soft and [2] _____. Others struck the heart, telling of anguish and [3] _____ suffering. These tunes would often cause Warren's audiences to [4] _____, weak with emotion. Sometimes Warren would play a(n) [5] _____ and simple melody—sober, serious, and solemn. He enjoyed both classical and jazz pieces. For Warren, each style had its own [6] _____ aspects and delicate shades of difference. When he was playing the trumpet, Warren felt he moved in a different world. The world of music was everlasting—[7] _____ beautiful and true. Everyday life could be difficult and [8] _____, but in the world Warren discovered in his music, everything flourished.

Exercise B *Decide whether each statement below is true or false. Circle T or F, and explain your answer.*

1. It is hard not to sympathize with people who live in <u>abject</u> poverty.
   T / F _____

2. A bully who picks on weaker classmates might be considered a <u>brute</u>.
   T / F _____

3. You can <u>glean</u> a lot of information from a book if you read it slowly and carefully.
   T / F _____

4. It is not desirable to have a garden that blooms <u>gorgeously</u> every year.
   T / F _____

5. An <u>increment</u> of your salary is twice the amount you are paid.
   T / F _____

6. A <u>sable</u> colored puppy has white fur.
   T / F _____

7. When you pick a flower or fruit, you pull it from its <u>stalk</u>.
   T / F _____

8. Productive agricultural land never <u>yields</u> a good harvest.
   T / F _____

Name _____ Date _____

Read the following passage. Pay special attention to the underlined words. Then, read it again, and complete the activities. Use a separate sheet of paper for your written answers.

Imagery of sowing and reaping dominates the severe, stark poems by Countee Cullen and Arna Bontemps in this grouping. These images have their roots in the sharecropping system of agriculture. This system, developed in the south after the Civil War, was a form of tenant farming. Landowners formed a partnership with tenants, who worked the land. In sharecropping, the owner provided all the operating expenses, food, clothing, and medical expenses for the tenants. In return, the tenants paid the owner in the form of a share of the crop, in cash, or in a combination of both.

Forms of tenant farming are still fairly common in many countries throughout the world. Abuses have occurred, however, when owners wield excessive power or when the tenants are poor or are of less powerful social status. This often happened with African American sharecroppers. Landowners found it easy to beguile and trick them. A slim, lean harvest in poor years left sharecroppers especially vulnerable to exploitation. Faced with a huge debt, a sharecropper would often crumple under the burden. This piteous situation aroused compassion in some and is recorded by Countee Cullen in the line from "From the Dark Tower": "We shall not always plant while others reap."

It takes no ingenious or subtle insight to see that black sharecroppers labored under extremely burdensome conditions. No one could be expected to live this way day after day, to tolerate the hardships of such a system eternally. It is not surprising that, several generations after the Civil War, many blacks migrated from the rural south to northern cities. They went in quest of a more fulfilling, mellow existence. This phenomenon, known as the Great Migration, set the stage in New York City for the great flowering of art and culture known as the Harlem Renaissance.

1. Underline the word in this sentence that means nearly the same as <u>stark</u>. What is an example of a *stark* landscape?

2. Circle the word in this sentence that means nearly the same as <u>beguile</u>. What are two synonyms for *beguile*?

3. Circle the word that means nearly the same as <u>lean</u>. What are two antonyms for *lean*?

4. Circle the phrase in this sentence that offers a clue to the meaning of <u>crumple</u>. Write a definition for *crumple*.

5. Underline the words in this sentence that give a clue to the meaning of <u>piteous</u>. What is a noun related to the adjective *piteous*?

6. Underline the word in this sentence that gives a clue to the meaning of <u>subtle</u>. What is the opposite of *subtle*?

7. Underline the phrase in this sentence that gives a clue to the meaning of <u>eternally</u>. What is a synonym for *eternally*?

8. Circle the word in this sentence that hints at the meaning of <u>mellow</u>. Give an example of how *mellow* music would sound.

Name _____ Date _____

Poems by Countee Cullen, Arna Bontemps, and Jean Toomer
Reading Warm-up B

Read the following passage. Pay special attention to the underlined words. Then, read it again, and complete the activities. Use a separate sheet of paper for your written answers.

When he first started golf lessons, Michael noticed the curious stares that greeted him at the golf course each morning. Not only was he the youngest person there, but also he was one of the few African Americans. Some of the other younger golfers made an effort to be friendly, but others seemed disapproving. Although no one ever said anything to him, somehow this bothered Michael even more. If his <u>sable</u> skin and youthful presence made them miserable, were they too <u>abject</u> to say what was on their minds?

Michael loved the game of golf, the way he could send a long drive down the fairway, arcing gracefully and <u>gorgeously</u> over the green grass. He knew that if he shifted his stance by even the smallest <u>increment</u>, the ball would end up in the trees, ruining his score. However, he had excellent form and concentration. As he swung the club, he kept a mental image of the tall pin that marked the hole, the tiny red flag like a flower on a delicate white <u>stalk</u>.

At first, no one gave him much credit for his talent. They acted as if he were just a wildly powerful freak, a small <u>brute</u> who could hit the ball well because of luck rather than skill. Eventually, though, they began to notice that his balls almost always traveled straight and true, while theirs often hooked or sliced off to the side. People got used to seeing Michael march determinedly down the fairway while other golfers searched for their lost balls, trying to <u>glean</u> the little white orbs in the knee-high grass.

On the putting green, Michael had the most delicate touch of anyone. Eventually, even those who had questioned his talent became his supporters. Michael learned that dedication provides rewards, and persistence <u>yields</u> respect.

1. Underline the words in a previous sentence that give a clue to the meaning of <u>sable</u>. Write a sentence of your own using *sable*.

2. Circle the word in this sentence that means nearly the same as <u>abject</u>. What are two synonyms for *abject*?

3. Underline the words in this sentence that give a clue to the meaning of <u>gorgeously</u>. What are two antonyms for *gorgeously*?

4. Circle the word in this sentence that gives a clue to the meaning of <u>increment</u>. Is an *increment* part of a whole or greater than the whole?

5. Underline the words in this sentence that give a clue to the meaning of <u>stalk</u>. What vegetable might *stalk* be used to describe?

6. Circle the words in this sentence that give a clue to the meaning of <u>brute</u>. Are the connotations of *brute* positive or negative?

7. Underline the words in this sentence that give a clue to the meaning of <u>glean</u>. What is a synonym for *glean*?

8. Circle the word in this sentence means nearly the same as <u>yields</u>. What are two synonyms for *yields*?

"From the Dark Tower" by Countee Cullen
"A Black Man Talks of Reaping" by Arna Bontemps
"Storm Ending" by Jean Toomer
Literary Analysis: Metaphor

A **metaphor** is a comparison between two seemingly dissimilar things that does not use a connecting word such as *like* or *as*. A metaphor may be directly stated or implied. By using a metaphor, the author can evoke images that may help to communicate his or her message.

DIRECTIONS: *Reread the poem "A Black Man Talks of Reaping." Briefly describe the metaphor in the poem on the lines provided. Underline words and images used to support the metaphor in the poem. Make notes in the margins identifying the images and emotions the metaphor evokes.*

Metaphor: _____

_____

_____

A Black Man Talks of Reaping by Arna Bontemps

I have sown beside all waters in my day.
I planted deep, within my heart the fear
that wind or fowl would take the grain away.
I planted safe against this stark, lean year.

I scattered seed enough to plant the land
in rows from Canada to Mexico
but for my reaping only what the hand
can hold at once is all that I can show.

Yet what I sowed and what the orchard yields
my brother's sons are gathering stalk and root;
small wonder then my children glean in fields
they have not sown, and feed on bitter fruit.

"From the Dark Tower" by Countee Cullen
"A Black Man Talks of Reaping" by Arna Bontemps
"Storm Ending" by Jean Toomer

Reading Strategy: Connect to Historical Context

The three poets featured in this selection were part of the cultural movement known as the Harlem Renaissance. This movement took place in the 1920s, mainly in Harlem, New York.

In the early 1900s, many Southern blacks moved to northern cities to escape discrimination, brutality, and crop losses. However, few found a good life there. Many found themselves working again as laborers or servants and living in poor, crowded, areas. Racial conflicts were common.

The Harlem Renaissance featured literature that showed black confidence and pride as well as literary skill. Many of these writers wrote about common experiences in the lives of African Americans throughout the country.

DIRECTIONS: *Reread the three poems in the selection and answer the following questions.*

1. How does knowing about life in the northern cities help you to understand "From the Dark Tower"?

   _____

   _____

   _____

   _____

2. How does knowing about how blacks in America lived—in the past and at the time this poem was written—help you to understand "A Black Man Talks of Reaping"?

   _____

   _____

   _____

   _____

3. How does knowing that the Harlem Renaissance produced literature that showed black confidence and pride, as well as literary skill, help you to understand "Storm Ending"?

   _____

   _____

   _____

   _____

4. Compare the authors' treatment of the subject of life in America for African Americans.

   _____

   _____

   _____

   _____

Name _____ Date _____

"From the Dark Tower" by Countee Cullen
"A Black Man Talks of Reaping" by Arna Bontemps
"Storm Ending" by Jean Toomer
Vocabulary Builder

Using the Root -cre-

A. DIRECTIONS: *The word* increment, *meaning "an increase, as one of a series," contains the root* -cre-, *which means "to grow." Each of the defined words below contains the word root* -cre-. *Rewrite each definition using the word* grow *or one of its forms.*

1. *concrescence*—a merging together of parts or cells

   _____

2. *create*—to cause to come into existence

   _____

3. *recreation*—any form of play that causes refreshment in the body or mind

   _____

Using the Word List

increment	countenance	beguile
stark	reaping	glean

B. DIRECTIONS: *Choose the word that best completes the meaning of each sentence and write it in the blank.*

1. He did not countenance their behavior; that is to say, he would not _____ their talking and laughing in class.
   A. like   B. acknowledge   C. understand   D. tolerate

2. The room was stark, as its furnishings were _____.
   A. few   B. lavish   C. bright   D. ornamental

3. Although she gleaned in the field all day, the amount she _____ was small.
   A. dug   B. plucked   C. collected   D. saw

4. The dance beguiled, or _____, the audience.
   A. bored   B. angered   C. delighted   D. puzzled

5. Late in the summer, the farmer was reaping, or _____, his crops.
   A. harvesting   B. planting   C. tending   D. pruning

6. The patron's yearly _____ helped the city's homeless population.
   A. pay check   B. taxation   C. pension   D. donation

Unit 5 Resources: Disillusion, Defiance, and Discontent

Name _____ Date _____

"**From the Dark Tower**" by Countee Cullen
"**A Black Man Talks of Reaping**" by Arna Bontemps
"**Storm Ending**" by Jean Toomer

Grammar and Style: Placement of Adjectives

The **placement of adjectives** can help set a mood in writing. Usually, adjectives precede the words they modify. However, for reasons of style, emphasis, or variety, they may be placed after the words they modify. When placed after the modified words, adjectives sometimes need to be set off with commas.

A. PRACTICE: *Underline the adjectives, circle the words they modify, and indicate whether the adjectives are placed before or after the modified words.*

1. "We shall . . . Not always countenance, abject and mute. . . ." _____

2. "That lesser men should hold their brothers cheap . . ." _____

3. "And there are buds that cannot bloom at all . . . but crumple, piteous, and fall. . . ."
_____

4. "I planted safe against this stark, lean year." _____

5. "I scattered seed enough to plant the land. . . ." _____

6. "my children glean in fields . . . and feed on bitter fruit." _____

7. "Great, hollow, bell-like flowers . . ." _____

8. "Full-lipped flowers . . . dripping rain . . ." _____

B. Writing Application: *Write a sentence using each of the nouns below and an adjective of your choice. Place the adjective either before or after the noun as indicated. The first sentence is written for you as an example.*

1. thunder (before)
   I heard loud thunder just before the rain fell. _____

2. grain (before)
_____

3. field (after)
_____

4. flower (after)
_____

5. house (before)
_____

6. night (after)
_____

"From the Dark Tower" by Countee Cullen
"A Black Man Talks of Reaping" by Arna Bontemps
"Storm Ending" by Jean Toomer
Support for Writing

Prepare to write a **compare-and-contrast essay** that discusses the structure and style of the poetry of Countee Cullen and Jean Toomer. Enter your ideas into the chart below:

The Poetry of Countee Cullen and Jean Toomer

"From the Dark Tower"	"Storm Ending"
What metaphors are used?	What metaphors are used?
What kind of imagery is used, and which senses does it appeal to?	What kind of imagery is used, and which senses does it appeal to?
What is the main theme or message?	What is the main theme or message?
Explain how the sound or musical quality is gentle or harsh.	Explain how the sound or musical quality is gentle or harsh.

On a separate page, write a draft, including the information from the chart. Give examples from the poetry to support your comparison-and-contrast development. When you revise, add descriptive language that supports your opinions.

"From the Dark Tower" by Countee Cullen
"A Black Man Talks of Reaping" by Arna Bontemps
"Storm Ending" by Jean Toomer

Support for Extend Your Learning

Listening and Speaking

Prepare a **dramatic reading** of two other poems by Countee Cullen. As you practice, follow these tips:

- Think about how the theme and image are connected in the poem you chose.
- As you read, emphasize key words.
- Make your reading dramatic and meaningful.

Read your poems to your classmates and ask for questions and helpful feedback.

Research and Technology

Do research with a group on an artist or musician from the Harlem Renaissance. Use the Internet and library resources to gather information about the person's life, talent, and accomplishments. Prepare a **research report** to present to the class and put in your classroom library. Use the graphic organizer below to organize your information.

[Artist's name]—A Significant Harlem Renaissance Figure

Biographical Highlights	Musical or Artistic Talent	Important Accomplishments	How He or She Is Remembered Today

Present your report to the class. Compare your report with others on the same artist.

Name _____ Date _____

"From the Dark Tower" by Countee Cullen
"A Black Man Talks of Reaping" by Arna Bontemps
"Storm Ending" by Jean Toomer
Enrichment: Social Studies

The Harlem Renaissance was a major development in American history that dealt with the expressed concerns of African Americans everywhere. The writers questioned whether they should use their natural speech and idioms or the accepted speech and traditional forms already in place. They had quandaries over whether to limit their themes and topics to the African American experience or to make their work more universal. Through their writing, they sought to advance their position in society as well as portray the inherent beauty in their people.

DIRECTIONS: *Choose one of the three poems and reread it. Then answer the following questions.*

1. Does the poem use natural speech and idioms or accepted speech and traditional forms? Explain.

   _____

   _____

   _____

   _____

2. Does the poet limit the theme and topics to the African American experience, or is the poem more universal? Explain.

   _____

   _____

   _____

   _____

3. In what ways does the poem touch on the theme of advancing African Americans' position in society?

   _____

   _____

   _____

   _____

4. In what ways does this poem portray the inherent beauty of African American people?

   _____

   _____

   _____

   _____

   _____

"From the Dark Tower" by Countee Cullen
"A Black Man Talks of Reaping" by Arna Bontemps
"Storm Ending" by Jean Toomer
Selection Test A

Critical Reading *Identify the letter of the choice that best answers the question.*

____ 1. In "From the Dark Tower," what are seeds most likely being compared to in this line: "And wait, and tend our agonizing seeds," as the poet describes the history of African Americans?
   A. seeds in a garden
   B. African-American achievement
   C. a crop of cotton
   D. a building with towers

____ 2. What is the historical context of "From the Dark Tower" that refers to the African American struggle for equality?
   A. the American Revolution
   B. the Civil War
   C. slavery and oppression
   D. the election of politicians

____ 3. Since "From the Dark Tower" was written to honor Charles S. Johnson, who edited an African-American journal, what might the references to *bursting fruit* refer to?
   A. the work of African American writers
   B. the work of African American farmers
   C. the work of African American inventors
   D. the work of African American businessmen

____ 4. What does the poet mean by saying in "From the Dark Tower" that the "night . . . is no less lovely being dark"?
   A. The night is as beautiful as the day.
   B. The night is as beautiful as the stars.
   C. African American culture is as beautiful as white culture.
   D. White culture is as beautiful as African American culture.

____ 5. In "A Black Man Talks of Reaping," what does the poet imply about African Americans by saying that others benefit from what he plants?
   A. They work only in farm and orchards.
   B. They work for others, not themselves.
   C. They work so their children don't have to.
   D. They plant only enough to feed themselves.

___ 6. To what does the poet compare the work farming in "A Black Man Talks of Reaping"?
A. making clothing and household goods
B. the work of African Americans
C. selling fruit at a farm stand
D. catching and cooking fish

___ 7. In "A Black Man Talks of Reaping," what is represented by the metaphor of planting?
A. safety
B. human effort
C. gathering fruit
D. watering

___ 8. In "Storm Ending," how is the storm a metaphor for the end of slavery?
A. They can both cause a war.
B. They both represent a force for change.
C. They can both create history.
D. They both represent freedom.

___ 9. In "Storm Ending," what are the "thunder blossoms . . . above our heads"?
A. bells
B. flowers
C. clouds
D. lightning

Vocabulary and Grammar

___ 10. Which word best replaces *reaping* in this sentence: "The farmers are *reaping* the corn they planted last year"?
A. harvesting
B. planting
C. writing
D. destroying

___ 11. Which word best replaces *countenance* in this sentence: "I do not *countenance* impolite behavior"?
A. remind
B. tolerate
C. discover
D. publish

_____ 12. In which sentence do adjectives modify a pronoun?
   A. The loud thunder rolled across the sky.
   B. The red sunset spread across the horizon.
   C. He was tired and muddy.
   D. A sudden wind hit the small boats.

_____ 13. In which sentence do adjectives modify a noun?
   A. The skater was quick and graceful.
   B. He was angry and ready for an argument.
   C. She was sleepy from studying for so long.
   D. Excited, we waited for the fireworks.

Essay

14. Some people have compared Jean Toomer's poem "Storm Ending," to a statement about the end of slavery. How could a storm be compared with slavery? What images would you use to compare a storm with slavery? Write a brief essay to give your ideas.

15. If "From the Dark Tower" is about African Americans and writing, what do you think the poem means to suggest by using terms such as *plant, reap, bursting fruit, buds,* and *seeds*? What might each of these terms mean as a metaphor for African-American culture and writing? Write a brief essay to give your ideas.

"From the Dark Tower" by Countee Cullen
"A Black Man Talks of Reaping" by Arna Bontemps
"Storm Ending" by Jean Toomer
Selection Test B

Critical Reading *Identify the letter of the choice that best completes the statement or answers the question.*

____ 1. What does the title of "From the Dark Tower" suggest about the poem?
A. The poem is from the heart of blacks facing inequality.
B. The poem was written in a tall, dark tower.
C. The reader should watch for a metaphor about a deep, dark well.
D. The poem is about a time before electricity was widely used.

____ 2. Which part of history probably most influenced "From the Dark Tower"?
A. the American Revolution
B. the Civil War
C. the recent slavery of blacks
D. the disdain for agriculturists by industrialists

____ 3. In "From the Dark Tower," which line is evidence of black pride at the time of the Harlem Renaissance writers?
A. "Not always countenance, . . . / That lesser men should hold their brothers cheap"
B. "Not everlastingly . . . Shall we beguile their limbs with mellow flute"
C. "The night whose sable breast . . . is no less lovely being dark"
D. "So in the dark we hide the heart that bleeds"

____ 4. In "From the Dark Tower," what does Cullen imply about the job situation during the 1920's for blacks as compared with whites?
A. It is equal after a long, hard fight.
B. It is the closest to equal it is ever going to be.
C. It is unequal, but the situation is much improved over a few years earlier.
D. It is unequal, but someday this will be changed.

____ 5. What is the theme of "A Black Man Talks of Reaping"?
A. Because generations of black people were poorly rewarded for honest work, their descendants have given up on honest work.
B. The early generations of black people made poor decisions when they planted their crops, and their descendants are suffering the results.
C. The hard work of black slaves is not appreciated by their descendants, who do not understand the value of labor.
D. When farmers have poor luck with their crops, it is not surprising that their children decide to seek other types of work.

____ 6. Which of the following lines from "A Black Man Talks of Reaping" most directly describes the results of inequality?
A. "I planted safe against this stark, lean year."
B. ". . . my children glean in fields they have not sown, and feed on bitter fruit."
C. ". . . wind or fowl would take the grain away."
D. "I scattered seed enough to plant the land in rows from Canada to Mexico."

_____ 7. Who is the speaker in "A Black Man Talks of Reaping"?
   A. the human race
   B. the black people
   C. the present-day farmers
   D. the Harlem youth

_____ 8. "A Black Man Talks of Reaping" is best described as
   A. a series of brief metaphors comparing the stages of a man's life to the seasons of the agricultural year and his feelings to a farmer's tasks.
   B. a single extended metaphor comparing the black race to a family of farmers trying to survive off the land in different parts of the world.
   C. a single extended metaphor comparing the work of the black race to one man's planting and harvest for a single year.
   D. three brief metaphors comparing a man's life to a season's planting, his death to a harvest, and his children's lives to bitter fruit.

_____ 9. In "A Black Man Talks of Reaping," what does the speaker's sowing represent in Bontemps's metaphor?
   A. human effort
   B. the passage of time
   C. the nobility of farming
   D. the futility of work

_____ 10. In "A Black Man Talks of Reaping," what does reaping represent?
   A. enjoying life
   B. dying
   C. being rewarded
   D. harvesting grain

_____ 11. In "Storm Ending," which word best describes Toomer's characterization of the thunder?
   A. beautiful
   B. destructive
   C. frightening
   D. invigorating

_____ 12. Which statement best describes the use of metaphor in "Storm Ending"?
   A. A brief metaphor compares the thunder to a flower, and then an extended metaphor compares it to a bell.
   B. In an extended metaphor comparing thunder to a bell, Toomer also compares it to a flower.
   C. The poem comprises several brief metaphors comparing thunder to various different kinds of flowers.
   D. In an extended metaphor comparing thunder to a flower, Toomer also compares it to a bell and a person.

Vocabulary and Grammar

____ 13. Which word is the closest in meaning to the word *increment*, as used in the following line of poetry?

The golden *increment* of bursting fruit

    A. excitement
    B. increase
    C. color
    D. flavor

____ 14. Which word is the closest in meaning to the word *beguile*, as used in the following line of poetry?

Shall we *beguile* their limbs with mellow flute

    A. relax
    B. charm
    C. surround
    D. drown

____ 15. Which of the following words is closest in meaning to the verb *countenance*?
    A. satisfy
    B. reap
    C. glean
    D. tolerate

____ 16. In the excerpt below, the adjective is _____, and it is _____ the word it modifies.

I scattered seed enough to plant the land

    A. seed; before
    B. seed; after
    C. enough; before
    D. enough; after

____ 17. In the excerpt below, the adjective is _____, and it is _____ the word it modifies.

they have not sown, and feed on bitter fruit.

    A. sown; before
    B. sown; after
    C. bitter; before
    D. bitter; after

Essay

18. Sometimes it is possible to capture the mood of a poem in a single word or phrase. Choose a word or phrase that you feel describes the mood of the poem, "A Black Man Talks of Reaping." In an essay, discuss your choice and why you made it. How does your word or phrase capture the mood of the poem? Support your decision with details from the poem.

19. All three of the poems in this section make use of metaphors to convey their meaning. Select one poem and write an essay explaining how it uses metaphors. What kinds of feelings do the metaphors evoke? Use examples from the poem to clarify your points.

Name _____ Date _____

Writing About Literature—Unit 5
Evaluate Literary Trends

Prewriting: Creating a Scorecard

Use your notes to complete the Imagist scorecard below by listing the criteria you will use to judge each poem. Place a *P* for each criterion that a given poem fulfills and an *F* for each criterion that the poem fails to meet.

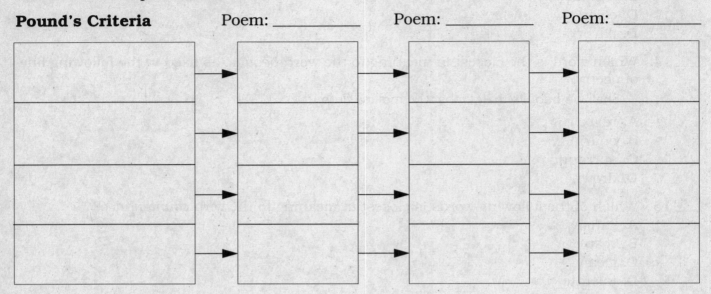

Pound's Criteria   Poem: _____   Poem: _____   Poem: _____

Drafting: Combining Sentences

Use the graphic organizer below to organize the sentences of your essay into paragraphs.

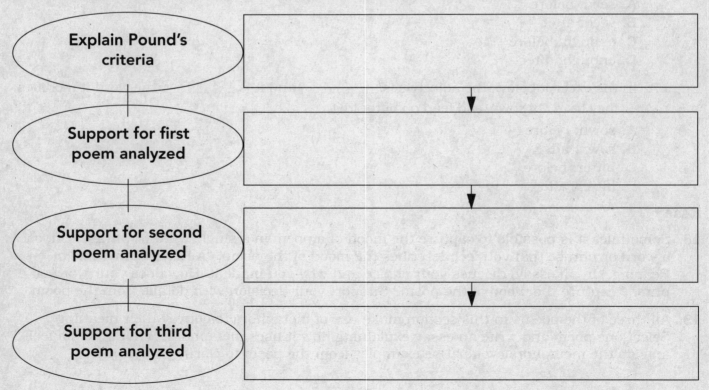

Explain Pound's criteria

Support for first poem analyzed

Support for second poem analyzed

Support for third poem analyzed

Writing About Literature—Unit 5
Evaluate Literary Trends: Integrating Grammar Skills

Varying Sentence Length and Word Choice

When revising your essay, work to avoid using the same words repeatedly. Also, revise your writing to avoid using sentences of the same length and structure.

Repetitive: Imagism is a modern poetic movement. Imagism lasted from 1909 to 1917. Imagism attracted poets in the United States, as well as England.

Varied: Imagism is a modern poetic movement that lasted from 1909 to 1917. It attracted poets in the United States, as well as England.

Identifying Repetitive Sentences

A. DIRECTIONS: *On the line, write whether each group of sentences is* repetitive *or* varied.

_____ 1. Ezra Pound was an Imagist poet. Amy Lowell was an Imagist poet. Hilda Doolittle (H. D.) was an Imagist poet, too.

_____ 2. Greek and Roman classics inspired the Imagists. Chinese and Japanese poetry inspired them too.

_____ 3. Rebelling against sentimental nineteenth-century poetry, the Imagists valued concrete images and everyday language. Their poems appeal directly to the reader's senses.

_____ 4. Ezra pound influenced many modern poets. He influenced Yeats.

Fixing Repetitive Sentences

B. DIRECTIONS: *Rewrite each passage to make the sentences more varied.*

1. William Carlos Williams tried to capture ordinary American life. Williams tried to use everyday language. He rejected some of Pound's views. Williams tried to avoid allusions to history.

_____

_____

_____

2. H. D.'s poems contain musical lines. H. D.'s poems to some important issues of the early 1900s. H. D.'s poems refer to World War I, movies, and new ideas about psychology.

_____

_____

_____

3. Imagist poems are brief and precise. Imagist poems use sensory images. Imagist poems capture the essence of their subject. Imagist poems freeze a single moment in time.

_____

Writing Workshop—Unit 5
Research: Multimedia Presentation

Prewriting: Choosing Your Topic

Use the chart below to create a media checklist by listing specific media that would be most useful for each topic.

Medical Checklist	**Topic:** _____
☐ Music	
☐ Videos	
☐ Art	
☐ Photographs	
☐ Computer presentation	
☐ Interviews	

Drafting: Shaping Your Presentation

Use the chart below to diagram what will occur at any given moment in your presentation.

Text	**Audio/Video**	**Stage Drirections**

Writing Workshop—Unit 5
Multimedia Presentation: Integrating Grammar Skills

Editing and Proofreading

When you proofread the text of the slides or printouts in your presentation, look for **sentence fragments**—groups of words that lack a subject or a verb. Replace sentence fragments with complete sentences. One way to revise a sentence fragment is to join it with another sentence.

Sentence + Fragment:	The coaster has two big climbs and drops. A 95-meter climb, followed by a drop, followed by a 76-meter peak and drop.
Combined:	The coaster has a 95-meter climb, followed by a drop, followed by a 76-meter peak and drop.

Identifying Sentence Fragments

A. DIRECTIONS: *Underline the sentence fragment in each numbered item.*

1. The midway includes international foods. Pizza, tacos, teriyaki, and falafel.
2. Sitting at the top of a big Ferris wheel. You can see for miles in all directions.
3. I remembered to bring my camera. To capture all those special memories.
4. Even standing in line can be fun. Laughing and talking with good friends.

Fixing Sentence Fragments

B. DIRECTIONS: *Rewrite each item so that it contains no sentence fragments.*

1. The sights and sounds of Town Day. Every year I enjoy them.

   _____

2. There is always a parade with marching bands in the morning. And a street fair at night.

   _____

3. Working in a booth can be fun. Waiting on your old friends.

   _____

4. I used to march in the parade with my baseball team. As a kid.

   _____

Spelling—Unit 5
Proofreading Practice

DIRECTIONS: *Proofread the following passage, looking for 24 misspelled words. Cross out each misspelled word, and write it correctly in the space above.*

The study of how we think and behave is called sychology. An important aspect of this study concerns our emotions and personalities. Why are some people caushus and prone to anxiety, while others are agressive and antagonisic? Can individuals increase their creativety or become more couragous? These are some of the mysteries that sychologists try to solve.

Life is always stressfull, and the ways we learn to cope with stress help to form our personalities. Studeous people, for example, find that concentrateing on books helps them to relax and escape their everyday fears. Artistic people find the same kind of release in taking photografs or listening to a symfony.

Active, outgoing people, on the other hand, find solitude and stillness dull and terrifying at the same time. Their syches seek adventure, and they apear to be in continous motion. Sitting still creates a nawing feeling that they're missing out on something. Other personality types might find fulfillment in being generous, reliable, or careing.

Increasing our knowlege of our own copeing stratejies can help us strengthen our helpful impulses and unlearn those that are bruteish or self-defeating. The more we no about ourselves, the better we can juge behaviors that will make us more adaptible and help us function better.

Name _____ Date _____

Communications Workshop—Unit 5
Evaluating Communication Methods

After choosing your news program or film documentary, fill out the following chart to help you evaluate the presentation.

Topic of news program or film documentary: _____

What is the general purpose of the presentation?
What structure is used?
What music or slogans are used?
What images are used?
Do you feel the events addressed by this medium were presented objectively and thoroughly? Explain.

Unit 5 Resources: Disillusion, Defiance, and Discontent
© Pearson Education, Inc., publishing as Pearson Prentice Hall. All rights reserved.
301

Suggestions for Further Reading—Unit 5

DIRECTIONS: *Think about the books suggested for this Unit that you have read. Then, on a separate sheet of paper, answer the discussion questions and take notes for your literature circle.*

The Great Gatsby by F. Scott Fitzgerald

Discussion Discuss the narrator's characterization of himself. What does Nick say directly about himself? What do we learn about him through his actions and from how other characters relate to him?

Connections—Literature Circle Discuss Nick's final judgments of Tom and Daisy. How do these judgments reflect how Nick has changed since the beginning of the novel?

Winesburg, Ohio by Sherwood Anderson

Discussion Evaluate George's interest in the stories of Enoch Robinson, Belle Carpenter, and Elmer. In whose story does he seem most or least interested? Why?

Connections—Literature Circle Discuss how George's attitude toward the residents of Winesburg changes by the end of the tales. Offer reasons for the change based on George's experiences and observations.

Black Voices: An Anthology of African-American Literature edited by Abraham Chapman

Discussion In "The Souls of Black Folk," W.E.B. Dubois said that "to be a poor man is hard, but to be a poor race in a land of dollars is the very bottom of hardships." Discuss your reactions to this statement.

Connections—Literature Circle Discuss the narrator's comments on violence in the Prologue to *Invisible Man*. Do you think his anger is justified? Why or why not?

Poems by Robert Frost: A Boy's Will and North of Boston by Robert Frost

Discussion Describe the speaker in "The Tuft of Flowers." What insight about life does the speaker convey?

Connections—Literature Circle Compare and contrast the two attitudes toward walls expressed in "Mending Wall." Explain which view you agree with, and tell why.

The Grapes of Wrath by John Steinbeck

Discussion Describe the opening setting of the novel. In your discussion, identify the place, the time of year, the agricultural conditions that prevail, and the general mood or atmosphere.

Connections—Literature Circle Describe the state of the Joad family at the end of the novel. Discuss whether the novel ends on a hopeful or a hopeless note.

ANSWERS

Unit 5 Introduction

Names and Terms to Know, p. 2

A. 1. F; 2. B; 3. C; 4. G; 5. D; 6. H; 7. B; 8. I; 9. E

B. Sample Answers

1. World War I was the war during which the use of the machine gun was introduced, making it impossible to attack an opponent's trenches.

2. The Great Depression followed a boom in the economy that was characterized by the creation of new buildings and the rise of entertainment such as radio and the movies.

3. World War II was started by the German invasion of Poland. The mood in America was one of isolationism, as it had been in World War I. However, even though most Americans wanted to stay out of the war, it could not be avoided when the Japanese attacked Pearl Harbor.

4. Expatriates were described by writer Gertrude Stein as "the lost generation," because they represented a sense of despair about modern life.

Focus Questions, p. 3

Sample Answers

1. Americans did not want to enter World War I, although they favored the Allies. When the British ship *Lusitania* sank, taking 128 Americans with it, American feelings were stirred. Two years later, German submarines began to attack the Allies again, and the United States felt compelled to join the war effort.

2. The Great Depression affected the entire nation. Massive numbers of people were unemployed. When Franklin Roosevelt offered Americans his New Deal plan for a return to prosperity, they elected him president. His policies brought about reform and strengthened the economy, bringing the country out of the Depression era.

3. The despair of writers came through in two ways—many of them chose to move abroad, and their subject matter was the grim state of modern living. T.S. Eliot's poem "The Waste Land" defines the sense of hopelessness felt by many. In addition, the uncertainty of the period led to the experimental nature of Modernist writing, the stream-of-consciousness naturalism of James Joyce, and the unique style of a poet like E. E. Cummings. There were other writers, such as William Carlos Williams, who used this period as an opportunity for closer exploration of the world of America, using informational language in his work.

"The Love Song of J. Alfred Prufrock" by T. S. Eliot

Vocabulary Warm-up Exercises, p. 5

A. 1. dusk
2. attendant
3. deferential
4. presume
5. digress
6. obtuse
7. snicker
8. ragged

B. Sample Answers

1. Omar fasted all month, abstaining from food.

2. Since the memory of them malingers, we recall them quite clearly.

3. A meticulous teacher always prepares lesson plans in advance.

4. A wrestler with overwhelming strength can seldom be defeated.

5. Animals that are scuttling across the floor generally move rapidly.

6. Someone sprawling in an armchair usually looks informal and relaxed.

7. If you find a book tedious, you may not even finish reading it.

8. The statue showed the hero's head wreathed with a crown.

Reading Warm-up A, p. 6

Sample Answers

1. <u>hide behind the bushes and gleefully</u>; *Snicker* means to "laugh mockingly."

2. (wrinkled clothes and battered hat); *elegant*

3. <u>sun had just begun to set . . . the dimming light</u>; At dusk it is often hard to distinguish objects clearly.

4. <u>you look too smart</u>; The opposite of *obtuse* is "intelligent."

5. (he had difficulty concentrating . . . to a story about a supermarket); *wander*

6. (just because he was old, people should not presume he was helpless); People often presume comedians are happy because they tell a lot of jokes.

7. (quiet . . . full of respect); *disrespectful*

8. <u>nurse holding him by the arm</u>; John hired an attendant gatekeeper during the resort's busy season.

Reading Warm-up B, p. 7

Sample Answers

1. <u>great . . . strength</u>; *slight, weak*

2. (with crowns symbolizing the tribute and admiration . . .); I wreathed my door with evergreen boughs.

3. <u>full of self-doubt and self-pity . . . fumbling efforts at romance</u>; The opposite of *tedious* is "interesting."

4. <u>detailed scrutiny</u>; *conscientious, painstaking*

5. (larger-than-life character . . . across the pages of the poem); *Sprawling* means "spreading awkwardly."

6. (frightened animal or insect . . . for safety); *strolling*

7. <u>choosing not to take part in the typical routines of everyday life</u>; Sarah read about a person who fasted one day a month for health reasons.

8. remember; The opposite of *malingers* is "departs" or "fades."

Literary Analysis: Dramatic Monologue, p. 8

Sample Responses

1. From earlier parts of the poem, it is clear that Prufrock is attending a party. These lines show how afraid he is of the social situation. He seems to want to turn back. Perhaps he is fearful of seeing the woman he secretly loves and being frustrated by his inability to express his feelings.

2. Prufrock seems to be afraid of the judgments people make about him. He feels like an insect that a scientist has impaled on a pin and is studying in a cold, analytic way. These lines may show his fear of revealing his true self when the world seems to "have him pegged."

3. He would like to be more daring and unconventional ("Shall I part my hair behind?"), enjoy sensual pleasure ("dare to eat a peach"), be more casual and enjoy nature and life ("wear white flannel trousers, and walk upon the beach").

Reading Strategy: Listening, p. 9

Suggested Responses

1. The repetition of *yellow, rubs, window-panes* forces the reader to pay attention to the non-repetitive elements and imparts a sense of expectation that the pattern will continue.

   The imagery of *rubs its back, rubs its muzzle* gives a visual picture of the fog as a cat-like animal, which draws out the first syllables of the first words. The repetition of these words gives the lines rhythm.

2. The alliteration of *t's* and *d's* force syllables to be stressed and that produces the meter of the lines. Repetition of the word *time* and the phrase *Do I dare?* forces the stress on these elements. The rhyme of *dare/stair/hair* (masculine rhyme) stresses these words, supporting the metric pattern.

3. The rhyme of *flicker/snicker* (end rhyme) produces emphasis to the musical effect. The repetition of *I have seen* slows the meter.

Vocabulary Builder, p. 10

A. 1. cut it apart; 2. taken away; 3. different from the others; 4. turn away from it; 5. break apart

B. 1. malingers; 2. meticulous; 3. obtuse; 4. insidious; 5. digress

Grammar and Style: Adjectival Modifiers, p. 11

A. 1. Arms <u>that are braceleted and white and bare</u> (adjective clause)

2. My necktie . . . <u>asserted by a simple pin</u> (participial phrase)

3. a bald spot <u>in the middle of my hair</u> (prepositional phrase)

4. Time <u>to turn back and descend the stair</u> (infinitive phrase)

5. the smoke <u>that rises from the pipes</u>/<u>Of lonely men</u> . . . (adjective clause)/(prepositional phrase)

B. Possible Responses

1. children's faces that shine with enthusiasm
2. a room to relax in
3. bright light from a glaring bulb
4. loud noise piercing my skull
5. bitter taste of lemons

Enrichment: Art, p. 14

Suggested Responses

1. Prufrock may be a balding middle-aged man who stands straight and acts in a proper manner. He is dressed in "correct" conventional clothing. His face has a dignified appearance, but his eyes give away his inner insecurity. His arms and legs are thin, and he appears to be aging.

2. Students might describe or sketch period hats, ties, and other clothing.

3. As students compare their sketches, they could focus on how their own mental images of Prufrock differed.

Selection Test A, p. 15

Critical Reading

1. ANS: B	DIF: Easy	OBJ: Literary Analysis
2. ANS: C	DIF: Easy	OBJ: Comprehension
3. ANS: B	DIF: Easy	OBJ: Reading Strategy
4. ANS: C	DIF: Easy	OBJ: Literary Analysis
5. ANS: A	DIF: Easy	OBJ: Interpretation
6. ANS: B	DIF: Easy	OBJ: Dramatic Monologue
7. ANS: C	DIF: Easy	OBJ: Reading Strategy
8. ANS: C	DIF: Easy	OBJ: Interpretation
9. ANS: A	DIF: Easy	OBJ: Comprehension
10. ANS: C	DIF: Easy	OBJ: Reading Strategy

Vocabulary and Grammar

11. ANS: B	DIF: Easy	OBJ: Vocabulary
12. ANS: B	DIF: Easy	OBJ: Grammar

Essay

13. Students should mention that the lack of a setting may reflect Prufrock's view of his life. He does not know where he is or where he is going. He goes through the motions of life but is unhappy.

   Difficulty: *Easy*

   Objective: *Essay*

14. Students should mention moments that they are aware of as opportunities for greatness, such as studying for a test, helping someone in need, or simply being kind.

They may also note that the word "flicker" refers to the temporary quality of time that goes by quickly.

Difficulty: *Easy*

Objective: *Essay*

Selection Test B, p. 18

Critical Reading

1. ANS: C	DIF: Easy	OBJ: Literary Analysis
2. ANS: D	DIF: Average	OBJ: Interpretation
3. ANS: B	DIF: Challenging	OBJ: Comprehension
4. ANS: B	DIF: Average	OBJ: Comprehension
5. ANS: D	DIF: Easy	OBJ: Literary Analysis
6. ANS: A	DIF: Average	OBJ: Reading Strategy
7. ANS: A	DIF: Challenging	OBJ: Reading Strategy
8. ANS: B	DIF: Average	OBJ: Reading Strategy
9. ANS: C	DIF: Easy	OBJ: Literary Analysis
10. ANS: D	DIF: Average	OBJ: Interpretation
11. ANS: C	DIF: Average	OBJ: Interpretation
12. ANS: D	DIF: Challenging	OBJ: Reading Strategy

Vocabulary and Grammar

13. ANS: A	DIF: Easy	OBJ: Vocabulary
14. ANS: D	DIF: Easy	OBJ: Vocabulary
15. ANS: B	DIF: Easy	OBJ: Vocabulary
16. ANS: B	DIF: Average	OBJ: Grammar
17. ANS: D	DIF: Average	OBJ: Grammar

Essay

18. Students should present their interpretations of Prufrock supported by specific details from the poems. For example, they may say that Prufrock feels his life is meaningless when he claims to "have measured out [his] in coffee spoons." They could see self-doubt in his realization that he is not Hamlet but only a minor character. They could find despair at his approaching death in the image of the eternal Footman. Students might suggest that Eliot meant Prufrock to exemplify a typical man living in an era of uncertainty and anxiety caused by rapid social, political, and technological change.

Difficulty: *Easy*

Objective: *Essay*

19. Students should explain how a dramatic monologue is the perfect vehicle for self-analysis and how the poetic images reveal Prufrock's personality and his response to his social environment. For example, students might mention that a monologue enables Prufrock not only to describe and comment on his external experiences but also to divulge his disconnected, half-formed but revealing thoughts and feelings. Students may mention how the poetic images both describe things and reveal Prufrock's emotional state. Evening, for example, spread "[l]ike a patient etherized upon a table" alerts the reader to Prufrock's depression.

Students will probably point out that a short story would normally rely less on images to convey a portrait of the character.

Difficulty: *Average*

Objective: *Essay*

20. Students should interpret the meaning and significance of the title using examples from the poem to support their ideas. They might, for example, point out the irony in the words "love song" and describe how Eliot undermines the conventions of a love poem to present a portrait of lovelessness. They might also state that the poem is a song only in the sense that it is a poem. In form, it is a dramatic monologue, nothing like a conventional song.

Difficulty: *Challenging*

Objective: *Essay*

Poems by Ezra Pound, William Carlos Williams, and H. D.

Vocabulary Warm-up Exercises, p. 22

A. 1. bashful
   2. scowling
   3. mediocre
   4. suspicion
   5. petals
   6. blunt
   7. rend
   8. clangs

B. Sample Answers
   1. T; An apparition might easily be supposed to be a ghost.
   2. F; *Bizarre* means "very strange" or "weird."
   3. F; A dogma is usually a deeply held belief.
   4. T; Eddies are like small whirlpools.
   5. T; *Instantaneously* means "suddenly."
   6. T; A rumbling sound is a deep-pitched noise.
   7. F; Tatters are usually worn and ragged.
   8. F; If advice is unheeded, it has failed to make much of an impression.

Reading Warm-up A, p. 23

Sample Answers

1. shy; Gwen was extremely bashful and felt awkward about meeting new people.
2. (from many hints and clues in the poem); *Suspicion* means an "underlying feeling."
3. at the area's industrial chaos; *smiling*
4. (tear at . . . his heart with sadness); *tear, rip*
5. (echoing . . . of a fire engine); a loud noise
6. sub-standard; *exceptional, excellent*
7. (toning down); Otis often blunts his criticism of student essays with praise for the paper's positive points.

8. <u>of a large exotic flower slowly opening and unfolding</u>; The garden paths were decorated with fallen rose petals.

Reading Warm-up B, p. 24

Sample Answers

1. <u>strange</u>; *weird*
2. (pleas to stay . . . he left home for good); My advice to train harder went unheeded, and Carol lost the competition.
3. <u>rejects all . . . and stresses the importance of serenity and an open mind</u>; *Dogma* means "something strongly believed in."
4. <u>ragged</u>; My shoes were so old they were in tatters.
5. (immediately); *slowly*
6. <u>"banished immortal" . . . of a deity spending time on earth</u>; *Apparition* means "ghost" or "supernatural being."
7. <u>crashing noisily</u>; We heard the rumbling of a train in the distance.
8. (the river's whirling); The kayaker enjoyed swirling in the river's eddies.

Literary Analysis: Imagist Poetry, p. 25

1. red wheelbarrow, rain water, white chickens
2. Sample response: rain, lights, figure 5, gold, red.
3. Sample response: Most of the objectives of the Imagist poets are achieved in this excerpt: the language is certainly of the everyday variety, no clichés are used, the rhythms are unique and new, the choice of subjects is unusual, the image is concrete, and the language is concentrated. Perhaps the only objective that is not achieved is that of suggesting rather than stating directly, unless the plums are seen as a symbol of something else.

Reading Strategy: Engage Your Senses, p. 26

Guidelines for student responses: Students will choose images that appeal to the senses. For example, from "The River-Merchant's Wife: A Letter," they might choose "pulling flowers," and list it under "See," "Touch," and "Smell."

Vocabulary Builder, p. 27

A. 1. apparent; 2. apparition; 3. appearance
B. 1. voluminous; 2. dogma; 3. apparition

Grammar and Style: Concrete and Abstract Nouns, p. 28

A. 1. gate, flowers (concrete)
2. leaves, wind (concrete); autumn (abstract)
3. apparition, faces, crowd, petals, bough (concrete)
4. wheel barrow, water, chickens (concrete)
5. dust, earth, arms (concrete)
6. wind, heat, tatters (concrete)

B. Sample Responses
2. The beauty of the pink and purple clouds at sunset was overwhelming.

3. Our love makes me think of moonlit nights and long walks along the beach.
4. With a courage beyond his years, the boy stood up to the bully who taunted him.
5. I envision a future with spaceships regularly traveling to interplanetary colonies in which thousands of people live and work.
6. Success to me doesn't mean a fancy house and car or a great deal of money, but rather friends and inner happiness.
7. I was moved by the kindness of the child who shared her sandwich with a homeless woman.
8. Justice is often pictured as a woman wearing a blindfold and holding a pair of scales in her hands.
9. The fear on the child's face stopped his mother from putting him on the roller coaster.
10. Your talent may be awakened someday by a paintbrush, a block of clay, a piano, or a camcorder.

Enrichment: Music, p. 31

Suggested Responses
A. Students should select an individual piece of music for each of the poems.
B. Students should explain the ways in which the music reflects the mood and the musical rhythms of the poems.

Selection Test A, p. 32

Critical Reading

1. ANS: C	DIF: Easy	OBJ: Comprehension
2. ANS: D	DIF: Easy	OBJ: Literary Analysis
3. ANS: D	DIF: Easy	OBJ: Literary Analysis
4. ANS: B	DIF: Easy	OBJ: Comprehension
5. ANS: D	DIF: Easy	OBJ: Interpretation
6. ANS: B	DIF: Easy	OBJ: Interpretation
7. ANS: D	DIF: Easy	OBJ: Literary Analysis
8. ANS: D	DIF: Easy	OBJ: Reading Strategy
9. ANS: B	DIF: Easy	OBJ: Reading Strategy
10. ANS: B	DIF: Easy	OBJ: Interpretation
11. ANS: B	DIF: Easy	OBJ: Vocabulary
12. ANS: C	DIF: Easy	OBJ: Grammar

Essay

13. Students should note that Pound is warning poets not to believe that a poet will be good just because it's a poem instead of prose. If the subject matter is not interesting enough to "go" or succeed as prose, it's also too dull for poetry.
Difficulty: *Easy*
Objective: *Essay*
14. Students' essays should note that sight is the sense mainly appealed to in this poem. The poem likely takes place in the yard of a farm. Students might sug-

gest a variety of other images, such as a barn, animals, and so on.

Difficulty: *Easy*
Objective: *Essay*

Selection Test B, p. 35

Critical Reading

1. ANS: C	DIF: Easy	OBJ: Comprehension
2. ANS: B	DIF: Average	OBJ: Interpretation
3. ANS: C	DIF: Average	OBJ: Reading Strategy
4. ANS: A	DIF: Average	OBJ: Interpretation
5. ANS: D	DIF: Average	OBJ: Literary Analysis
6. ANS: B	DIF: Average	OBJ: Literary Analysis
7. ANS: C	DIF: Challenging	OBJ: Literary Analysis
8. ANS: A	DIF: Challenging	OBJ: Literary Analysis
9. ANS: D	DIF: Easy	OBJ: Reading Strategy
10. ANS: B	DIF: Challenging	OBJ: Interpretation
11. ANS: D	DIF: Average	OBJ: Interpretation
12. ANS: B	DIF: Easy	OBJ: Reading Strategy
13. ANS: C	DIF: Challenging	OBJ: Comprehension
14. ANS: C	DIF: Average	OBJ: Interpretation

Vocabulary and Grammar

15. ANS: A	DIF: Easy	OBJ: Vocabulary
16. ANS: D	DIF: Easy	OBJ: Vocabulary
17. ANS: D	DIF: Average	OBJ: Grammar

Essay

18. Students may take either position as long as they illustrate it with examples from the poems. Students who agree that the statement is a simplistic way of looking at life, for example, may not feel that a red wheelbarrow and two white chickens reflect enough of life to move the reader. Those who feel that the statement has some value may argue that such images allow the reader to consider personal meanings or implications, rather than having them imposed by the poet.

Difficulty: *Easy*

Objective: *Essay*

19. Students may either agree or disagree with Williams's statement but should support their ideas with examples from the three poems. Those who agree, for example, may state that in a poem like "The Great Figure," the fleeting impression of the fire truck with its gold figure 5 is true to life, but nothing more. It represents nothing, and so it is trivial. They may point out that such poetry might have been difficult for people used to complex subjects and elevated language to accept. Those who disagree may state that the Imagists really didn't make such a huge divergence but merely took poetry back to its roots, when poets and readers were connected by,

and found significance in, moments such as a red wheelbarrow and two chickens.

Difficulty: *Average*
Objective: *Essay*

20. Students should develop Pound's vision imaginatively and display an understanding of the image in the poem. For example, they may suggest that Pound's use of the word "apparition" means that the sight of the faces was unexpected, perhaps as the train pulled rapidly into the station. The beauty of the faces is expressed in the choice of the word "petals." The "wet, black bough" may mean that Pound's original poem described a rainy day with people in dark raincoats carrying umbrellas.

Difficulty: *Challenging*
Objective: *Essay*

"Winter Dreams" by F. Scott Fitzgerald

Vocabulary Warm-up Exercises, p. 39

A. 1. catering
2. obnoxious
3. imperceptible
4. irrelevant
5. justified
6. veranda
7. insincere
8. involuntarily

B. Sample Answers
1. We resented it when Ronnie greeted us so <u>contemptuously</u>.
2. Sam was fond of <u>exaggeration</u> and used overstatement in many anecdotes he told.
3. Mel's <u>haughty</u> expression signaled that he had an arrogant outlook on life.
4. The story was so <u>poignant</u> that it moved us deeply.
5. We feared that the vase might fall over because it was balanced so <u>precariously</u> on the shelf.
6. As the tide began to <u>recede</u>, we no longer worried about getting wet.
7. That writer's works <u>transcended</u> her times and appeal greatly to modern readers.
8. Tricia was <u>unconsciously</u> pleased by the music but had no idea how to analyze it.

Reading Warm-up A, p. 40

Sample Answers
1. <u>offensive and even . . . in shady, maybe even illegal, business deals</u>; Tad's behavior at the party was loud and *obnoxious*.
2. (<u>showy, extravagant parties . . . and hypocritical</u>); *sincere, honest*
3. <u>to his guests as a means of impressing</u>; Zena, a successful hotel manager, was used to *catering* to her guests' every whim.

4. <u>this goal . . . all the attention and expense . . .</u>; *validated*

5. (congregating regularly on his splendid . . . and mani-cured lawns); The *veranda* was beautifully decorated with pots of exotic flowering plants.

6. <u>it is not . . . to note at the same time that . . .</u>; The oppo-site of *irrelevant* is *relevant*.

7. (slowly and almost . . .); *noticeably*

8. <u>struggling in a trap that he has misidentified</u>; *unintentionally*

Reading Warm-up B, p. 41

Sample Answers

1. <u>who looked down on everyone else at school</u>; *arrogant*

2. (straight ahead in scorn, as if he wasn't there); *respectfully, politely*

3. <u>into the background</u>; As the memories of that painful crisis began to *recede* in his mind, Sam gradually became more optimistic and confident.

4. <u>the two of them perched . . . a thousand feet above the ground</u>; *stably*

5. (Joshua didn't realize it); Ernie sensed *unconsciously* that he'd found his true career: interior design.

6. (the gulf between them); *bridged, went beyond*

7. <u>suddenly his fantasies of her seemed like a ridiculous . . .</u>; *understatement*

8. <u>he could hardly look at his journal after that, for it had become a lost dream . . .</u>; *painful*

Literary Analysis: Characterization, p. 42

1. In Dexter's mind, anything was attainable.

2. The already rich may have been squandering their wealth, but Dexter's quest for riches makes him deter-mined in his business.

3. Dexter's financial success reflects that of many people after World War I: People who had been the servants became the served.

4. Though a wealthy man by middle age, Dexter came from humble beginnings like other young men of his time.

5. Judy's ideas about love and affection are influenced by a need for wealth.

Reading Strategy: Draw Conclusions About Characters, p. 43

Sample Responses

1. Sometimes Dexter behaves impetuously.

2. Judy probably does not feel sorry about it, and perhaps feels she has been inconvenienced by hitting him.

3. The fact that Judy does not go out of her way to impress Dexter reveals that she does not consider him to be important.

4. Dexter seems to be ashamed of his background.

5. Judy uses her physical attractiveness to cause men to want her and probably forgive her for anything she does.

Vocabulary Builder, p. 44

A. 1. somnambulate; 2. somniferous; 3. insomnia; 4. somniloquy

B. 1. B; 2. D; 3. A; 4. D; 5. B; 6. C; 7. C; 8. A

Grammar and Style: Dashes, p. 45

A. 1. And one day it came to pass that Mr. Jones—himself and not his ghost—came up to Dexter with tears in his eyes. . . .

2. There was a general ungodliness in the way her lips twisted down at the corners when she smiled, and in the—Heaven help us!—in the almost passionate quality of her eyes.

3. He knew that if he moved forward a step his stare would be in her line of vision—if he moved backward he would lose his full view of her face.

4. [His parents] persuaded Dexter several years later to pass up a business course at the State university—his father, prospering now, would have paid his way—for the precarious advantage of attending an older and more famous university in the East. . . .

B. Suggested Responses

1. "That Judy Jones!" remarked Mr. Hedrick on the next tee, as they waited—some moments—for her to play on ahead.

2. He had a rather priggish notion that he—the young and already fabulously successful Dexter Green—should know more about such things.

3. He loved her, and he would love her until the day he was too old for loving—but he could not have her.

4. Early in that summer morning the sun—reddish and swollen—rose slowly up into the hazy sky.

Enrichment: Film, p. 48

Possible Responses

1. Both Dexter Green and Jay Gatsby have fallen deeply in love with, and would do anything for, a beautiful woman who had several suitors in her youth.

2. Both Judy Jones and Daisy Buchanan are beautiful socialites who care a great deal about image and who want only for the world to treat them beautifully.

3. Although the general plots of the short story and the movie are different, the common element is that a man is completely in love with a woman, who returns his love but ultimately sacrifices him for her own convenience.

4. Whether or not "Winter Dreams" is a first draft of *The Great Gatsby* is a matter for student interpretation, although students should support their answers with specific scenes or images.

Selection Test A, p. 49

Critical Reading

1. ANS: C	DIF: Easy	OBJ: Literary Analysis
2. ANS: C	DIF: Easy	OBJ: Comprehension

3. ANS: D   DIF: Easy   OBJ: Literary Analysis
4. ANS: B   DIF: Easy   OBJ: Reading Strategy
5. ANS: A   DIF: Easy   OBJ: Reading Strategy
6. ANS: B   DIF: Easy   OBJ: Interpretation
7. ANS: A   DIF: Easy   OBJ: Literary Analysis
8. ANS: C   DIF: Easy   OBJ: Interpretation
9. ANS: B   DIF: Easy   OBJ: Interpretation
10. ANS: B   DIF: Easy   OBJ: Reading Strategy

Vocabulary and Grammar

11. ANS: C   DIF: Easy   OBJ: Vocabulary
12. ANS: B   DIF: Easy   OBJ: Grammar

Essay

13. Students' essays should reflect that Devlin's view of Judy challenges Dexter's reasons for living his life as he has. To hear that she is just an ordinary, aging housewife makes him realize that his dreams about her have kept him from living a fuller life.
   Difficulty: *Easy*
   Objective: *Essay*

14. Students' essays should reflect that Dexter wanted to have wealth and power. Judy is one of these "glittering things." Dexter never saw Judy as a real person. This quotation shows that Dexter would probably always be disappointed in his life.
   Difficulty: *Easy*
   Objective: *Essay*

Selection Test B, p. 52

Critical Reading

1. ANS: A   DIF: Challenging   OBJ: Literary Analysis
2. ANS: C   DIF: Average   OBJ: Reading Strategy
3. ANS: B   DIF: Easy   OBJ: Reading Strategy
4. ANS: D   DIF: Easy   OBJ: Interpretation
5. ANS: D   DIF: Easy   OBJ: Interpretation
6. ANS: D   DIF: Challenging   OBJ: Literary Analysis
7. ANS: A   DIF: Average   OBJ: Comprehension
8. ANS: B   DIF: Average   OBJ: Literary Analysis
9. ANS: A   DIF: Easy   OBJ: Comprehension
10. ANS: C   DIF: Average   OBJ: Reading Strategy
11. ANS: A   DIF: Challenging   OBJ: Interpretation
12. ANS: C   DIF: Average   OBJ: Interpretation
13. ANS: D   DIF: Challenging   OBJ: Literary Analysis

Vocabulary and Grammar

14. ANS: C   DIF: Average   OBJ: Vocabulary
15. ANS: A   DIF: Easy   OBJ: Vocabulary
16. ANS: D   DIF: Average   OBJ: Vocabulary

17. ANS: A   DIF: Average   OBJ: Grammar

Essay

18. Students' essays should identify traits, supported with examples from the story, that are contradictory in nature. For example, Dexter Green shows contradictory traits in the way he carefully and meticulously plans his professional life compared with the impetuous and often destructive decisions he makes about Judy Jones.
   Difficulty: *Easy*
   Objective: *Essay*

19. Students should cite the attributes of Judy Jones and Dexter Green that relate to the biographer's statement. Students will probably state that the "superlative" qualities that Judy Jones possesses are both exquisite beauty and a high social position, as well as a number of suitors. Dexter Green could be called a "buccaneer" because he is dashing and intelligent, and he is considered a "good catch" by many unmarried women and their families.
   Difficulty: *Average*
   Objective: *Essay*

20. Students should identify two characters and focus on how they embody Fitzgerald's fascination with and distrust of wealthy society. For example, they might identify Dexter Green as a character who is fascinated by wealthy society. Early in the story he excels at golf, a sport of the wealthy. Later he becomes infatuated with Judy Jones, who seems to embody the beauty and flair but also the callousness and coldness of wealthy society.
   Difficulty: *Challenging*
   Objective: *Essay*

"The Turtle" from *The Grapes of Wrath*
by John Steinbeck

Vocabulary Warm-up Exercises, p. 56

A. 1. clamped
   2. plodding
   3. embankment
   4. trench
   5. fraction
   6. boosted
   7. flick
   8. skidded

B. **Sample Answers**

   1. T; An *armored* vehicle is fortified and protected, often with weapons.
   2. T; Immigrants often *dispersed*, or scattered, to different destinations.
   3. F; A *parapet* is usually constructed high above ground level.
   4. F; *Passive* means "inactive."

5. T; *Peered* means "stared" or "gazed intently."

6. F; *Quartz* is a type of crystallized rock.

7. T; *Swerved* means "turned suddenly."

8. F; *Waggling* implies slight, wobbling movement.

Reading Warm-up A, p. 57

Sample Answers

1. the shell, which is . . . on a turtle's back to protect the vital organs of the body; *detached*

2. (or at least improved); *lifted, raised*

3. riverside; From our position high up on the *embankment*, we could see downstream for several miles.

4. (that has been dug to serve as a canal or artificial watercourse); *ditch*

5. slowest-moving creatures in nature . . . at one-third of a mile per hour; *trudging*

6. a large . . . of turtle species are aquatic or sea turtles; *part*

7. (all four flippers rapidly); Every few seconds, the horse would *flick* its tail to chase the flies away.

8. "tourists . . . to a halt and gazed at the mother turtles in fascination"

Reading Warm-up B, p. 58

Sample Answers

1. agricultural interests . . . suddenly, and millions of acres were plowed under; When I saw the raccoon at the last minute, I *swerved* in order to avoid hitting it.

2. (. . . into the future and seem the consequences of this change); *stared, gazed intently*

3. the flat prairie land shimmers

4. . . . their limbs to and fro; *wobbling*

5. (. . . with the water-retaining roots of native grasses . . . unprotected); The opposite of *armored* is *vulnerable* or *unprotected.*

6. the unprotected soil with such force that the dust storms were called "black blizzards"; *gathered, collected*

7. (if you stood high up on a . . . you could see the wind-blown dust being carried for huge distances)

8. (in the face of such a disaster); The opposite of *passive* is *active* or *aggressive.*

Literary Analysis: Theme, p. 59

Possible Responses

1. Story detail: The turtle crawls over the grass, "turning aside for nothing."

   How it connects to theme: Like the Joads, the turtle has a goal—to get across the road—and he won't be deterred.

2. Story detail: "A red ant ran into the shell, into the soft skin inside the shell, and suddenly head and legs snapped in, and the armored tail clamped in sideways."

   How it connects to theme: Anything that might threaten the turtle will be dealt with in whatever way necessary.

3. Story detail: After being hit by the truck, the turtle is flipped over and rolled off the highway. "Lying on its back, the turtle was tight in its shell for a long time. But at last its legs waved in the air, reaching for something to pull it over."

   How it connects to theme: Even though the turtle runs into a temporary setback, it will do all it can to survive and keep going.

Reading Strategy: Find Clues to Theme, p. 60

Sample Responses

1. Oat beards, foxtails, clover burrs, etc.; these seeds all contain the potential for reproduction and renewal.

2. Wild oats become attached to turtle; the turtle picks up seeds from one side of the road—in the same way the Joads start from Oklahoma with the potential for renewal, or having children.

3. Oat seeds are deposited on far side of road and covered with dirt; perhaps the Joads arrive in California and are planted there with the potential for growth.

Vocabulary Builder, p. 61

A. 1. procrastinate; 2. promote; 3. project

B. 1. raised structure; 2. thrust forward

Grammar and Style: Parallel Structure, p. 62

A. For a long moment the turtle lay still, and then the neck crept out and the old humorous frowning eyes looked about and the legs and tail came out.

B. 1. The apples were dipped in caramel before they were placed in chocolate.

2. The faster train arrived in Seattle before the slower train arrived in Portland.

3. A caterpillar changes into a chrysalis before it changes into a butterfly.

4. Marcy's younger sister swung on the swing set before she climbed on the monkey bars.

5. At night, you should turn on a light before you switch on the television.

6. Jamie sleeps on his side, whereas Matt sleeps on his back.

Enrichment: Survival, p. 65

Possible Responses

1. Shell; armorlike covering protects turtle from physical harm; being tough-skinned (not easily ruffled) can be a good characteristic in the workplace; also, hard hats protect construction workers in a similar way.

2. Ability to withdraw within shell; protects vulnerable body parts from harm when danger is present; when going gets tough at work, ability to withdraw for a moment to regroup can be useful.

Selection Test A, p. 66

Critical Reading

1. ANS: C	DIF: Easy	OBJ: Comprehension
2. ANS: B	DIF: Easy	OBJ: Interpretation
3. ANS: B	DIF: Easy	OBJ: Reading Strategy
4. ANS: A	DIF: Easy	OBJ: Literary Analysis
5. ANS: C	DIF: Easy	OBJ: Literary Analysis
6. ANS: B	DIF: Easy	OBJ: Reading Strategy
7. ANS: D	DIF: Easy	OBJ: Reading Strategy
8. ANS: A	DIF: Easy	OBJ: Literary Analysis
9. ANS: B	DIF: Easy	OBJ: Comprehension
10. ANS: B	DIF: Easy	OBJ: Interpretation
11. ANS: B	DIF: Easy	OBJ: Vocabulary
12. ANS: B	DIF: Easy	OBJ: Grammar

Essay

13. Students should say that the truck driver represents an uncaring attitude that nonhuman life is not worth anything. They may suggest that Steinbeck is trying to teach the reader that animal and plant life is more valuable than we realize.
Difficulty: *Easy*
Objective: *Essay*

14. Students' essays should reflect that both the Joads and the turtle travel in a vehicle, a truck and a turtle shell. Both are traveling across a barren landscape which carries with it certain dangers. Both are carrying "seeds" of new generations of life.
Difficulty: *Easy*
Objective: *Essay*

Selection Test B, p. 69

Critical Reading

1. ANS: A	DIF: Easy	OBJ: Comprehension
2. ANS: B	DIF: Average	OBJ: Interpretation
3. ANS: D	DIF: Average	OBJ: Comprehension
4. ANS: A	DIF: Challenging	OBJ: Literary Analysis
5. ANS: D	DIF: Average	OBJ: Reading Strategy
6. ANS: A	DIF: Average	OBJ: Literary Analysis
7. ANS: C	DIF: Average	OBJ: Literary Analysis
8. ANS: D	DIF: Challenging	OBJ: Literary Analysis
9. ANS: A	DIF: Average	OBJ: Interpretation
10. ANS: B	DIF: Average	OBJ: Interpretation
11. ANS: C	DIF: Easy	OBJ: Reading Strategy
12. ANS: B	DIF: Easy	OBJ: Reading Strategy

Vocabulary and Grammar

13. ANS: C	DIF: Average	OBJ: Grammar
14. ANS: A	DIF: Easy	OBJ: Grammar

15. ANS: B	DIF: Average	OBJ: Vocabulary
16. ANS: C	DIF: Easy	OBJ: Vocabulary
17. ANS: D	DIF: Challenging	OBJ: Vocabulary

Essay

18. Students should use examples from the story to show how Steinbeck humanizes the turtle. For example, Steinbeck refers to the turtle as "he" or "him" throughout, calls his front feet "hands," and speaks of his "fierce, humorous eyes." Students might also mention that focusing closely on the turtle's journey across the road makes it seem larger than life and heroic, as when the turtle hoists himself over the parapet. Students will probably agree that humanizing the turtle makes the reader care about him and identify with his struggles.
Difficulty: *Easy*
Objective: *Essay*

19. Students may take either position as long as they support it with details from the story. Those who agree with the statement will characterize many events of the turtle's life as hardships or sufferings. They could cite such examples as scaling the embankment, having the red ant run into his shell, and being hit by the truck. Students who disagree might argue that because the turtle is an animal, the term "hardships" doesn't really apply. The turtle is just following instincts to survive in trying to make his way across the road.
Difficulty: *Average*
Objective: *Essay*

20. Students can either agree or disagree with the statement but should support their position with details from the story. Those who agree might conclude that the seeds are more important to the theme of reproduction than the turtle, who is just one of many vehicles for seeds. They might cite the first paragraph, in which the focus is on seeds and the turtle has not yet appeared, and the last few sentences, in which the "planting" of the seeds is described. Those who disagree could mention the detailed emphasis on the turtle throughout the body of the story, which leads the reader to forget the earlier focus. They may argue that without the turtle, the seeds it carries would not survive.
Difficulty: *Challenging*
Objective: *Essay*

"old age sticks" and "anyone lived in a pretty how town" by E. E. Cummings
"The Unknown Citizen" by W. H. Auden

Vocabulary Warm-up Exercises, p. 73

A. 1. community
   2. statistics
   3. official
   4. scold
   5. folk

6. dues
7. yanked
8. interfere

B. Sample Answers

1. Their argument was so <u>absurd</u> that we could not take it seriously.
2. His smiling, happy face showed that he felt <u>content</u> with our proposal.
3. Louise decided to use the <u>installment plan</u> and paid $40 a month for the TV.
4. Steve purchased a <u>phonograph</u> so that he could listen to his favorite classical music.
5. If you wish to study the mind and human motivations, take a course in <u>psychology</u>.
6. Fred <u>reaped</u> the harvest by picking the plants carefully by hand.
7. Evan was <u>sensible</u> to our point of view, entering into many discussions with us.
8. Jane thought she would join a <u>union</u> to negotiate better with the factory's management.

Reading Warm-up A, p. 74

Sample Answers

1. <u>a neighborhood</u>; The spirit of civic involvement in our *community* is very strong.
2. (seems designed to make Alan afraid. "Vengeance is mine, and I will repay"); The opposite of *scolds* is *praises*.
3. <u>dates of birth and death</u>; almanac, encyclopedia
4. *formal, authoritative; unofficial, informal*
5. (common . . . ordinary people like Alan himself); Over the centuries, ordinary *folk* in that region have produced hundreds of fascinating oral tales.
6. <u>they pay their union . . .</u> ; *fees*
7. <u>tried to . . . it back into place with his hands, but it won't budge</u>; *jerk, pull hard*
8. <u>trying to alter the past</u>; *came between, intervened*

Reading Warm-up B, p. 75

Sample Answers

1. <u>irrational or . . .</u>; The opposite of *absurd* is *logical* or *rational*.
2. (a lot of attention . . . the recognition he gained); figuratively
3. <u>and pleased</u>; *displeased, unhappy, discontent*
4. <u>the dangers of conformity and complacency</u>; *aware of*
5. (appliances, such as a dishwasher, a refrigerator . . .)
6. (reducing their debt by a little every month)
7. <u>the product of a healthy mindset</u>; Since he was interested in the workings of the unconscious mind, Zach majored in *psychology*.
8. (an anonymous laborer who worked hard and belong to a . . .); They might join to bargain collectively for better wages and improved working conditions.

Literary Analysis: Satire, p. 76

Students should write a satirical slogan for each ad campaign and explain how they would present it. For example, to educate drivers about the importance of obeying traffic signs, they might suggest an image of a person being rolled on a gurney to an ambulance with the slogan, "When it said 'Stop,' it couldn't have meant *you*, Bob. After all, you were late to a party."

Reading Strategy: Relate Structure to Meaning, p. 77

1. In time, two children grow up and fall in love. The people in love are everything to each other.
   Structural Elements: The use of a regular stanza, rhythm, and rhyme reinforce the concept of falling in love as a typical aspect of life. The unusual syntax and absence of punctuation accentuate the quick passage of time and the unpredictability of life.
2. Older people give young people warnings about life's pitfalls, but young people usually disregard them.
   Structural Elements: the stanza and rhythm patterns reinforce the predictability of life. The capitalization accentuates the negative nature of older people's warnings. The unusual use of parentheses emphasizes the battle between the generations.
3. According to the authorities, the person fit perfectly into society's mold, purchasing all the customary consumer goods that living like everybody else requires.
   Structural Elements: The use of regular rhythm and thyme accentuate the sameness, anonymity, and predictability of life in modern society. The use of capitalization reinforces the concept that authorities tend to intrude into people's lives, prescribing how people should live.

Vocabulary Builder, p. 78

A. 1. psychokinesis: the movement of physical things with the mind alone
2. psychotherapy: treatment of mental and emotional disorders
3. psychopath: someone who suffers from severe mental illness

B. 1. D; 2. B

Grammar and Style: Parentheses, p. 79

A. 1. (at least in my opinion)
2. (so I've read)
3. (and probably most other people)
4. (if that's the right word)
5. (you'd have to say)
6. (if you'll pardon the expression)
7. (if I'm not mistaken)
8. (and I'm glad of this)

B. Student reviews should use parentheses to set off material that is truly unimportant and interruptive in nature.

Unit 5 Resources: Disillusion, Defiance, and Discontent

Enrichment: Art, p. 82

Suggested Responses

1. Students should recognize that both paintings are drab in color. The palette of the painting by Sample consists mainly of browns, yellows, and grays, in addition to black and white, while the Grant Wood painting is black, gray, and white. The limited colors of the Sample painting suggest that old age is limited, colorless, and melancholy. The monochrome of the Wood painting seems to comment on the dullness of the factory worker's job. The forbidding colors of *Remember Now . . .* reinforce the negative, obstructive nature of old age in the poem. The black, white, and grays of *Turret Lathe Operator* mirror the lack of color and distinction in the life of Auden's unknown citizen.

2. Students should note the stern expressions on the faces of the elderly men as they look out on various younger people in the picture. These men no longer participate, but they do appear to pass judgment. The old age of "old age sticks" is, of course, not represented by actual old people, but by their actions; it is more active and negative than the old age shown in the painting. Wood's lathe operator could be a portrait of Auden's unknown citizen in his lack of distinguishing characteristics.

3. Students may mention that the painting depicts an attractive town and shows people, some of them feature-less, in various life stages, going about their business, just as the poem does. The judgmental expressions of the older men suggest the small-mindedness that Cummings touches on in his poem.

4. Students will probably note that Wood's lathe operator is as nameless as Auden's citizen. Both are singled out only in terms of their job or the role they play.

5. Students should cite some of these points: In *Remember Now the Days of Thy Youth,* youth operates in the light, while old age is in darkness, producing a separation of generations parallel to that in "old age sticks." The figures in the light, like Cummings's youth, seem oblivious to the darkness of old age to which they will move. The figures beyond the porch in the painting are as general-ized as those in the Cummings work. Although the lathe operator Wood paints stands out because the light falls on him, his features are generalized. He seems less an individual than a part of his machine. His position to the side of the machine de-emphasizes his importance. He is as unremarkable a cog in society as Auden's unknown citizen.

Selection Test A, p. 83

Critical Reading

1. ANS: C	DIF: Easy	OBJ: Interpretation
2. ANS: C	DIF: Easy	OBJ: Interpretation
3. ANS: A	DIF: Easy	OBJ: Reading Strategy
4. ANS: B	DIF: Easy	OBJ: Interpretation
5. ANS: D	DIF: Easy	OBJ: Reading Strategy
6. ANS: C	DIF: Easy	OBJ: Literary Analysis
7. ANS: B	DIF: Easy	OBJ: Literary Analysis
8. ANS: A	DIF: Easy	OBJ: Comprehension
9. ANS: D	DIF: Easy	OBJ: Literary Analysis
10. ANS: D	DIF: Easy	OBJ: Interpretation

Vocabulary and Grammar

11. ANS: A	DIF: Easy	OBJ: Vocabulary
12. ANS: B	DIF: Easy	OBJ: Grammar

Essay

13. Students' essays should reflect that all the time youth is ignoring the signs put up by old age, they are growing old themselves. The poet may be suggesting that young people should take advantage of their freedom while they have it.
Difficulty: *Easy*
Objective: *Essay*

14. Students' essays should reflect that the society in the poem does not care about individual feelings. The citizen may or may not have feelings, but no one has asked about them.
Difficulty: *Easy*
Objective: *Essay*

Selection Test B, p. 86

Critical Reading

1. ANS: D	DIF: Average	OBJ: Reading Strategy
2. ANS: A	DIF: Average	OBJ: Reading Strategy
3. ANS: C	DIF: Average	OBJ: Interpretation
4. ANS: C	DIF: Challenging	OBJ: Literary Analysis
5. ANS: B	DIF: Challenging	OBJ: Reading Strategy
6. ANS: C	DIF: Average	OBJ: Interpretation
7. ANS: C	DIF: Easy	OBJ: Comprehension
8. ANS: B	DIF: Average	OBJ: Literary Analysis
9. ANS: C	DIF: Challenging	OBJ: Interpretation
10. ANS: C	DIF: Average	OBJ: Interpretation
11. ANS: D	DIF: Easy	OBJ: Comprehension
12. ANS: C	DIF: Challenging	OBJ: Reading Strategy
13. ANS: B	DIF: Average	OBJ: Comprehension
14. ANS: D	DIF: Challenging	OBJ: Literary Analysis

Vocabulary and Grammar

15. ANS: A	DIF: Average	OBJ: Vocabulary
16. ANS: A	DIF: Average	OBJ: Vocabulary
17. ANS: B	DIF: Easy	OBJ: Grammar

Essay

18. In their responses, students should interpret how the citizen might feel about being treated as a statistic.

They should also suggest how he might want to be treated instead. For example, they might say he would be upset to be considered a statistic. He might wish that the government had been more actively concerned with his happiness and freedom, rather than with his conformity.

Difficulty: *Easy*
Objective: *Essay*

19. Students should support their speculations with evidence from "The Unknown Citizen." For example, Auden dislikes a society that puts a high premium on conforming. He appears suspicious of the materialistic focus of modern life, by which people are encouraged to react to advertisements by buying things they can't really afford (the Installment Plan).

Difficulty: *Average*
Objective: *Essay*

20. Students should choose appropriate elements to support the statement. For example, the poem mixes subject matter about human rituals such as marriage and burials with repeated lines about natural cycles— "spring summer autumn winter" and "sun moon stars rain." Students might also argue that Cummings writes about faceless people (someones and everyones), instead of individual characters, to convey a sense of the universal.

Difficulty: *Challenging*
Objective: *Essay*

Benchmark Test 7, p. 89

MULTIPLE CHOICE

1. ANS: C
2. ANS: A
3. ANS: A
4. ANS: B
5. ANS: D
6. ANS: C
7. ANS: D
8. ANS: B
9. ANS: C
10. ANS: A
11. ANS: B
12. ANS: D
13. ANS: D
14. ANS: B
15. ANS: A
16. ANS: D
17. ANS: C
18. ANS: C
19. ANS: A
20. ANS: B
21. ANS: B

22. ANS: A
23. ANS: C
24. ANS: C
25. ANS: D
26. ANS: C
27. ANS: D
28. ANS: A

ESSAY

29. Possible response: The pig with the brick house in "The Three Little Pigs" has a relationship with his mother, his brothers, and the wolf. Each of these relationships can be explored, for example. Students should use clear, descriptive language in their analyses.

30. Students should begin with a general statement in which they highlight the topic of their essay. They should provide information about the character's relationships and interactions with other characters. Students should include information about ways the character changes, citing events that cause the change or changes.

31. Students' essays should provide historical context to support their descriptions.

Diagnostic Test 8, p. 95

MULTIPLE CHOICE

1. ANS: B
2. ANS: D
3. ANS: A
4. ANS: B
5. ANS: B
6. ANS: D
7. ANS: C
8. ANS: D
9. ANS: C
10. ANS: B
11. ANS: C
12. ANS: D
13. ANS: B
14. ANS: C
15. ANS: B

"The Far and the Near" by Thomas Wolfe

Vocabulary Warm-up Exercises, p. 99

A. 1. lordly
2. meager
3. peril
4. grandeur
5. falter

6. perplexity
7. paralyzed
8. stammering

B. Sample Answers

1. F; *Converging* means "meeting" or "joining."
2. T; *Receding* means "going backward," so the water level would diminish.
3. F; A gloomy or bad-tempered person would not usually be good company.
4. T; The conductor sets the pace of the music.
5. F; *timorous* means "fearful."
6. T; A *tragedy* typically ends in disaster.
7. T; A person's face often reveals clues to his or her emotions.
8. T: A mountaintop might be expected to offer a broad, impressive view.

Reading Warm-up A, p. 100

Sample Answers

1. and break down; *hesitate*
2. (compared to Blenkinsop's. It could pull eight wagons . . .); The Rolls Royce is a *lordly* car: carefully made, very elegant, and extremely expensive.
3. although its hauling capacity may seem very . . . today; *small, modest, lean, inadequate*
4. *magnificence; austerity*
5. (puzzlement, confusion, or . . .); The opposite of *perplexity* is *comprehension* or *confidence*.
6. standing stock still . . . with wonder; The word is used figuratively.
7. unable to get their words out; *stuttering*
8. to pose great danger or . . .; The opposite of *peril* is *safety*.

Reading Warm-up B, p. 101

Sample Answers

1. with a frown . . . depressed at the idea . . .; *gloomy, bad-tempered*
2. (like an old person, winding its careful way over the land . . . slow and . . .); The opposite of *timorous* is *confident*.
3. whose foggy eyes and wrinkled . . .; *face, countenance*
4. the painfully slow . . . of the train's movement; *pace*
5. (silently contemplate the passing . . . outside her window); From the mountain's summit, the *vista* of the surrounding countryside was truly splendid.
6. (appearing and then . . . into the distance); The opposite of *receding* is *advancing*.
7. the complicated network of different tracks . . . like streams into a single river; *diverging, separating*
8. had its advantages . . . it was not such a . . . to be traveling in this old-fashioned way; sad ending

Literary Analysis: Climax and Anticlimax, p. 102

Sample Responses

1. The woman has made a positive impression on the engineer. The engineer expects the woman to be cheerful and friendly to strangers.
2. This passage is anticlimactic because it disappoints the reader's expectation that there is something interesting or exciting to be learned about the women. The reader might have expected, with the engineer, that there was some connection between the engineer and the women, but it turns out that there is none.

Reading Strategy: Predict, p. 103

Sample Responses

1. The engineer will retire soon.
2. Something will happen to change the vision of the little house and the women waving.
3. The town is not as the engineer expected, and the women may not be either.
4. The engineer is about to make some unpleasant discovery.
5. Something about the woman is disappointing to the engineer: she may not be the same woman, or something about her may seem terribly wrong.

Vocabulary Builder, p. 104

A. 1. contemporary; 2. extemporaneous; 3. temporary; 4. temporal
B. 1. sullen; 2. timorous; 3. visage; 4. sallow; 5. tempo

Grammar and Style: Restrictive and Nonrestrictive Participial Phrases, p. 105

A. 1. "To one side of the house there was a garden neatly patterned with plots of growing vegetables. . . ." restrictive
2. ". . . now, schooled by the qualities of faith and courage and humbleness that attended his labor, he had grown old." nonrestrictive
3. "And finally, stammering a crude farewell, he departed." nonrestrictive

B. Sample Responses

1. Her hair, swept back in a ponytail, was red and wavy.
2. Behind the house was a rose garden neatly planted within a brick border.
3. The model, posing gracefully on the couch, looked bored.
4. The lawyer carefully studied the words written on the page.

Enrichment: Art, p. 108

Sample Responses

1. The painting shows mostly houses and barns.
2. It is a farming community.

3. The train might carry passengers and grain.

4. One person is depicted on a horse near the center of the painting. This town probably has a small population, and the people probably spend most of their time working at home on their farms.

5. No, people in this town probably meet strangers rarely. The town is small, and there would be little reason for strangers to come here.

6. People in small towns can be very hospitable and friendly because they live in a community where everyone knows each other and they feel safe. They might be interested to hear the train engineer's news about faraway train destinations and to hear what brought him to their town.

7. Because people in small towns often know most of the people in town, they are sometimes suspicious of strangers. They may live in a small town in part because they do not like the anonymity of cities. Or they may simply feel shy around people they don't know.

Selection Test A, p. 109

Critical Reading

1. ANS: B	DIF: Easy	OBJ: Comprehension
2. ANS: D	DIF: Easy	OBJ: Reading Strategy
3. ANS: B	DIF: Easy	OBJ: Interpretation
4. ANS: B	DIF: Easy	OBJ: Reading Strategy
5. ANS: A	DIF: Easy	OBJ: Literary Analysis
6. ANS: A	DIF: Easy	OBJ: Reading Strategy
7. ANS: D	DIF: Easy	OBJ: Interpretation
8. ANS: B	DIF: Easy	OBJ: Literary Analysis
9. ANS: B	DIF: Easy	OBJ: Comprehension
10. ANS: B	DIF: Easy	OBJ: Comprehension
11. ANS: A	DIF: Easy	OBJ: Interpretation

Vocabulary and Grammar

12. ANS: D	DIF: Easy	OBJ: Vocabulary
13. ANS: B	DIF: Easy	OBJ: Grammar

Essay

14. Students' essays should reflect that Wolfe might be suggesting that one's expectations about others can lead to horrible disappointment, as they do in this story. The engineer's happiness at the place of the women in his life all these years is ruined, and he is destroyed.

Difficulty: *Easy*

Objective: *Essay*

15. Students' essays should note that the writer is warning the reader that the engineer will face a situation he has not expected. Students might reflect that the engineer must now face the real world. In the real world, the women have no interest in him except as way to break up their workdays by waving to him.

Difficulty: *Easy*

Objective: *Essay*

Selection Test B, p. 112

Critical Reading

1. ANS: C	DIF: Easy	OBJ: Comprehension
2. ANS: C	DIF: Challenging	OBJ: Interpretation
3. ANS: D	DIF: Average	OBJ: Literary Analysis
4. ANS: C	DIF: Easy	OBJ: Reading Strategy
5. ANS: C	DIF: Challenging	OBJ: Reading Strategy
6. ANS: B	DIF: Easy	OBJ: Reading Strategy
7. ANS: C	DIF: Easy	OBJ: Literary Analysis
8. ANS: D	DIF: Average	OBJ: Literary Analysis
9. ANS: B	DIF: Challenging	OBJ: Literary Analysis
10. ANS: D	DIF: Average	OBJ: Interpretation
11. ANS: D	DIF: Challenging	OBJ: Comprehension
12. ANS: A	DIF: Challenging	OBJ: Interpretation
13. ANS: C	DIF: Average	OBJ: Interpretation

Vocabulary and Grammar

14. ANS: D	DIF: Easy	OBJ: Vocabulary
15. ANS: A	DIF: Average	OBJ: Vocabulary
16. ANS: A	DIF: Average	OBJ: Vocabulary
17. ANS: C	DIF: Average	OBJ: Grammar

Essay

18. Students should use details from the story to support their interpretation of the engineer's feelings. For example, students might say that the women always make time during their day for this one gesture. This otherwise insignificant gesture makes the engineer feel hopeful and believe that there is always some good in the world.

Difficulty: *Easy*

Objective: *Essay*

19. In their responses, students should clearly demonstrate why the story's ending is anti-climactic. They should use details from the story to support their assertions. For example, when the engineer visits the women, he discovers that there is no particular reason why they wave—their wave is not really the brave, free gesture that he imagined it to be.

Difficulty: *Average*

Objective: *Essay*

20. Students should interpret the engineer's state of mind at the end of the story by explaining why he feels confusion, doubt, and hopelessness and what has changed. For example, students might say that the engineer feels the way he does because his perspective has completely changed. As a person with an important job, he had confidence that led him to shape what he saw from the majestic distance of his train into idealized, magical visions. Up close, from a more realistic perspective, the

people and things he embellished in his visions are ordinary and even unpleasant.

Difficulty: *Challenging*
Objective: *Essay*

"Of Modern Poetry" and "Anecdote of the Jar"
by Wallace Stevens
"Ars Poetica" by Archibald MacLeish
"Poetry" by Marianne Moore

Vocabulary Warm-up Exercises, p. 116

A. 1. meditation
2. script
3. wilderness
4. quest
5. mute
6. suffice
7. genuine/valid
8. valid/genuine

B. Sample Answers
1. We felt those art works were derivative, displaying little original talent.
2. Aldo had an insatiable appetite and could not stop eating between meals.
3. We were shocked at Randy for his insolence during the meeting.
4. The bronze medallions commemorating the anniversary were very attractive.
5. When we met Sally, the tension was palpable and we were very uncomfortable.
6. If you want to remember a journey or trip, you should buy a souvenir.
7. The triviality of her action was such that we forgot about it almost at once.
8. The lecturer's accent made him unintelligible, and we couldn't understood the lecture.

Reading Warm-up A, p. 117

Sample Answers
1. or search; The heroes of epic poems often set out on a dangerous *quest* or mission.
2. (or acceptable); *invalid, unacceptable*
3. as adequate; *sufficient*
4. *jungle, wasteland;* It is dangerous to go hiking in the *wilderness* without a compass.
5. (or text); The *script* for the movie was full of suspense and special effects.
6. or considered treatment; *deep consideration*
7. a place for authentic and true feelings; The opposite of *genuine* is *fake, false,* or *inauthentic.*
8. have tried to define poetry and have scarcely been . . . on this subject; *silent*

Reading Warm-up B, p. 118
Sample Answers
1. soon became an . . . urge and before long Cyrus had enough poems to fill five notebooks; *greedy*
2. (gold . . . like those from the Olympic Games, attached to silk ribbons that the winners got to wear around their necks)
3. but now the darkness and the hush made the tension inside him; When he learned he had passed the exam, his feeling of relief was *palpable.*
4. (lacked originality . . . copying famous rap songs almost line-by-line); The opposite of *derivative* is *original.*
5. bored the audience with ordinary situations; *minor, insignificant*
6. (the meaning was lost); The opposite of *unintelligible* is *intelligible* or *clear.*
7. (raising his fist in anger); *politeness, respect*
8. he would be taking home one of the gold medals; *memento*

Literary Analysis: Simile, p. 119
Suggested Response
Students will describe the associations each simile evokes and then explain possible reasons the poet had for choosing the simile. For example, the simile *like an insatiable actor* might evoke associations of a dramatic moment in a movie or play and of an actor who has a deep and interesting voice. Students might think the poet chose the simile to emphasize the importance of the words and the sounds of the words in a poem.

Reading Strategy: Paraphrase, p. 120
Sample Answers
1. Then the poem's scene changed / The past was in the past.
2. It has to be relevant to the people of the time.
3. wholly / enveloping the mind / so that it cannot go below or rise above
4. Human civilization [The jar] was sterile. / It did not show nature, / It had no part of nature.
5. A poem should be touchable and quiet / As inviting as fruit.
6. A poem should stand still in time / Like the moon as it moves in the sky.
7. A poem should not have an abstract meaning; it should instead really exist in a concrete way. / A poem should just exist.
8. Even as you despise flowery language, / You can find reality in it.
9. these things are important not / because of some deep meaning we read into it / but because they have practical value to us.
10. and can illustrate / fantasy with reality mixed in it.

Vocabulary Builder, p. 121

A. 1. He was <u>dissatisfied</u> with the quality of the food.

2. She had an <u>insatiate</u> desire for fame.

3. The student's incomplete report was graded <u>unsatisfactorily</u> by the teacher.

B. 1. palpable; 2. dominion; 3. literalists; 4. slovenly; 5. insatiable; 6. derivative; 7. suffice

Grammar and Style: Subject Complements, p. 122

A. 1. The actor is a <u>metaphysician</u> in the dark—a noun identifying the subject

2. The jar was <u>gray</u>—an adjective describing the subject

3. A poem should be <u>motionless</u>—an adjective describing the subject

4. all these phenomena are <u>important</u>—an adjective describing the subject

B. Sample Answers

1. The piano is Steve's favorite musical instrument.

2. The experience was very emotional for Sarah.

3. This area is considered a wilderness.

4. The eagle is a bird of prey.

5. The brightest light in the night sky is the moon.

Enrichment: Photography, p. 125

Possible Responses

1. Wallace Stevens felt that the goal of poetry is to capture the interaction between the imagination and the real world. He might interpret the scene in the photograph as a piece of the real world to be ordered by the imagination. The moon may symbolize using the mind to create a perspective on the natural world. A line that supports this interpretation is "It took dominion everywhere" from "Anecdote of the Jar."

2. Archibald MacLeish wrote "Ars Poetica" in an experimental, Modernist form. He might interpret the scene in the photograph as an image that portrays an idea. A line that supports this interpretation is "A poem should be motionless in time/As the moon climbs."

3. Marianne Moore's "Poetry" suggests that a good poem describes "imaginary gardens with real toads in them." She might interpret the scene in the photograph as a real-world setting for an imagined action. A line that supports this interpretation, in addition to the quoted line about imaginary gardens, is "If you demand on the one hand,/the raw material of poetry in/all its rawness and/that which is on the other hand/genuine, you are interested in poetry."

Selection Test A, p. 126

Critical Reading

1. ANS: C	DIF: Easy	OBJ: Comprehension
2. ANS: B	DIF: Easy	OBJ: Reading Strategy
3. ANS: B	DIF: Easy	OBJ: Comprehension
4. ANS: B	DIF: Easy	OBJ: Literary Analysis
5. ANS: B	DIF: Easy	OBJ: Interpretation
6. ANS: B	DIF: Easy	OBJ: Literary Analysis
7. ANS: C	DIF: Easy	OBJ: Literary Analysis
8. ANS: C	DIF: Easy	OBJ: Reading Strategy
9. ANS: A	DIF: Easy	OBJ: Interpretation
10. ANS: B	DIF: Easy	OBJ: Comprehension
11. ANS: C	DIF: Easy	OBJ: Reading Strategy

Vocabulary and Grammar

12. ANS: C	DIF: Easy	OBJ: Vocabulary
13. ANS: B	DIF: Easy	OBJ: Grammar

Essay

14. Students' essays should reflect that Stevens believes modern poetry has to use speech that is familiar to people. Students may suggest that modern poetry must address the concerns of the poet's audience, such as war or hunger.

Difficulty: *???*

Objective: *Essay*

15. Students' essays should suggest that MacLeish says that poetry is most effective when it creates images that stand apart from the words used. When MacLeish says a poem should not mean, but be, perhaps he is suggesting that a good poem should not talk about meaning anything, but be a new thing in itself.

Difficulty: *???*

Objective: *Essay*

Selection Test B, p. 129

Critical Reading

1. ANS: B	DIF: Average	OBJ: Interpretation
2. ANS: D	DIF: ???	OBJ: ???
3. ANS: C	DIF: Average	OBJ: Literary Analysis
4. ANS: C	DIF: Challenging	OBJ: Interpretation
5. ANS: B	DIF: Challenging	OBJ: Reading Strategy
6. ANS: B	DIF: Easy	OBJ: Literary Analysis
7. ANS: B	DIF: Easy	OBJ: Literary Analysis
8. ANS: A	DIF: Challenging	OBJ: Literary Analysis
9. ANS: C	DIF: Easy	OBJ: Interpretation
10. ANS: D	DIF: Average	OBJ: Reading Strategy
11. ANS: A	DIF: Average	OBJ: Reading Strategy
12. ANS: A	DIF: Average	OBJ: Interpretation

Vocabulary and Grammar

13. ANS: A	DIF: Average	OBJ: Grammar
14. ANS: D	DIF: Easy	OBJ: Vocabulary

15. ANS: A   DIF: Average   OBJ: Grammar
16. ANS: C   DIF: Average   OBJ: Vocabulary
17. ANS: D   DIF: Average   OBJ: Vocabulary

Essay

18. Students may choose any of the other three poems in the selection and identify lines or images that are memorable to them. For example, they might choose MacLeish's "A poem should not mean/But be" because it is such a strong and simple definition of a poem. Or students might consider the opening lines of Moore's "Poetry" significant because the poet admits to sharing readers' negative feelings about poetry. Students will probably feel that the "imaginary gardens" image is effective because it gives a vivid impression of fantasy mixed with reality, which captures what poetry is all about.
Difficulty: *Easy*
Objective: *Essay*

19. Students may take either position as long as it is supported by details from the two poems. Those who feel that examples are most effective might suggest that if a poem cannot be explained, it can only be likened to something else, like a "globed fruit" or "the flight of birds." They may point out that Stevens also uses examples in likening a poem to "an insatiable actor." Students who prefer Stevens's approach may argue, for example, that his description of what a poem does or must do, such as "learn the speech of the place," makes it easier to grasp his idea of poetry.
Difficulty: *Average*
Objective: *Essay*

20. Students may take either position as long as it is supported by examples from "Anecdote of the Jar." Some students may think the poem is realistic because it is filled with realistic, concrete images. Other students may think the poem is unrealistic because the concrete image of the jar symbolizes the much broader abstraction of human civilization and because the concrete image of the Tennessee wilderness stands for the natural world in general.
Difficulty: *Challenging*
Objective: *Essay*

"In Another Country" by Ernest Hemingway
"The Corn Planting" by Sherwood Anderson
"A Worn Path" by Eudora Welty

Vocabulary Warm-up Exercises, p. 133

A. 1. grave
2. detached
3. invalid
4. notion
5. ceremonial
6. illustrated

7. inclined
8. rigidity

B. **Sample Answers**
1. T; Since *blurted* means "uttered rapidly," this statement is true.
2. F; *Citations* are normally issued to soldiers for bravery.
3. F; *Illumined* means "lit up."
4. F; Since *intent* means "engrossed" or "focused," the person would be interested.
5. T; Hours of exercise would make a gymnast's body flexible.
6. F; *Loitered* means "dawdled," so it is unlikely that the students would get home early.
7. F; *Lurched* means "staggered" or "rolled suddenly."
8. F; Shrunken, dried-up flowers would not look attractive.

Reading Warm-up A, p. 134
Sample Answers
1. and lasting impression; Bank robbery is a *grave* offense, and the law punishes it severely.
2. (was wounded . . . at a hospital); Aunt Rose suffered from severe rheumatoid arthritis, and she was an *invalid* for many years.
3. it was almost impossible to remain uninvolved; *aloof*
4. (a graphically . . . magazine article); *illustration*
5. (or idea); Pam had a *notion* that she would like to travel to France sometime soon.
6. far from being . . . or noble activity, warfare was a brutal, chaotic pursuit; *informal, casual*
7. (the selfishness . . . with which nations pursued their nationalistic self-interest); The opposite of *rigidity* is *flexibility*.
8. The phrase "toward waging war" serves as a clue; *leaned, had a tendency toward*

Reading Warm-up B, p. 135
Sample Answers
1. . . . on learning everything she can about the subject; Thatcher was *intent* on improving his tennis game, and he spent hours practicing on the court.
2. (. . . for several hours after school); *hurried, rushed*
3. she was so excited that she . . . all the details
4. a bit awkwardly into her narration; *staggered, rolled suddenly*
5. (could keep its body . . . and agile); The opposite of *limber* is *stiff* or *inflexible*.
6. dried-up; *fresh, vigorous*
7. (the fire . . . with brightness)
8. (as the symbol of immortality); positive

Literary Analysis: Point of View, p. 136
1. second-person; 2. first-person; 3. third-person;
4. first-person

Reading Strategy: Identify with Characters, p. 137

Sample Responses

1. In this passage, the major appears to be very particular about grammar. If he were a grotesque, he might not be interested in anything else and might go through life correcting everyone's grammar.

2. The old people are curious and eager. If they were grotesques, they might go to the city and explore every part of it.

Vocabulary Builder, p. 138

A. 1. B; 2. D; 3. C; 4. A
B. 1. grave; 2. obstinate; 3. invalided; 4. limber

Grammar and Style: Punctuating Dialogue, p. 139

A. 1. character's words; 2. entire sentence; 3. character's words; 4. entire sentence; 5. entire sentence

Enrichment: Health, p. 142

Sample Responses

Story: "In Another Country"; *Character:* the Major; *Reason for Grief:* death of his wife; *Ways of Coping:* working out on the machines; *What the Character Hopes For:* that his hand may get better

Story: "The Corn Planting"; *Character:* the Hutchensons; *Reason for Grief:* death of their son; *Ways of Coping:* planting corn; *What the Character Hopes For:* that the corn will grow

Story: "A Worn Path"; *Character:* Phoenix Jackson; *Reason for Grief:* illness of her grandson; *Ways of Coping:* walking to get medicine and a present for her grandson; *What the Character Hopes For:* that her grandson will heal or at least be happy

1. Each of the characters uses hard work to cope with grief.

2. The characters feel that their work and effort may help them get what they hope for.

From the Author's Desk

Tim O'Brien Introduces "Ambush", p. 143

1. He means that it has a beginning, a middle, and an end; it can be understood and appreciated with no additional information.

2. The story is fiction, since the character Tim in the narrative is not identical with the author in real life, even though their names are the same.

3. Sample answers: **Factual Details:** mosquitoes, trail junction, dark night, tension, three shadowy enemy soldiers; **Fictional Details:** throwing a hand grenade, inspection of the body, gaping at the dead soldier.

4. Answers will vary. Some students will agree that O'Brien is responsible, since his participation in the violence implicates him; others will argue he is not responsible, since he cannot be sure that it was a bullet from his weapon that killed the enemy soldier.

5. The main purpose in writing the story was to express a kind of confession or a lament. The story was the author's effort to acknowledge his responsibility for the death of a fellow human being.

Tim O'Brien

Listening and Viewing, p. 144

Sample answers and guidelines for evaluation:

Segment 1: In both fiction and magic, one must create the illusion that something is really happening even though the audience knows it is not real. Fictional books are true in an emotional and spiritual sense as they connect with human experiences, whether or not they actually happened.

Segment 2: The story "Ambush" includes real events, places, and names while most of the details of the story are entirely fictional. Using the word *I* gives the story a sense of authority and actuality. Students may answer that reading a story from a first-person perspective makes the story more realistic and credible.

Segment 3: Students may answer that revision is important because it allows them the opportunity to improve their writing. He knows that his story is finished when it "feels finished" and when the story has a harmony and sounds resolved.

Segment 4: Stories have the power to console, inspire, lead through tough times, and help us heal. Students may suggest that writing stories can bring out the most exciting and interesting parts of their lives and personalities.

Selection Test A, p. 145

Critical Reading

1. ANS: B	DIF: Easy	OBJ: Comprehension
2. ANS: B	DIF: Easy	OBJ: Literary Analysis
3. ANS: C	DIF: Easy	OBJ: Reading Strategy
4. ANS: C	DIF: Easy	OBJ: Interpretation
5. ANS: D	DIF: Easy	OBJ: Literary Analysis
6. ANS: C	DIF: Easy	OBJ: Interpretation
7. ANS: A	DIF: Easy	OBJ: Interpretation
8. ANS: C	DIF: Easy	OBJ: Literary Analysis
9. ANS: B	DIF: Easy	OBJ: Reading Strategy
10. ANS: B	DIF: Easy	OBJ: Comprehension
11. ANS: B	DIF: Easy	OBJ: Interpretation

Vocabulary and Grammar

12. ANS: C	DIF: Easy	OBJ: Vocabulary
13. ANS: B	DIF: Easy	OBJ: Grammar

Essay

14. Students' should mention that the narrator feels he has not done brave deeds in battle, and he thinks the others have done so. The narrator has gotten his medals because he is an American, while the other men have received their medals specifically for their wounds.

Difficulty: *Easy*

Objective: *Essay*

15. Students' essays might reflect that the grandson is dead because it takes Phoenix so long to answer the nurse's question about him. Other students may think he is still alive, because Phoenix has come to get his medicine and plans to buy him a Christmas gift. Students may take either position and justify it with evidence from the story.

Difficulty: *Easy*

Objective: *Essay*

Selection Test B, p. 148

Critical Reading

1. ANS: A	DIF: Challenging	OBJ: Interpretation
2. ANS: A	DIF: Easy	OBJ: Reading Strategy
3. ANS: C	DIF: Easy	OBJ: Comprehension
4. ANS: B	DIF: Average	OBJ: Interpretation
5. ANS: A	DIF: Challenging	OBJ: Comprehension
6. ANS: C	DIF: Challenging	OBJ: Literary Analysis
7. ANS: A	DIF: Average	OBJ: Literary Analysis
8. ANS: B	DIF: Easy	OBJ: Reading Strategy
9. ANS: A	DIF: Challenging	OBJ: Reading Strategy
10. ANS: B	DIF: Average	OBJ: Interpretation
11. ANS: C	DIF: Average	OBJ: Literary Analysis
12. ANS: A	DIF: Easy	OBJ: Literary Analysis
13. ANS: D	DIF: Average	OBJ: Reading Strategy

Vocabulary and Grammar

14. ANS: D	DIF: Average	OBJ: Grammar
15. ANS: A	DIF: Average	OBJ: Vocabulary
16. ANS: B	DIF: Average	OBJ: Vocabulary
17. ANS: D	DIF: Easy	OBJ: Vocabulary

Essay

18. Students should describe Hal's character, using details from the story that relate to his involvement with the Hutchensons. They might mention that he appears to be a good person in befriending Will in Chicago. He appears to be very kind and caring, since he visits the Hutchensons regularly and is reluctant to give the Hutchensons the news of their son's death. Except that he was educated in Chicago and is a high school principal, we know nothing else about him.

Difficulty: *Easy*

Objective: *Essay*

19. Students should use examples from the stories to compare Phoenix Jackson and the major. For example, both characters respond to their troubles by maintaining a hard discipline with little complaint: Phoenix regularly makes the difficult journey, and the major comes to the hospital daily and keeps his grief mostly to himself. If students believe that Phoenix's grandson is dead, then she and the major are alike in their difficulty in accepting the death of a loved one. For differences, students could refer to their nationalities, gender, education, and circumstances.

Difficulty: *Average*

Objective: *Essay*

20. Students should use examples from the stories in discussing the role of the narrators and their involvement with the events. They may mention, for example, that the narrator of "In Another Country" plays a more direct role in the story's events, although he also tells about other characters. The first-person point of view brings the reader closer to the tragedies of war. In "The Corn Planting," much of what the narrator reports is hearsay from Hal, such as the letters from Will and his parents' reaction to them. At the end, the narrator becomes a direct observer and provides a unique perspective on the strangeness of the old couple's act.

Difficulty: *Challenging*

Objective: *Essay*

"Chicago" and "Grass" by Carl Sandburg

Vocabulary Warm-up Exercises, p. 152

A.
1. butcher
2. vivid
3. conductor
4. flinging
5. freight
6. husky
7. luring
8. wicked

B. Sample Answers

1. Carl, <u>bragging</u> about his ability at math, was very arrogant about his grades.
2. We found the children <u>brawling</u>, fighting together like cats and dogs.
3. The fabric of that shirt is <u>coarse</u>, extremely rough and irregular to the touch.
4. When you go shopping, it is never advisable to trust a <u>cunning</u> salesperson.
5. A person's <u>destiny</u> often lies far off in the future.
6. I always disliked it when Jeremy would <u>sneer</u> at other people.
7. Yanick found that work at the factory was very difficult, amounting to endless <u>toil</u>.

8. Paul's inconsiderate, irresponsible behavior struck us as almost <u>wanton</u>.

Reading Warm-up A, p. 153

Sample Answers

1. <u>big . . . with huge wrists and forearms</u>; The captain of the wrestling team was a *husky* senior named Dennis.
2. <u>(. . . that Jacob could see the people and the action as if in a movie)</u>; The opposite of *vivid* is *vague* or *indistinct.*
3. <u>full of criminals and every other kind of . . . person</u>; *evil, immoral*
4. <u>(at the slaughterhouses, whose job was cutting cattle up into steaks)</u>
5. <u>(the doors . . . on their hinges from his mighty shove)</u>; *energetic, wild*
6. <u>(his eyes . . . away from the slaughterhouse)</u>; *repelling*
7. <u>collecting tickets on the trains</u>
8. <u>a train arriving in town . . . of copper wire</u>; *cargo*

Reading Warm-up B, p. 154

Sample Answers

1. <u>fate or</u>; From an early age, Alexander the Great seems to have been aware of his special *destiny* to become a great conqueror.
2. <u>(fights of the urban masses)</u>; excited, aggressive
3. <u>cockiness of a tough industrial city on the move</u>; *Bragging* about her ability as a gardener, old Mrs. Thwackum showed us her roses.
4. <u>rough . . . of Chicago's working class</u>; *refined*
5. <u>(long days of backbreaking)</u>; *strain*
6. <u>(deceived and exploited)</u>; negative
7. <u>mocking them for their poverty and ignorance</u>

<u>irresponsible and . . . disregard</u>; *prudent, conscient*

Literary Analysis: Apostrophe, p. 155

Sample Responses

1. Clue #1: The address at the beginning of the poem: "Hog Butcher of the World," etc.; Clue #2: The use of *you* in the first section of the poem; Clue #3: The use of the imperative in the second half of the second section of the poem
2. Chicago and its critics
3. The conversation might have been a debate between Chicago and its critics.
4. Sandburg might have written a first-person account of his experiences in Chicago, or he might have written a poem that neutrally compared the good and bad points of Chicago.

Reading Strategy: Respond, p. 156

Suggested Response

Students should find appropriate passages from the poems to analyze using the table. They may need to use encyclope-

dias or other reference sources to fill in the column relating to background knowledge. Their opinions or responses about the passages will vary, but should be connected in some way to the poems.

Vocabulary Builder, p. 157

A. 1. C; 2. A; 3. B
B. 1. cunning; 2. wanton; 3. brutal; 4. brutal; 5. cunning

Grammar and Style: Sentence Types, p. 158

A. 1. declarative; 2. imperative; 3. interrogative; 4. imperative
B. Sample Answers
1. Have you seen the painted women under the gas lamps luring the farm boys?
2. The gunman killed and was set free to kill again!
3. Look at the tall bold slugger set vivid against the little soft cities.
4. The bodies are piled high at Austerlitz and Waterloo.

Enrichment: Career in Marketing, p. 161

Suggested Responses

1. Students should choose an appropriate plant, animal, or force of nature for comparison to their community.
2. Have students consider the predominant type of worker in their community. For example, a coastal fishing town might be best compared to, or exemplified by, a person who fishes for a living.
3. Have students consider the basis of their community's economy. For example, a rural farming community might provide food, such as milk and produce, to a large city within the state.
4. Paragraphs should reflect a student's community and cast it in a positive light.

Selection Test A, p. 162

Critical Reading

1. ANS: C	DIF: Easy	OBJ: Literary Analysis
2. ANS: B	DIF: Easy	OBJ: Comprehension
3. ANS: C	DIF: Easy	OBJ: Interpretation
4. ANS: A	DIF: Easy	OBJ: Reading Strategy
5. ANS: D	DIF: Easy	OBJ: Comprehension
6. ANS: C	DIF: Easy	OBJ: Literary Analysis
7. ANS: C	DIF: Easy	OBJ: Literary Analysis
8. ANS: B	DIF: Easy	OBJ: Reading Strategy
9. ANS: C	DIF: Easy	OBJ: Comprehension
10. ANS: B	DIF: Easy	OBJ: Reading Strategy
11. ANS: A	DIF: Easy	OBJ: Interpretation

Vocabulary and Grammar

12. ANS: B   DIF: Easy   OBJ: Vocabulary
13. ANS: C   DIF: Easy   OBJ: Grammar

Essay

14. Students' essays should suggest that Sandburg is proud of Chicago's size, activity, loudness, and all the qualities that set it apart from smaller, quieter, rural cities and towns. Using the word "slugger" suggests an active person, such as a fighter or a baseball player.
   Difficulty: *Easy*
   Objective: *Essay*

15. Students' essays should reflect either that the grass does not care about humankind's wars or that the grass is trying to awaken humans about the pointlessness of war.
   Difficulty: *Easy*
   Objective: *Essay*

Selection Test B, p. 165

Critical Reading

1. ANS: D   DIF: Challenging   OBJ: Interpretation
2. ANS: B   DIF: Easy   OBJ: Literary Analysis
3. ANS: A   DIF: Challenging   OBJ: Literary Analysis
4. ANS: B   DIF: Easy   OBJ: Reading Strategy
5. ANS: D   DIF: Easy   OBJ: Reading Strategy
6. ANS: D   DIF: Average   OBJ: Comprehension
7. ANS: C   DIF: Challenging   OBJ: Comprehension
8. ANS: A   DIF: Average   OBJ: Interpretation
9. ANS: D   DIF: Average   OBJ: Reading Strategy
10. ANS: B   DIF: Average   OBJ: Reading Strategy
11. ANS: A   DIF: Challenging   OBJ: Interpretation
12. ANS: A   DIF: Easy   OBJ: Literary Analysis
13. ANS: A   DIF: Average   OBJ: Interpretation

Vocabulary and Grammar

14. ANS: B   DIF: Average   OBJ: Grammar
15. ANS: D   DIF: Easy   OBJ: Vocabulary
16. ANS: C   DIF: Average   OBJ: Vocabulary
17. ANS: D   DIF: Average   OBJ: Grammar

Essay

18. Student essays should discuss the charges against the city and the verdict of the speaker, using examples from the poem. For example, they might point out that the speaker actually agrees with the critics that Chicago is a city of poverty and crime, yet he finds its youthful vitality, its will to work hard, and its ability to laugh at adversity admirable.
   Difficulty: *Easy*
   Objective: *Essay*

19. Students should pick an image that captures other aspects of the city giving strong reasons for their choices. For example, they might choose an image of building: structures rising from the prairie created by the people—architects, businesspeople, and workers interacting as a team to make a better life for all.
   Difficulty: *Average*
   Objective: *Essay*

20. Students may choose either interpretation as long as they support it with details from the poem. For example, students who understand the poem as a reflection on the statement "Time heals all wounds" may say that it stresses the fact that the physical scars of war are quickly erased by nature. Those who read the poem as an illustration of the point-lessness of war might suggest that as the physical scars of war disappear, so the reasons for fighting the war may be forgotten.
   Difficulty: *Challenging*
   Objective: *Essay*

"The Jilting of Granny Weatherall"
by Katherine Anne Porter

Vocabulary Warm-up Exercises, p. 169

A.
1. circulation
2. exchanged
3. tactful
4. fumbled
5. marvel
6. rummaging
7. jilted
8. huddled

B. Sample Answers
1. F; An *amethyst* is typically colored purple or violet.
2. T; *Everlasting* means "perpetual."
3. F; A *flimsy* piece of furniture would be fragile.
4. T; A *hypodermic* needle can be used to give shots.
5. F; *Piety* connotes respect and devotion.
6. F; Children who create a nuisance or who pester would not be delightful to be around.
7. F; A *scandal* on the record would be a drawback.
8. T; An emergency room would provide the necessary, immediate care.

Reading Warm-up A, p. 170

Sample Answers

1. of the blood; One of the early symptoms of diabetes can be poor *circulation.*
2. (through some encyclopedia articles to find out more about the oath); *searching*
3. to share what we had learned; *gave in return*
4. (and a model doctor); *wonder, admiration*

5. (but they have not come up with a really satisfactory title); *touched nervously*

6. and respectful attitude; *tactless, rude, undiplomatic*

7. (and abandoned by a suitor); The opposite of *jilted* is *cherished.*

8. The word "together" is a clue to the meaning; *separated, dispersed*

Reading Warm-up B, p. 171

Sample Answers

1. her body looked as . . . as a paper doll; The opposite of *flimsy* is *strong, robust.*

2. (needle . . . used to inject his grandmother's arm with pain medicine)

3. (. . . trying to lighten the mood); tense

4. before cancer had started to . . . making her so weak; *annoyed, pestered, attacked*

5. that might ruin her career; disgrace, outrage

6. bluish-purple, the color of an . . . stone

7. (serious and proper); *devotion*

8. (her bright spirit would continue); *temporary, ephemeral, impermanent*

Literary Analysis: Stream of Consciousness, p. 172

Sample Responses

A. 1. Her first sight of Doctor Harry makes her feel that everyone is floating. When she sees him again, she feels the presence of God but also worries about sugar ants; then her thoughts turn to Hapsy.

2. Granny recalls her daily routine, focusing on dusting a clock. Thoughts of cleaning make her recall cleaning the attic and finding love letters, and that thought leads to contemplating death itself.

3. Thoughts of Lydia lead Granny into a comparison of her children; from there, her thoughts turn to John, her long-dead husband.

4. Granny imagines herself being smothered by the pillow and then recalls being jilted on her wedding day.

5. Granny's thoughts naturally turn to the state of her soul but suddenly refocus on how John comforted her when George jilted her.

B. John felt he could float forever on that pillow. Look, Ma, I can swim! I can swim! The sand was so warm, and the water was so salty; I never wanted to go home. It was good to feel so right about the world, but there were so many things he'd always meant to do. Well, he'd start doing some of these things when he came home from the hospital.

Reading Strategy: Clarify Sequence of Events, p. 173

Possible Responses

1. I was pretty. I wore a Spanish comb in my hair, and I often carried a fan.

2. We had a good, loving relationship. We worked hard and loved our children.

3. I fenced in the fields on my own, with just a little help. I raised the children. I rode out in all sorts of weather to help sick people and to take care of the livestock.

4. When the children were young, I was their protector. They looked to me to solve all their problems. Sometimes they still come to me for help. But most of the time now, I find that I am dependent on *them.* And I don't see them as often as I would like to.

5. When I was sixty, I became very ill. My children thought I was going to die, but I've lived on twenty more years. Also, I'm not afraid of death because I've made peace with God; I think I've been a good person and lived an honest life.

6. George was a man I was engaged to before I met John. George jilted me on our wedding day. I've never forgotten the grief and anger I experienced on that day. The grief and anger have stayed with me for sixty years.

Vocabulary Builder, p. 174

A. 1. D; 2. C; 3. G; 4. A; 5. B; 6. F; 7. E

B. 1. A; 2. C; 3. D

Grammar and Style: Imperative Sentences, p. 175

A. 1. "'Well, Missy, excuse me,' Doctor Harry patted her cheek. 'But I've got to warn you, haven't I?'"

2. "Don't let good things rot for want of using. You waste life when you waste good food. Don't let things get lost. It's bitter to lose things."

3. "There, wait a minute, here we are!' John, get the doctor now, Hapsy's time has come. But there was Hapsy standing by the bed in a white cap. 'Cornelia, tell Hapsy to take off her cap. I can't see her plain.'"

B. Sample Responses

1. Respect your elders, young man.
2. Correct
3. Correct
4. Pick all the fruit this year and see that nothing is wasted.
5. Find George.
6. Correct
7. Ellen, believe what I tell you.
8. Cornelia, take the amethyst set.

Enrichment: Film Biography, p. 178

Suggested Responses

Students should pick three pivotal or important events from the lifetime of the subject of the film biography. Students might suggest using Katherine Anne Porter's stream-of-consciousness technique in at least one of the scenes, as it is the technique studied in this selection.

Selection Test A, p. 179

Critical Reading

1. ANS: B	DIF: Easy	OBJ: Comprehension
2. ANS: D	DIF: Easy	OBJ: Reading Strategy
3. ANS: C	DIF: Easy	OBJ: Comprehension
4. ANS: A	DIF: Easy	OBJ: Literary Analysis
5. ANS: D	DIF: Easy	OBJ: Interpretation
6. ANS: A	DIF: Easy	OBJ: Reading Strategy
7. ANS: D	DIF: Easy	OBJ: Interpretation
8. ANS: B	DIF: Easy	OBJ: Literary Analysis
9. ANS: B	DIF: Easy	OBJ: Interpretation
10. ANS: D	DIF: Easy	OBJ: Comprehension
11. ANS: C	DIF: Easy	OBJ: Reading Strategy

Vocabulary and Grammar

12. ANS: B	DIF: Easy	OBJ: Vocabulary
13. ANS: C	DIF: Easy	OBJ: Grammar

Essay

14. Students' essays should suggest that to "weather all" means to be able to withstand much pain and hardship and still have a rewarding life. This is true of Granny Weatherall, who has weathered bad memories but also has good ones. Students may find other examples of Granny's strength in the story.

Difficulty: *Easy*
Objective: *Essay*

15. Students' essays should reflect that even at the point of death, Granny cannot let go of the memory of being jilted. Even the deaths of her husband and daughter are nothing in the face of this one terrible memory.

Difficulty: *Easy*
Objective: *Essay*

Selection Test B, p. 182

Critical Reading

1. ANS: B	DIF: Easy	OBJ: Comprehension
2. ANS: B	DIF: Easy	OBJ: Literary Analysis
3. ANS: D	DIF: Easy	OBJ: Interpretation
4. ANS: C	DIF: Average	OBJ: Reading Strategy
5. ANS: A	DIF: Easy	OBJ: Reading Strategy
6. ANS: D	DIF: Average	OBJ: Reading Strategy
7. ANS: C	DIF: Easy	OBJ: Literary Analysis
8. ANS: C	DIF: Challenging	OBJ: Interpretation
9. ANS: A	DIF: Challenging	OBJ: Literary Analysis
10. ANS: B	DIF: Challenging	OBJ: Interpretation
11. ANS: B	DIF: Easy	OBJ: Comprehension
12. ANS: D	DIF: Average	OBJ: Interpretation

Vocabulary and Grammar

13. ANS: B	DIF: Average	OBJ: Vocabulary
14. ANS: A	DIF: Average	OBJ: Vocabulary
15. ANS: A	DIF: Average	OBJ: Grammar
16. ANS: B	DIF: Average	OBJ: Grammar
17. ANS: D	DIF: Average	OBJ: Grammar

Essay

18. Students may choose different interpretations as long as they support their opinions with events from the story. For example, they might feel that the title signifies the importance of the jilting to Granny and its continuing effect on her. Others might suggest that Granny's approaching death evokes many of the same feelings in her that her jilting did.

Difficulty: *Easy*
Objective: *Essay*

19. Students may choose either position, as long as it is supported with details from the story. For example, students who agree might suggest that Granny committed a blunder in her youth by agreeing to marry George. She admits her adulthood was a struggle, especially after John died. Most students will probably state that Granny Weatherall would disagree with the last part of the statement, as she does not seem to regret much in her old age, except a chance to tell George he did no lasting damage. Those who disagree might say that Granny seems too spunky to agree with such a depressing blanket indictment of life.

Difficulty: *Average*
Objective: *Essay*

20. Students should define stream of consciousness and state how well it indicates how close Granny is to death, supporting their answers with specific details. For example, they might say that stream of consciousness reflects the thoughts coming directly from a character's mind and that it creates a realistic and vivid personal view of death approaching a character. They could contrast Granny's coherence at the beginning, where she carries on a conversation with the doctor, with her growing difficulty in communicating as the story progresses. They might also say that, at first, she can distinguish between present events and memories of her past but loses this ability toward the end of the story.

Difficulty: *Challenging*
Objective: *Essay*

"A Rose for Emily" and "Nobel Prize Acceptance Speech" by William Faulkner

Vocabulary Warm-up Exercises, p. 186

A. 1. acclaim
   2. universal
   3. dense

4. compassion
5. confidence
6. anguish
7. agony
8. glade

B. Sample Answers

1. Once in town, we made a <u>beeline</u> for the music store without stopping anywhere else first.
2. A salary <u>commensurate</u> with experience has a relationship to a person's previous knowledge.
3. The <u>dedication</u> of a charitable donation is the destination of the gift.
4. If you are <u>dodging</u> snowballs, you are trying to avoid them.
5. An <u>ephemeral</u> feeling usually lasts for only a few minutes.
6. We slowly clambered up the hillside to reach the <u>pinnacle</u>.
7. The squirrel was <u>scrabbling</u> through the underbrush, moving quickly and irregularly.
8. Because of a large <u>thicket</u> of tall trees, our visibility across the meadow was impaired.

Reading Warm-up A, p. 187

Sample Answers

1. <u>because of their position as insiders</u>; Joanna, who was always optimistic, faced the future with *confidence*.
2. (with many critics praising his radical experiments); *renown, praise*
3. <u>of suffering and resentment afflicting a Southern family</u>; *ecstasy, pleasure*
4. <u>sympathy and</u>; Mother Teresa had great *compassion* for the poor of Calcutta in India.
5. *thick; diffuse*
6. (strikingly mingles . . . with humor); *delight, pleasure, satisfaction*
7. <u>many points of view to gain . . . truly comprehensive</u>; The opposite of *universal* is *local* or *parochial*.
8. The phrase "or clearing" serves as a clue.

Reading Warm-up B, p. 188

Sample Answers

1. <u>all the way up to the mountain's</u>; *summit, apex*
2. (hastily through low trees); The small hermit crabs were *scrabbling* through the seaweed, trying to get away from us
3. <u>made a . . . directly for the steep chute</u>
4. <u>with the fear . . . was the desire</u>; *proportional*
5. (if he had the necessary focus and . . . to keep going)
6. (. . . of trees which meant a certain crash)
7. <u>weaving turns to slow down . . . barely in control</u>; *avoiding*

8. <u>over in a split second</u>; The opposite of *ephemeral* is *permanent* or *perpetual*.

Literary Analysis: Conflict and Resolution, p. 189

A. 1. Miss Emily does not pay her taxes, and the town authorities try to bring her into compliance with the law. The conflict is external.
2. She is firm, with no emotion. She may have lost touch with reality, or she may be trying to avoid responsibility.
3. An awful smell begins to come from Miss Emily's house, and the neighbors complain. A party is organized to go in the night and sprinkle lime in her cellar and around her outbuildings.
4. The narrator appears to have a high level of respect and even awe for Miss Emily, yet he feels both pity and revulsion. Examples will vary.
5. The discovery of the body resolves what most likely caused the awful smell, why Miss Emily purchased the arsenic, and why Homer Baron was never seen again.

B. Students may mention that Faulkner says that the modern world is frightening, and people read to gain hope and relief from this external conflict. Students may also mention that when people have internal conflicts, they can find support or wisdom through reading.

Reading Strategy: Clarify Ambiguities, p. 190

A. 1. B

Supporting details: The smell is so foul that complaints are brought to the mayor. The man is eventually found dead in Miss Emily's bed.

2. C

Supporting details: She carried her head high, demanding recognition of her dignity.

3. A

Supporting details: A Grierson would not think seriously of a Northerner, a day laborer.

B. Sample response: The voices of humans are expressed in writing that gets left behind for others to read. In this way, humans do not die, because their message continues.

Vocabulary Builder, p. 191

Sample Responses

A. 1. N; Slaves often received *inhumane* treatment.
2. D; The importance of eating properly is often *ingrained*.
3. D; Please *input* the most recent information.
4. N; The bee sting was *insignificant* to Emma.
5. N; Jake was screaming so loudly that he was *incoherent*.

B. 1. Someone might use the information you provided.
2. There will be a shortage of produce and prices will rise.
3. I might work as a volunteer or go to summer school.

4. I might have to ask someone for a ride.
5. They get in trouble.
6. The mouse would probably keep trying.
7. Usually the more experienced team wins easily.
8. It suggests that the person is not guilty.
9. Doctors would tell people to get vaccinated immediately.
10. I would ask him to respect my privacy.

Grammar and Style: Semicolons, p. 192

A. 1. The men went to her father's funeral out of respectful affection; the women went out of curiosity.

2. Miss Emily did not invite them inside to sit down; she stood in the doorway and listened.

3. After her father's funeral, a few ladies tried to visit Miss Emily to offer their condolences; they were not received.

4. The four men crept about Miss Emily's house in the middle of the night; they sprinkled lime in the cellar and around all the outbuildings.

5. The Griersons held themselves above everyone else; no one was quite good enough.

B. Sample response: Faulkner discussed the fear of destruction that all of us face, and he encouraged writers to look beyond that fear. He believes that writers have a special responsibility; they need to write about the human heart and its problems.

Enrichment: Journalism, p. 195

Sample Response

Headline: Second Badly Decomposed Body Found in Grierson Home

Who? County coroner William Brady reported today the discovery of a second body believed to that of Homer Baron.

What? Officials had just removed the body of Emily Grierson, who appears to have died from natural causes, when a search revealed a badly decomposed skeleton.

Where? The Grierson home was located in what was once Jefferson's best neighborhood, but years of disregard had turned the area into an eyesore.

Why? Officials are not yet certain why the body had been confined to the upstairs bedroom of the Grierson home for so long or if foul play was involved.

How? There is an investigation underway to determine the cause of death.

Students' news stories should include all key details, with the most important details appearing first.

Selection Test A, p. 196

Critical Reading

1. ANS: B	DIF: Easy	OBJ: Literary Analysis
2. ANS: C	DIF: Easy	OBJ: Reading Strategy
3. ANS: A	DIF: Easy	OBJ: Comprehension
4. ANS: D	DIF: Easy	OBJ: Interpretation
5. ANS: B	DIF: Easy	OBJ: Reading Strategy
6. ANS: D	DIF: Easy	OBJ: Interpretation
7. ANS: A	DIF: Easy	OBJ: Literary Analysis
8. ANS: B	DIF: Easy	OBJ: Reading Strategy
9. ANS: B	DIF: Easy	OBJ: Comprehension
10. ANS: A	DIF: Easy	OBJ: Interpretation
11. ANS: A	DIF: Easy	OBJ: Comprehension

Vocabulary and Grammar

12. ANS: B	DIF: Easy	OBJ: Grammar
13. ANS: B	DIF: Easy	OBJ: Grammar

Essay

14. Students' essays should suggest that it is reasonable to think that Homer simply abandoned Emily. The author describes certain events, such as the bad smell and Emily's purchase of rat poison, out of order, so readers might not connect them with Homer's disappearance unless they read very carefully.

Difficulty: *Easy*

Objective: *Essay*

15. Students' essays should reflect that Faulkner says that fear keeps writers from writing from their heart. Therefore, people no longer have books to read that are about love, honor, compassion, pride, and sacrifice.

Difficulty: *Easy*

Objective: *Essay*

Selection Test B, p. 199

Critical Reading

1. ANS: B	DIF: Average	OBJ: Literary Analysis
2. ANS: B	DIF: Challenging	OBJ: Reading Strategy
3. ANS: A	DIF: Challenging	OBJ: Interpretation
4. ANS: B	DIF: Average	OBJ: Comprehension
5. ANS: C	DIF: Average	STO: Reading Strategy
6. ANS: D	DIF: Challenging	OBJ: Interpretation
7. ANS: C	DIF: Average	OBJ: Reading Strategy
8. ANS: B	DIF: Average	OBJ: Literary Analysis
9. ANS: D	DIF: Average	OBJ: Comprehension
10. ANS: A	DIF: Average	OBJ: Reading Skill
11. ANS: C	DIF: Average	OBJ: Literary Analysis
12. ANS: D	DIF: Average	OBJ: Comprehension
13. ANS: B	DIF: Challenging	OBJ: Interpretation

Vocabulary and Grammar

14. ANS: C	DIF: Average	OBJ: Vocabulary
15. ANS: B	DIF: Average	OBJ: Vocabulary
16. ANS: C	DIF: Average	OBJ: Grammar

17. ANS: C   **DIF:** Average   **OBJ:** Grammar

Essay

18. Students should recognize the Grierson family's history of enjoying privileges in the town of Jefferson that were a tradition. At the same time, Miss Emily's unusual behavior concerning her taxes and the smell might be seen as a duty placed upon the town. Finally, her behavior during the death of her father required that the people of Jefferson look in on her and take care of her.

    Difficulty: *Average*

    Objective: *Essay*

19. Student should recognize that the Grierson's best days are behind them, and this makes Emily look to the past. Students may certainly interpret the story as a study of a particular disorder based on Miss Emily's inability to accept change. However, Miss Emily could also be said to represent the things in ourselves and our lives that we do not wish to change.

    Difficulty: *Challenging*

    Objective: *Essay*

20. Students should note that the narrator speaks for the people of Jefferson, yet there are subtle clues about his true opinions. Occasionally he appears to depart from that will, or at least is confused. Miss Emily poses a more difficult challenge. Student will need to infer the internal conflicts she may be facing as the story develops and she resists changes.

    Difficulty: *Challenging*

    Objective: *Essay*

Robert Frost's Poetry

Vocabulary Warm-up Exercises, p. 203

A. 1. mischief
   2. proclaimed
   3. subdued
   4. boulders
   5. shed
   6. poise
   7. limp
   8. offense

B. Sample Answers
   1. T; Vehicles traveling *abreast* can move in a double file.
   2. T; Since *artless* means "naïve" or "straightforward," this statement is true.
   3. F; *Downy* means "soft" or "feathery."
   4. T; *Forthwith* means "immediately."
   5. T; *Outright* means "unconditional."
   6. T; A *rueful* expression might plausibly convey regret or sorrow.
   7. T; The verb *snarled* implies intense annoyance, so the animal might be dangerous.

8. F; Neighbors who acted stubbornly or irresponsibly would not motivate praise.

Reading Warm-up A, p. 204

Sample Answers

1. loudly . . . only a fool would break his ankle on a raft trip; After the attack, the president *proclaimed* a day of national mourning.
2. (standing up and dancing around the raft like a clown); The opposite of *mischief* is good behavior.
3. dancing around the raft like a clown . . . of stupidity; *wrong, mistake*
4. (rocks and . . . the size of wheelbarrows); large
5. (flop and twirl without . . . like a stuffed toy); *balance*
6. ankle cast made him; *stiff, inflexible*
7. *conquered*; "Uncle Bob would never stand for a temper tantrum"
8. it was 90 degrees outside and he was already sweating . . . his jeans jacket; *cast off, doffed*

Reading Warm-up B, p. 205

Sample Answers

1. seems a bit sad; After failing the math exam, Ron returned home with a *rueful* look.
2. (a little stubbornly); The opposite of *willfully* is *cooperatively* or *pleasantly*.
3. *side by side*
4. buzz saw has come to life as an enemy, determined to injure; negative
5. *naïve, straightforward; cunning, sly*
6. *soft; rough*
7. surrender to the temptations; He wanted to make an *outright* gift of the land to his daughter.
8. (immediate); *eventual, belated*

Literary Analysis: Blank Verse, p. 206

And <u>so</u> I <u>dream</u> of <u>going</u> <u>back</u> to <u>be</u>.
It's <u>when</u> I'm <u>weary</u> <u>of</u> considerations,
And <u>life</u> is <u>too</u> much <u>like</u> a <u>pathless</u> <u>wood</u>
Where <u>your</u> face <u>burns</u> and <u>tickles</u> <u>with</u> the <u>cobwebs</u>
Broken <u>across</u> it, <u>and</u> one <u>eye</u> is <u>weeping</u>
From a <u>twig's</u> <u>having</u> <u>lashed</u> <u>across</u> it open.

Reading Strategy: Read Blank Verse, p. 207

A. 1. 7; 2. 1

B. Poem

   "Birches"

   "Mending Wall"

   "'Out, Out—'"

   "Stopping by Woods on a Snowy Evening"

   "Acquainted with the Night"

   "The Gift Outright"

Number of Sentences

20

21

23

6

7

5

Vocabulary Builder, p. 208

A. Sample Responses

1. Robert Frost remains a luminary of American poetry.
2. The luminary glow of the stars lit the path for the weary travelers.
3. The young film star's face seemed luminous through the eye of the camera.
4. Her luminosity was apparent to all her fans.
5. Robert Frost's poems illuminate a time and a place in American history.

B. 1. luminary; 2. rueful; 3. poise

Grammar and Style: Uses of Infinitives, p. 209

A. 1. to get; noun
2. to keep; adverb
3. to build; adjective

B. Sample Responses

1. Robert Frost was asked to give many speeches during his lifetime.
2. He liked to write about New Englanders and the rural landscape of the eastern part of the United States.
3. "Mending Wall" is about two neighbors working to put up a fence between their property.
4. "Stopping by Woods on a Snowy Evening" is about a man pausing to reflect on the beauty of nature.

Enrichment: Photography, p. 212

A. Sample Responses

1. Many students will feel that photographs suit the realism of Frost's poetry.
2. walking through forest; delight
3. farming; wonder
4. rustic beauty; calm
5. clean, cold climate; peace

B. Suggested Responses

Students' poems will vary but should stem from a well-chosen photograph and address the emotion it evokes.

Selection Test A, p. 213

Critical Reading

1. ANS: B	DIF: Easy	OBJ: Literary Analysis
2. ANS: B	DIF: Easy	OBJ: Interpretation
3. ANS: A	DIF: Easy	OBJ: Reading Strategy
4. ANS: D	DIF: Easy	OBJ: Literary Analysis
5. ANS: C	DIF: Easy	OBJ: Comprehension
6. ANS: C	DIF: Easy	OBJ: Interpretation
7. ANS: A	DIF: Easy	OBJ: Interpretation
8. ANS: B	DIF: Easy	OBJ: Comprehension
9. ANS: D	DIF: Easy	OBJ: Comprehension
10. ANS: C	DIF: Easy	OBJ: Reading Strategy
11. ANS: A	DIF: Easy	OBJ: Literary Analysis

Vocabulary and Grammar

12. ANS: A	DIF: Easy	OBJ: Vocabulary
13. ANS: D	DIF: Easy	OBJ: Grammar

Essay

14. Students' essays should reflect that death is common when people work with farming equipment. The family members are not heartless, but they know that they could not have done anything to save the boy, and farming means working long hours, so they continue their work.

Difficulty: *Easy*

Objective: *Essay*

15. Students' essays should suggest that the speaker is suspicious of walls and the reasons for building them. He is asking if walls are built to protect people and their property, or to keep people from getting to know one another.

Difficulty: *Easy*

Objective: *Essay*

Selection Test B, p. 216

Critical Reading

1. ANS: B	DIF: Average	OBJ: Interpretation
2. ANS: A	DIF: Easy	OBJ: Comprehension
3. ANS: B	DIF: Challenging	OBJ: Interpretation
4. ANS: A	DIF: Challenging	OBJ: Interpretation
5. ANS: D	DIF: Average	OBJ: Comprehension
6. ANS: C	DIF: Average	OBJ: Comprehension
7. ANS: C	DIF: Average	OBJ: Literary Analysis
8. ANS: A	DIF: Easy	OBJ: Literary Analysis
9. ANS: C	DIF: Challenging	OBJ: Reading Strategy
10. ANS: B	DIF: Average	OBJ: Literary Analysis
11. ANS: D	DIF: Easy	OBJ: Reading Strategy

Vocabulary and Grammar

12. ANS: A	DIF: Average	OBJ: Vocabulary
13. ANS: C	DIF: Average	OBJ: Vocabulary
14. ANS: D	DIF: Average	OBJ: Grammar
15. ANS: D	DIF: Average	OBJ: Grammar
16. ANS: B	DIF: Average	OBJ: Vocabulary

17. ANS: A   **DIF:** Easy   **OBJ:** Grammar

Essay

18. Students' essays should reflect a number of different examples of Frost's thematic use of regret. For example, students may cite the example of the boy who is killed by the saw in "'Out, Out—.'" ("Then the boy saw all—/ since he was old enough to know, big boy/Doing a man's work, though a child at heart—/He saw all spoiled.") They may point out the mournful refrain at the end of "Stopping by Woods on a Snowy Evening" or the speaker's wish to return to childhood and simple joy in "Birches." Students may mention that such longings are a part of human nature that is instantly recognizable and familiar. They may note that even at their relatively young age, they have a sense of lost childhood or regret about times gone by.

Difficulty: *Easy*

Objective: *Essay*

19. Students' essays should reflect that while the story told in the poem seems a simple one, it actually reflects complicated ideas about the human condition and the American sensibility. The reasons for not wanting walls might include unspoiled natural beauty, easier access to the countryside, a stronger bonding with neighbors, and so on. Reasons for building and keeping walls might include such ideas as maintaining privacy and land rights, avoiding legal battles, and a desire to keep family affairs within the family. The poem points up the American ideas of open spaces and pioneering on the one hand, and rugged individualism and ownership on the other.

Difficulty: *Average*

Objective: *Essay*

20. Students should explore "Stopping by Woods on a Snowy Evening" in terms of the three parts Frost considered essential: the point or idea, the details that develop it, and the technique. For example, they might state the main idea as the conflict between desire for rest and duty; the details in the attractiveness of the woods and the little horse's eagerness to keep going; and the rhythm and rhyme scheme that sound like a moving sleigh.

Difficulty: *Challenging*

Objective: *Essay*

"The Night the Ghost Got In" by James Thurber from *Here Is New York* by E. B. White

Vocabulary Warm-up Exercises, p. 220

A. 1. commendably
   2. aspiration
   3. ceased
   4. compelled
   5. retreat
   6. vigorous
   7. intervene
   8. perpetual

B. Sample Answers
   1. Because of her <u>claustrophobia</u>, she would not enter that windowless room.
   2. The <u>confines</u> of a building are defined by the space inside it.
   3. Because the theory was so <u>implausible</u>, we refused to believe it.
   4. She felt she had given an <u>incomparable</u> performance, and she could now relax.
   5. When we realized the problem was <u>insoluble</u>, we abandoned work on it.
   6. A person who works <u>intuitively</u> does not depend on analytical ability.
   7. Because he was a <u>transient</u> by nature, he often moved from place to place.
   8. He is known throughout the neighborhood as a <u>vagrant</u>, aimlessly wandering around.

Reading Warm-up A, p. 221

Sample Answers
   1. <u>Jimmy could not stop clowning</u>; Randy was a *perpetual* source of amusement, with a joke for every occasion.
   2. (getting an answer right); *creditably*
   3. *stopped; continued*
   4. *forced*; Jimmy's jokes and insults never ceased.
   5. (nothing could make Jimmy . . . from his outrageous behavior); The opposite of *retreat* is *advance*.
   6. (practicing for a future career as a stand-up comedian); *goal, hope, objective*
   7. *energetic, strong*; We enjoyed two hours of *vigorous* exercise at the fitness club.
   8. <u>and make him stop</u>; *remain neutral*

Reading Warm-up B, p. 222

Sample Answers
   1. <u>or matchless essays</u>; "not"
   2. (their instincts lead them unconsciously in the right direction); *instinctively*
   3. <u>within the limited . . . of a short piece</u>; Within the *confines* of an essay, you can expect to cover only a limited, focused topic.
   4. <u>to discuss the meaning of life within 500 words or so . . . you sacrifice the reader's interest and belief</u>; The opposite of *implausible* is *plausible* or *believable*.
   5. (huge questions are simply . . . so narrow your topic so that it is focused); *solvable*
   6. (hopping around from topic to topic)
   7. <u>wandering aimlessly in and around the topic's twists and turns</u>; *drifter*
   8. <u>essays are a good remedy for . . . since they are a means of escaping enclosed spaces</u>

Literary Analysis: Informal Essay, p. 223

Sample Responses

1. Students should realize that in this passage Thurber wanders charmingly from the subject—the strange night. He tells us more about Bodwell than is strictly necessary. He digresses even further in stating that his family seemed to be in constant contact with people suffering "attacks." Examples of everyday language include "in a rather bad way" and "Most everybody."

   Students might conclude that italicizing *some* for emphasis would not be done in more formal writing. The last sentence stresses the unusual situations his family members tend to find themselves in.

2. Thurber tries to reproduce the way the police talk ("Looky here, Joe.") and refers to them as *cops.* This would not be the case in a more formal essay. Here and elsewhere the author makes no secret of his unflattering opinion of the police. On the other hand, what he himself says to the cops is weird—and foolish, as he admits in his after-the-fact opinion. Again, the details he gives are digressions from the events and his language is simple and straightforward.

3. Students will note the everyday examples White uses here: people brushing their teeth and lovers writing notes, as well as everyday language: "his girl," "pfft," "just like that."

Reading Strategy: Recognize Hyperbole, p. 224

1. The brother's tone, compared to the "low, hopeless tone of a despondent beagle," is exaggerated. The image of a sad beagle is just one more funny detail in the scene.

2. The brother's color is exaggerated. The idea that he would be "a light green" is amusing.

3. The neighbor's attitude is exaggerated. The idea that he would be "frothing a little" is funny, and the idea that the Bodwells would consider moving back to Peoria because of the incident is also funny.

4. The narrator's mother's actions are exaggerated. The image of her "whooping and carrying on and slamming doors" is an amusing vision.

5. The image of the grandfather is exaggerated, and the description of his clothing is funny.

Vocabulary Builder, p. 225

A. 1. *terrestrial*; because it refers to things that live and grow on earth

2. *territorial*; because areas of land are called territories

3. *terrier*; because terriers are hunting dogs trained to go after game that lives underground

4. *terrace*; because it is a level piece of ground or land

B. 1. subterranean

2. claustrophobia

3. blaspheming

4. aspiration

5. cosmopolitan

6. intuitively

Grammar and Style: Commas in Series, p. 226

A. 1. [D]oors were yanked open, drawers were yanked open, windows were shot up and pulled down, furniture fell with dull thumps.

2. They began to ransack the floor: pulled beds away from walls, tore clothes off hooks in the closets, pulled suitcases and boxes off shelves.

3. [T]hey sit in stalled subways without claustrophobia, they extricate themselves from panic situations by some lucky wisecrack, they meet confusion and congestion with patience and grit. . . .

B. Sample Responses

1. As I left for the airport, I turned on my alarm system, danced out the door, slammed it joyfully behind me, and suddenly realized I had left all my keys on the kitchen counter.

2. A stuffed woodchuck in a lifelike pose dominated the shelf, which also held a ceramic mug bearing the image of a long-forgotten politician, an assortment of dusty quartz crystals, six or seven tiny plastic dolls scattered like casualties on a battlefield, and, last but not least, a grimy ball of aluminum foil the size of a human head.

Enrichment: The Police, p. 229

Suggested Responses

Students should conduct enough research to answer the questions accurately. They should compare the events in the story with actual events and use information about police procedure to enhance their understanding of the story.

Selection Test A, p. 230

Critical Reading

1. ANS: B	DIF: Easy	OBJ: Literary Analysis
2. ANS: D	DIF: Easy	OBJ: Reading Strategy
3. ANS: A	DIF: Easy	OBJ: Comprehension
4. ANS: C	DIF: Easy	OBJ: Comprehension
5. ANS: A	DIF: Easy	OBJ: Interpretation
6. ANS: D	DIF: Easy	OBJ: Literary Analysis
7. ANS: B	DIF: Easy	OBJ: Literary Analysis
8. ANS: B	DIF: Easy	OBJ: Interpretation
9. ANS: A	DIF: Easy	OBJ: Reading Strategy
10. ANS: B	DIF: Easy	OBJ: Interpretation
11. ANS: C	DIF: Easy	OBJ: Comprehension

Vocabulary and Grammar

12. ANS: A	DIF: Easy	OBJ: Vocabulary
13. ANS: D	DIF: Easy	OBJ: Grammar

Essay

14. Students' essays should suggest that the police act strangely. First, they tear the house apart rather than looking for evidence of burglary. They question the author about what he is doing there when he obviously lives there. After one of them is shot by Grandfather, they go away without arresting him. All these actions add humor to the story and are not realistic.

Difficulty: *Easy*

Objective: *Essay*

15. Students' essays should reflect that E. B. White thinks New Yorkers are unique and strong enough to put up with the challenges New York throws at them. They put up with crowds, noise, and with not having enough air or water or space. They do all these things because they realize what a unique place New York is.

Difficulty: *Easy*

Objective: *Essay*

Selection Test B, p. 233

Critical Reading

1. ANS: C	DIF: Average	OBJ: Interpretation
2. ANS: D	DIF: Challenging	OBJ: Literary Analysis
3. ANS: B	DIF: Average	OBJ: Reading Strategy
4. ANS: C	DIF: Easy	OBJ: Comprehension
5. ANS: D	DIF: Average	OBJ: Interpretation
6. ANS: A	DIF: Average	OBJ: Comprehension
7. ANS: D	DIF: Average	OBJ: Reading Strategy
8. ANS: B	DIF: Average	OBJ: Literary Analysis
9. ANS: C	DIF: Average	OBJ: Comprehension
10. ANS: B	DIF: Average	OBJ: Reading Strategy
11. ANS: B	DIF: Challenging	OBJ: Literary Analysis
12. ANS: C	DIF: Easy	OBJ: Interpretation
13. ANS: D	DIF: Easy	OBJ: Literary Analysis

Vocabulary and Grammar

14. ANS: C	DIF: Average	OBJ: Grammar
15. ANS: A	DIF: Average	OBJ: Vocabulary
16. ANS: B	DIF: Average	OBJ: Vocabulary
17. ANS: C	DIF: Easy	OBJ: Vocabulary

Essay

18. Students' responses should give a clear idea of the eccentricities of these characters through specific examples of their personalities and actions. For example, students might cite the mother's urge to throw another shoe and her belief that the wounded policeman really was a deserter as eccentric features, which come close to crossing the line of credibility. They might find the grandfather's reception of the police eccentric, but somewhat believable, given the implication that the old man is not in his right mind.

Difficulty: *Easy*

Objective: *Essay*

19. Students should show White's wide-ranging interests and feeling for humanity through specific examples. For example, they might cite his sympathetic admiration for New Yorkers living under pressure, as an example that nothing human is alien to him. They could see evidence of his keen eye in such vivid examples as the young man writing to his girl or the overwhelmed newlywed visitors eating a dispirited meal. As evidence of White's intelligence, they might mention his clear analysis of New York's neighborhood pattern.

Difficulty: *Average*

Objective: *Essay*

20. Students should give some general criteria for where they draw the line between humor and unkindness and illustrate it with specific examples. For example, they might state that when Thurber calls attention to things people can't help, such as the grandfather's mental problems or the police's speech patterns, and exaggerates them, he crosses the line. In contrast, they might decide that White's depiction of tourists doesn't cross the line because he is more descriptive than critical.

Difficulty: *Challenging*

Objective: *Essay*

Benchmark Test 8, p. 236

MULTIPLE CHOICE

1. ANS: C
2. ANS: A
3. ANS: A
4. ANS: C
5. ANS: D
6. ANS: C
7. ANS: A
8. ANS: B
9. ANS: D
10. ANS: A
11. ANS: B
12. ANS: A
13. ANS: C
14. ANS: B
15. ANS: B
16. ANS: A
17. ANS: A
18. ANS: D
19. ANS: A
20. ANS: D
21. ANS: A
22. ANS: D
23. ANS: D

24. ANS: C
25. ANS: D
26. ANS: C
27. ANS: D
28. ANS: B
29. ANS: C
30. ANS: A

ESSAY

31. Students should choose any two stories, poems, or other selections to compare and contrast. They should begin with a statement giving their general critical assessment of both works. They should then organize their essays by making point-by-point comparisons and contrasts or by discussing first one work and then the other. They should supply details from the works to illustrate more general points they make.

32. Students should identify the author and explain the sad occasion for the speech. They should then provide details about the author's life and achievements in a speech that pays respect to the deceased and that might also offer comfort to the listeners. Students might organize the details in their speech in order of importance or chronological order.

33. Students should attempt to capture the way the human mind works by leaping from one association to another in presenting a character's thoughts. Students' passages should be clear enough so that most readers can follow them, even if they go from one association to another. Students who write the thoughts of a character created by another writer should reflect the character's personality and situation.

Diagnostic Test 9, p. 242

MULTIPLE CHOICE

1. ANS: C
2. ANS: A
3. ANS: B
4. ANS: C
5. ANS: D
6. ANS: B
7. ANS: D
8. ANS: A
9. ANS: D
10. ANS: B
11. ANS: B
12. ANS: D
13. ANS: A
14. ANS: C
15. ANS: B

from *Dust Tracks on a Road*
by Zora Neale Hurston

Vocabulary Warm-up Exercises, p. 246

A. 1. tingled
2. angelic
3. consciousness
4. duration
5. experimentally
6. monarch
7. realm
8. avarice

B. Sample Answers
1. F; A shy person would not be acting with *brazenness*.
2. T; A *caper* might reasonably be expected to involve mischief.
3. F; *Chums* are pals or good friends.
4. T; *Foreknowledge* in advance would be helpful.
5. F; Since *indifferent* means "uncaring," this statement is false.
6. T; If the fruit were ripe, it would be time to pluck it from a vine or stem.
7. T; Pride and satisfaction would be signaled by someone who *sported* a new hat.
8. F; *Tread* means "footfall."

Reading Warm-up A, p. 247

Sample Answers
1. mindset . . . of an entire people; *awareness*
2. (. . . or time span . . . may be centuries long); *seven*
3. alter some of the details; *scientists, inventors*
4. (a king or queen); *ruler*
5. (or region); *kingdom*
6. with excitement; *set on edge*
7. (a tale about a miser . . . the dangers of); The opposite of *avarice* is *generosity*.
8. one of them angelic and the other two envious and wicked; *well-behaved*

Reading Warm-up B, p. 248

Sample Answers
1. known all over the school . . . "bold and beautiful" . . . musical trailblazers, audaciously blending styles in brand-new ways; The opposite of *brazenness* is *modesty* or *timidity*.
2. (friendly); *pals, friends*
3. before
4. a stunning new . . . would really make a mark on the audience
5. (. . . and jaded, unwilling to pay you respect); The opposite of *indifferent* is *involved* or *caring*.
6. the strings of his guitar; *fruit, flowers*

7. (the heavy . . . as they plodded up the stairs)

8. (a bright orange cap, tilted to the side at a rakish angle); positive

Literary Analysis: Social Context in Autobiography, p. 249

1. She reveals that her family functioned in a completely segregated world, where they often lived in fear of the actions of white people. The forwardness she shows in offering to walk a while with the white folks frightens her family.

2. She reveals that her community was made up of people like herself. To Hurston, the homogeneity of the village was isolated and boring.

3. Hurston reveals here that her school was a spectacle for whites—they were intrigued by an all-black school and watched the proceedings much like they would have watched a show or performance.

Student responses about their own social context will vary. Generally, students can make a connection to feelings of isolation, awkwardness, and boredom.

Reading Strategy: Analyze How a Writer Achieves Purpose, p. 250

Sample Responses

1. This event shows that Hurston hasn't really had much experience with white people, especially sophisticated ones. It helps the reader to see how separated she was from white people, perhaps because her community was totally African American.

2. The white ladies' request may show that they don't trust her abilities, thinking perhaps the reading she did in school was memorized. Hurston may want the reader to see that although well-intentioned, these women refused to take her fluent reading at face value because it contradicted their stereotypes about African Americans.

3. Her thoughts about these characters show that Hurston has a strong moral bent and admires people who take action rather than talking about things. She chooses these details to reveal aspects of her character.

4. Hurston rides about half a mile with the white travelers and walks back. This shows that she is bored with Orlando and gives the reader the idea that she will get out of Orlando as soon as she can.

5. Hurston is most pleased with the red coat and red tam in the box of clothes sent by the white women. This shows her appreciation of good clothes and suggests that she might have more style than most of the residents of Orlando.

Vocabulary Builder, p. 251

A. 1. *graphology*; Since *-ology* means "the study of," *graphology* would be the study of handwriting.

2. *graphic*; He is making use of the powers of writing to create a picture in his readers' minds.

3. *lithograph*; A lithograph is a drawing made using stone.

4. *calligraphy*; Calligraphy is "beautiful writing."

B. 1. C; 2. F; 3. E; 4. A; 5. B; 6. D

Grammar and Style: Parallelism in Coordinate Elements, p. 252

A. 1. I was <u>fifth</u> (or) <u>sixth</u> down the line.

2. Last thing, I was <u>given a handkerchief to carry,</u> <u>warned again about my behavior,</u> (and) <u>sent off</u>. . . .

3. I seemed to remember seeing Thor swing his mighty short-handled hammer as he sped across the sky in rumbling thunder, lightning flashing from <u>the tread of his steeds</u> (and) <u>the wheels of his chariot.</u>

B. 1. The two white ladies who visited her school had fingers that were long and white but pink near the tips.

2. Zora liked to read mythological stories, study geography, and play games.

3. Zora didn't know whether she would get a reward or be whipped.

Enrichment: Community and Personal Identity, p. 255

Suggested Responses

Students should use the questions to get ideas for their pen pal letter. Student letters should focus on their communities and the values they have learned from living there.

Selection Test A, p. 256

Critical Reading

1. ANS: D	DIF: Easy		OBJ: Interpretation
2. ANS: B	DIF: Easy		OBJ: Comprehension
3. ANS: B	DIF: Easy		OBJ: Literary Analysis
4. ANS: A	DIF: Easy		OBJ: Comprehension
5. ANS: C	DIF: Easy		OBJ: Reading Strategy
6. ANS: B	DIF: Easy		OBJ: Reading Strategy
7. ANS: A	DIF: Easy		OBJ: Interpretation
8. ANS: D	DIF: Easy		OBJ: Literary Analysis
9. ANS: B	DIF: Easy		OBJ: Comprehension
10. ANS: B	DIF: Easy		OBJ: Interpretation
11. ANS: C	DIF: Easy		OBJ: Reading Strategy

Vocabulary and Grammar

12. ANS: C	DIF: Easy		OBJ: Vocabulary
13. ANS: C	DIF: Easy		OBJ: Grammar

Essay

14. Students' essays should reflect that Hurston's grandmother grew up as a slave and knew that any white person could cause her death and get away with it. Hurston grew up as a free person, though in a racist society, and she was not as

aware of the power of white people when she was young. She also had a lot of self-confidence.

Difficulty: *Easy*

Objective: *Essay*

15. Students' essays should suggest that Zora knew that she was acting a part, but she was a very curious person and wanted to learn about the world. Also, she probably felt that reading well and dressing up and being polite to the white women couldn't hurt her in any way and might help her learn something useful.

Difficulty: *Easy*

Objective: *Essay*

Selection Test B, p. 259

Critical Reading

1. ANS: A	DIF: Easy	OBJ: Comprehension
2. ANS: B	DIF: Average	OBJ: Interpretation
3. ANS: C	DIF: Challenging	OBJ: Interpretation
4. ANS: B	DIF: Challenging	OBJ: Interpretation
5. ANS: A	DIF: Average	OBJ: Interpretation
6. ANS: C	DIF: Average	OBJ: Comprehension
7. ANS: B	DIF: Average	OBJ: Reading Strategy
8. ANS: B	DIF: Challenging	OBJ: Reading Strategy
9. ANS: C	DIF: Average	OBJ: Literary Analysis
10. ANS: B	DIF: Average	OBJ: Reading Strategy
11. ANS: D	DIF: Challenging	OBJ: Reading Strategy
12. ANS: A	DIF: Average	OBJ: Literary Analysis

Vocabulary and Grammar

13. ANS: A	DIF: Average	OBJ: Vocabulary
14. ANS: D	DIF: Average	OBJ: Vocabulary
15. ANS: C	DIF: Easy	OBJ: Vocabulary
16. ANS: D	DIF: Easy	OBJ: Grammar
17. ANS: B	DIF: Easy	OBJ: Grammar

Essay

18. Student responses should include several character traits revealed by specific information in the text. For example, they might mention Zora's self-confidence, eagerness to learn, sense of responsibility, and love of action. They might cite her hailing of white people from her gatepost as an example of self-confidence. Her sense of responsibility can be seen in her admiration for Heracles, who chose a life of duty over pleasure.

Difficulty: *Easy*

Objective: *Essay*

19. Students should mention attitudes and give examples that illustrate them. As an example of an attitude to which Zora refers directly, students may cite the amusement white people probably felt when she asked to ride with them. On the other hand, it can be inferred

from the fuss the white ladies make over Zora's reading ability that they had low expectations of African American schooling or intelligence. Students may suggest that the women wanted to help Zora out of a life they considered impoverished and inadequate and that it made them feel good.

Difficulty: *Average*

Objective: *Essay*

20. Students should cite specific examples in discussing both how the critic's view is supported by the selection and how it is not. For example, they may say that Zora's descriptions of white people are generally positive enough to support the critic's view: she is curious about differences, but not critical; her view of the white women's hands arouses wonder, not distaste. In contrast, students might suggest that Zora implies criticism when she mentions white curiosity about a "Negro school." The fact that the ladies had Zora read from a magazine at the hotel implies that they had suspicions about her performance at school.

Difficulty: *Challenging*

Objective: *Essay*

"The Negro Speaks of Rivers," "I, Too," "Dream Variations," and "Refugee in America" by Langston Hughes
"The Tropics in New York" by Claude McKay

Vocabulary Warm-up Exercises, p. 263

A.
1. longing
2. lull
3. pale
4. dawns
5. fit
6. liberty
7. slim
8. whirl

B. Sample Answers
1. One hardly expects judges to give their benediction to violations of the law.
2. She wanted to stay at home, safe in the bosom of her family.
3. The flower's petals were dewy and moist from the rain shower.
4. In the dusky light of evening, it is hard to see the line of hills on the horizon.
5. He wanted badly to gaze at the temple ruins, but his eyes were irritated and itchy.
6. Laden with blossoms, the cherry trees were in full flower.
7. For Paul, the concert was a mystical experience that he found stirring and significant.
8. The entire parish consisted of twenty medium-sized villages.

Reading Warm-up A, p. 264

Sample Answers

1. (slender); clarinets, piano keys, drumsticks, flutes
2. (twirl); a top, a drill
3. (yearning); When I saw the photos of my native country, I was filled with longing.
4. soothed; The opposite of *lulled* is *pained* or *aggravated*.
5. freedom . . . social justice or equality of opportunity; *freedom*
6. origins; figuratively
7. (suitable); *unfit, unsuitable*
8. muted; The pale colors of sparrows are less dramatic than the brilliant colors of most parrots.

Reading Warm-up B, p. 265

Sample Answers

1. in the midst of; in or near the center
2. (sighted); *stared, peered*
3. favorable and graceful words; The minister offered a benediction as we left the service.
4. unfathomable; *comprehensible*
5. (as counties are called); a county
6. spectacular sunsets . . . dinner by candlelight; After football practice, we rode our bikes home through the dusky twilight.
7. (moisture); in the early morning
8. heavily with many; *loaded, burdened*

Literary Analysis: Speaker, p. 266

Sample Responses

"Refugee in America": The speaker is probably an ex-slave. The poem is written in the first person. The speaker "knows" something about the worth of freedom, and this knowledge makes the speaker almost cry.

"I, Too": The speaker is a black man experiencing discrimination and is being segregated. The poem is written in the first person. The speaker is saying that people like him are Americans and should be viewed as having the same rights and freedoms as others.

"The Negro Speaks of Rivers": The speaker is the black people as a race. Although the poem is written in the first person, the span of history that is covered is too long for a single person's lifetime. All of the remembrances told in the poem are part of black history.

"Dream Variations": The speaker is a black person who takes great pride in his or her race. The poem is written in the first person, with the clues "Dark like me—", and "Black like me" telling that the speaker is a black person.

"The Tropics in New York": The speaker is a former resident of a tropical area, probably Jamaica, who now lives in New York. The poem is written in the first person, and describes the sights found in a tropical area. The last verse of the poem tells of homesickness, indicating that the

speaker is no longer in this tropical area. The title indicates the speaker is now in New York.

Reading Strategy: Draw Inferences About the Speaker, p. 267

Sample Responses

"Refugee in America": Words, ideas, and details: freedom sings, make me cry. Inferences: The speaker is probably an ex-slave who remembers what it was like to be enslaved and now rejoices in his or her freedom. The title indicates that the speaker feels that America is his or her adopted home, but not the original one.

"The Negro Speaks of Rivers": Words, ideas, and details: ancient, pyramids. Inferences: The speaker is black people as a race. The speaker feels great pride and has a sense of the people's history.

"The Tropics in New York": Words, ideas, and details: bananas, memories. Inferences: The speaker is a former resident of a tropical area, probably Jamaica, who now lives in New York. He or she is very homesick for the native land—both for its sights and its way of life—so much that the speaker is moved to tears by sadness and longing.

Vocabulary Builder, p. 268

A. 1. liberalize; 2. liberal arts; 3. liberally; 4. libertarian
B. 1. D; 2. B; 3. A

Grammar and Style: Verb Tenses: Past and Present Perfect, p. 269

A. 1. I've known rivers ancient as the world; present perfect
2. I built my hut near the Congo; past
3. and it lulled me to sleep; past
4. I heard the singing of the Mississippi; past
5. I've seen its muddy bosom; present perfect
6. My soul has grown deep like the rivers; present perfect

B. 1. They saw the rivers. (past); They've seen the rivers. (present perfect)
2. I went home. (past); I have gone home, (present perfect)
3. Palo studied history during study hall, (past); Palo has studied history during study hall. (present perfect)
4. You took pride in your work. (past) You have taken pride in your work. (present perfect)

Enrichment: Science, p. 272

A. Suggested Responses

1. Student research may focus on several aspects of rivers. For example, students may find information on flooding, such as the annual floods that occur in many rivers or the occasional floods that have disastrous results.
2. Students may find specific information on how pollution, such as agricultural runoff, has affected rivers.
3. Students can research the efforts made to solve problems concerning rivers. For example, there are organi-

zations that evaluate and diagnose the health of rivers and other waterways. Other organizations focus on the cleanup and environmental restoration of rivers.

B. Using their research, students should write a poem to a particular river or to rivers in general. The poem should encompass some of the information they found.

Selection Test A, p. 273

Critical Reading

1. ANS: B	DIF: Easy	OBJ: Reading Strategy
2. ANS: A	DIF: Easy	OBJ: Interpretation
3. ANS: A	DIF: Easy	OBJ: Comprehension
4. ANS: D	DIF: Easy	OBJ: Comprehension
5. ANS: C	DIF: Easy	OBJ: Literary Analysis
6. ANS: B	DIF: Easy	OBJ: Comprehension
7. ANS: C	DIF: Easy	OBJ: Reading Strategy
8. ANS: C	DIF: Easy	OBJ: Interpretation
9. ANS: B	DIF: Easy	OBJ: Literary Analysis
10. ANS: A	DIF: Easy	OBJ: Literary Analysis
11. ANS: C	DIF: Easy	OBJ: Comprehension

Vocabulary and Grammar

12. ANS: B	DIF: Easy	OBJ: Vocabulary
13. ANS: D	DIF: Easy	OBJ: Grammar

Essay

14. Guidelines for evaluation: Students' essays should reflect that the speaker of the poem could be an African American who thinks of himself as a refugee. That is, he sees himself as someone who does not know what freedom and liberty are because he comes from a history of slavery.
    Difficulty: *Easy*
    Objective: *Essay*

15. Guidelines for evaluation: Students' essays should suggest that black people have been on Earth for thousands of years, so they are *ancient* with *deep* memories. They are *dusky* and *muddy*, like the color of rivers at night. Students may suggest other comparisons if they wish.
    Difficulty: *Easy*
    Objective: *Essay*

Selection Test B, p. 276

Critical Reading

1. ANS: A	DIF: Easy	OBJ: Literary Analysis
2. ANS: A	DIF: Average	OBJ: Reading Strategy
3. ANS: C	DIF: Average	OBJ: Reading Strategy
4. ANS: A	DIF: Challenging	OBJ: Interpretation
5. ANS: C	DIF: Average	OBJ: Reading Strategy
6. ANS: C	DIF: Average	OBJ: Comprehension
7. ANS: A	DIF: Average	OBJ: Interpretation
8. ANS: B	DIF: Average	OBJ: Literary Analysis
9. ANS: C	DIF: Challenging	OBJ: Reading Strategy
10. ANS: D	DIF: Average	OBJ: Comprehension
11. ANS: B	DIF: Average	OBJ: Literary Analysis

Vocabulary and Grammar

12. ANS: A	DIF: Easy	OBJ: Vocabulary
13. ANS: B	DIF: Average	OBJ: Vocabulary
14. ANS: A	DIF: Easy	OBJ: Grammar
15. ANS: D	DIF: Average	OBJ: Grammar

Essay

16. Students should mention some specific ways in which the poem is effective in contributing to African American awareness and pride. For example, they might cite how the association with ancient rivers from the earliest times reminds African Americans of their roots. Students might also suggest that the use of the pronoun I enables the African American reader to identify with the history of his or her people. The connection of the Nile and Pyramids, representing one of the world's greatest civilizations, to the African American people provides a source of pride.
    Difficulty: *Easy*
    Objective: *Essay*

17. In their essays, students should compare and contrast the speakers in the three poems, telling who the I represents and what effect the use of this pronoun has on the reader. For example, in "Refugee in America" students might decide that the speaker is the poet who has experienced a lack of liberty, although a reader who shared these experiences might see the I as representing the African American race. In "The Tropics in New York," they might suggest that I is the poet, and any reader might identify with his feelings of homesickness. In "The Negro Speaks of Rivers," they might recognize that speaker is the whole African American race throughout time. The use of I invites the reader to become part of the narration and to identify with the race.
    Difficulty: *Average*
    Objective: *Essay*

"From the Dark Tower" by Countee Cullen
"A Black Man Talks of Reaping" by Arna Bontemps
"Storm Ending" by Jean Toomer

Vocabulary Warm-up Exercises, p. 280

A. 1. beguile
2. mellow
3. piteous
4. crumple

5. stark
6. subtle
7. eternally
8. lean

B. **Sample Answers**

1. T; People living in utter poverty often evoke sympathy or pity.
2. T; Since *brute* means "a cruel person," such a bully might be considered a brute.
3. T; You would be able to gather much information by reading slowly and carefully.
4. F; Since *gorgeously* means "splendidly," such a garden would be desirable.
5. F; Since an increment is a portion or part, it would not equal double the amount.
6. F; *Sable* means "black" or "dark brown."
7. T; The stalk is the main stem of a plant.
8. F; Productive land would normally yield or provide a good harvest.

Reading Warm-up A, p. 281

Sample Answers

1. severe; A desert landscape might be considered stark.
2. (trick); *trick, deceive*
3. (slim); *rich, full*
4. (under the burden): *Crumple* means "crush" or "collapse."
5. aroused compassion; *pity*
6. ingenious; The opposite of *subtle* is *gross* or *unrefined*.
7. live this way day after day; *forever*
8. (fulfilling); Mellow music would sound soft and soothing.

Reading Warm-up B, p. 282

Sample Answers

1. African American; The puppy's fur was a soft sable color.
2. (miserable); *miserable; degraded*
3. arcing gracefully . . . over the green grass; *miserably, wretchedly*
4. (smallest); part of a whole
5. the tall pin that marked the whole; *corn, celery*
6. (wildly powerful freak); negative
7. searched for; *collect*
8. (provides); *provides, offers*

Literary Analysis: Metaphor, p. 283

Suggested Response

One possible interpretation of the metaphor in the poem is that being black in America is like being a laborer or a servant. Students will underline words and images that indicate the tasks of a laborer or farmer. Students should write notes in the margins explaining any images and emotions the metaphor in the poem evokes.

Reading Strategy: Connect to Historical Context, p. 284

Sample Responses

1. Life was not much better for black people living in the cities than it had been in the rural South. In many cases, they seemed to exchange one form of servitude for another. "From the Dark Tower" suggests that life will not always be one of servitude for black Americans.
2. Many people from the time period were probably familiar with the agricultural images, as well as with the feelings of inequality and despair.
3. "Storm Ending" is a vivid poem that evokes strong images. The poem may be interpreted as a comment on the times or just as a skillfully written poem.
4. Cullen's poem presents the plight of the African American with confidence and strength. Bontempt's poem is more negative and despairing. Toomer's poem uses strong images that may connote judgment about past injustices.

Vocabulary Builder, p. 285

A. 1. a growing together of parts or cells
2. to cause to "grow" into existence
3. any form of play that causes the body or mind to grow more refreshed

B. 1. D; 2. A; 3. C; 4. C; 5. A; 6. D

Grammar and Style: Placement of Adjectives, p. 286

A. 1. We shall . . . Not always countenance, abject and mute. . . . (after)
2. That lesser men should hold their brothers cheap . . . (before)
3. And there are buds that cannot bloom at all . . . but crumple, piteous, and fall. . . . (after)
4. I planted safe against this stark, lean year. (before)
5. I scattered seed enough to plant the land. . . . (after)
6. my children glean in fields . . . and feed on bitter fruit. (before)
7. Great, hollow, bell-like flowers . . . (before)
8. Full-lipped flowers . . . dripping rain . . . (before)

B. **Sample Responses**

2. The amber grain waved in the breeze.
3. I gazed out upon the field, still burning, destroyed.
4. The flower, wilted, still gave off an air of romance.
5. That old house was just sold.
6. The night, cool and quiet, reminded me of my youth.

Enrichment: Social Studies, p. 289

Sample Responses

1. "From the Dark Tower" and "A Black Man Talks of Reaping" use traditional poetry forms. "Storm Ending" may use some natural speech and idioms.

2. "From the Dark Tower" and "A Black Man Talks of Reaping" have themes about the African American experience. "Storm Ending" may have a more universal theme, depending on one's interpretation.

3. "From the Dark Tower" and "A Black Man Talks of Reaping" may have been intended to motivate African Americans to advance their position in society. "Storm Ending" may show that African American writers can produce the same quality of literature as other writers.

4. All three poems may be interpreted as showing the inherent beauty of African American people and the African American experience.

Selection Test A, p. 290

Critical Reading

1. ANS: B	DIF: Easy	OBJ: Literary Analysis
2. ANS: C	DIF: Easy	OBJ: Reading Strategy
3. ANS: A	DIF: Easy	OBJ: Reading Strategy
4. ANS: C	DIF: Easy	OBJ: Interpretation
5. ANS: B	DIF: Easy	OBJ: Interpretation
6. ANS: B	DIF: Easy	OBJ: Comprehension
7. ANS: B	DIF: Easy	OBJ: Literary Analysis
8. ANS: B	DIF: Easy	OBJ: Literary Analysis
9. ANS: C	DIF: Easy	OBJ: Comprehension

Vocabulary and Grammar

10. ANS: A	DIF: Easy	OBJ: Vocabulary
11. ANS: B	DIF: Easy	OBJ: Vocabulary
12. ANS: C	DIF: Easy	OBJ: Grammar
13. ANS: A	DIF: Easy	OBJ: Grammar

Essay

14. Students' essays should reflect that storms are violent events that can be very dangerous to people. Slavery was an ongoing event that was a constant danger to slaves. When a storm ends, people in its path sigh with relief, just as African Americans were relieved when slavery was finally ended.

Difficulty: *Easy*
Objective: *Essay*

15. Students' essays should suggest that *plant*, *reap*, and *seeds* might be metaphors for writing manuscripts and being published. *Bursting fruit* might be used as a metaphor for a completed work. *Buds* might be partially finished works that may or may not be completed satisfactorily.

Difficulty: *Easy*
Objective: *Essay*

Selection Test B, p. 293

Critical Reading

1. ANS: A	DIF: Average	OBJ: Interpretation

2. ANS: C	DIF: Average	OBJ: Reading Strategy
3. ANS: C	DIF: Challenging	OBJ: Reading Strategy
4. ANS: D	DIF: Average	OBJ: Reading Strategy
5. ANS: A	DIF: Challenging	OBJ: Interpretation
6. ANS: B	DIF: Challenging	OBJ: Comprehension
7. ANS: B	DIF: Easy	OBJ: Interpretation
8. ANS: C	DIF: Challenging	OBJ: Literary Analysis
9. ANS: A	DIF: Average	OBJ: Literary Analysis
10. ANS: C	DIF: Average	OBJ: Literary Analysis
11. ANS: A	DIF: Average	OBJ: Interpretation
12. ANS: D	DIF: Challenging	OBJ: Literary Analysis

Vocabulary and Grammar

13. ANS: B	DIF: Easy	OBJ: Vocabulary
14. ANS: B	DIF: Easy	OBJ: Vocabulary
15. ANS: D	DIF: Average	OBJ: Vocabulary
16. ANS: D	DIF: Average	OBJ: Grammar
17. ANS: C	DIF: Average	OBJ: Grammar

Essay

18. Students' essays should give a word or phrase describing the mood of the poem and cite details that show how it captures the mood of the poem. For example, students may choose the word "bitter" or a synonym, citing references to sowing much but reaping little and the detail of the speaker's children eating "bitter fruit."

Difficulty: *Easy*
Objective: *Essay*

19. Students may select any one of the poems as long as they explain how it uses metaphors. For example, students might choose "From the Dark Tower" or "A Black Man Talks of Reaping," citing the comparison of African American life to planting without reaping, which reminds readers of the agricultural slavery of that life and evokes feelings of anger and despair. If they select "Storm Ending," they might mention that thunder is compared to bell-like flowers, which convey the noise and beauty of the storm and evoke a sense of awe.

Difficulty: *Average*
Objective: *Essay*

20. Students may agree or disagree with the statement but should support their position with examples. For example, students agreeing that Toomer intended to write about the African American experience might assert the thunder represents the trials of African Americans and, like other writers of the Harlem Renaissance, his purpose was to call attention to their life. Students who disagree might reason that the images of the storm give no hint of any further meaning and that the poem was written to show that African American writers could produce literature equal in quality to that of white writers.

Difficulty: *Challenging*
Objective: *Essay*

Writing About Literature—Unit 5

Evaluate Literary Trends: Integrating Grammar Skills, p. 297

A.
1. repetitive
2. repetitive
3. varied
4. repetitive

B. Sample Revisions

1. Using everyday language, William Carlos Williams tried to capture ordinary American life. Because he rejected some of Pound's views, Williams avoided allusions to history.
2. With musical lines, the poetry of H. D. refers to some important issues of the early 1900s. Among the subjects she explores are World War I, movies, and new ideas about psychology.
3. Brief and precise, Imagist poems use sensory imagery to capture the essence of their subject. They freeze a single moment in time.

Writing Workshop—Unit 5

Multimedia Presentation: Integrating Grammar Skills, p. 299

A.
1. Pizza, tacos, teriyaki, and falafel
2. Sitting at the top of a big Ferris wheel
3. To capture all those special memories
4. Laughing and talking with good friends

B.
1. Every year I enjoy the sights and sounds of Town Day.
2. There is always a parade with marching bands in the morning and a street fair at night.
3. Working in a booth and waiting on your old friends can be fun.
4. As a kid, I used to march in the parade with my baseball team.

Spelling—Unit 5

Proofreading Practice, p. 300

1. psychology; 2. cautious; 3. aggressive;
4. antagonistic; 5. creativity; 6. courageous;
7. psychologists; 8. stressful; 9. studious;
10. concentrating; 11. photographs; 12. symphony;
13. psyches; 14. appear; 15. continuous;
16. gnawing; 17. caring; 18. knowledge; 19. coping;
20. strategies; 21. brutish; 22. know; 23. judge;
24. adaptable